LITERATURE WORKS

A Collection of Readings

COLLECTION 6

Silver Burdett Ginn
A Division of Simon & Schuster
160 Gould Street
Needham Heights, MA 02194

Acknowledgments appear on pages 606–608, which constitute an extension of this copyright page.

ISBN: 0-663-61227-6   1 2 3 4 5 6 7 8 9 10 VHP 03 02 01 00 99 98 97 96

LITERATURE WORKS

A Collection of Readings

COLLECTION 6

THEMES

Perspectives

Uncovering the Past: Ancient Egypt

Finding Common Ground

Strange Encounters

Survival

Journeys of Change

SILVER BURDETT GINN

Needham, MA   Parsippany, NJ
Atlanta, GA   Deerfield, IL   Irving, TX   Santa Clara, CA

Theme 1

Perspectives

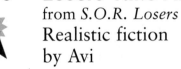

Theme
Trade
Books

Theme 2

Uncovering the Past: Ancient Egypt

Theme
Trade
Books

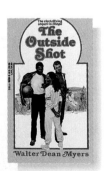

Theme Trade Books

Theme 4

Strange Encounters

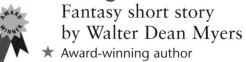

**Theme
Trade
Books**

Survival

Theme
Trade
Books

Journeys of Change

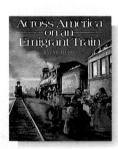

Theme
Trade
Books

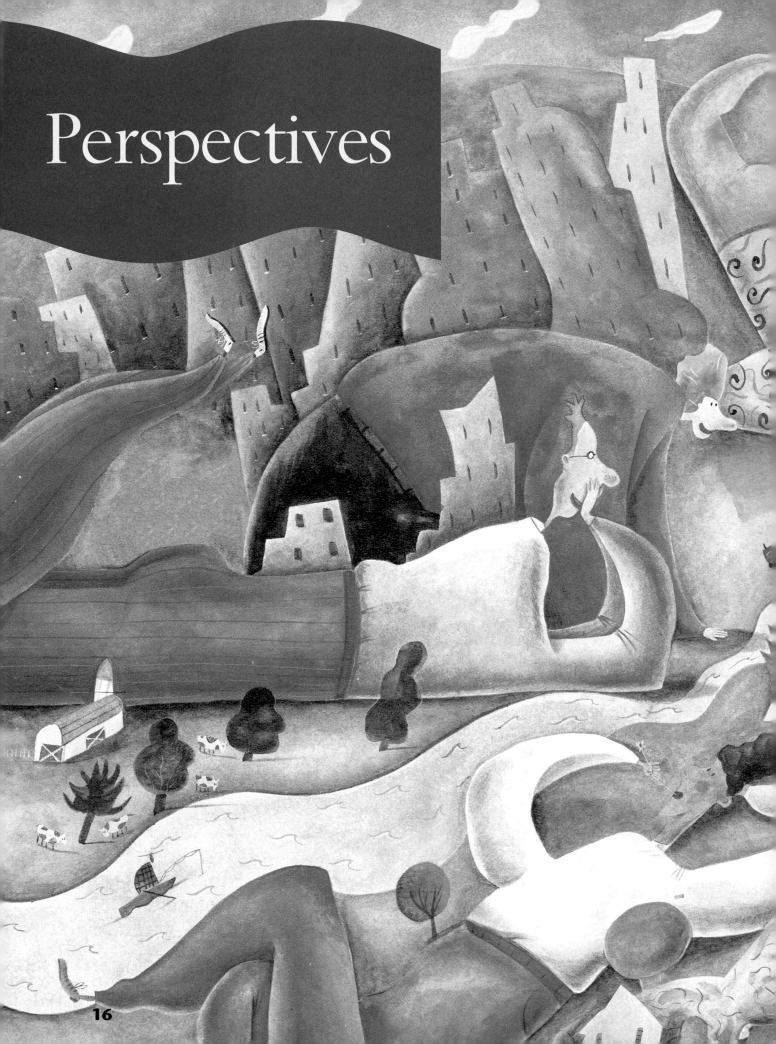

Perspectives

"Each person has a way of looking at the world."

—Avi

17

Perspectives

CONTENTS

Theme Trade Books

Mop, Moondance, and the Nagasaki Knights
by Walter Dean Myers
While preparing for a baseball tournament, three friends learn lessons about communicating with foreign students, helping a teammate in crisis, and winning.

Journey Home
by Yoshiko Uchida
After months of hardship in a United States detention camp during World War II, Yuki and her Japanese American family rebuild their lives with their unyielding faith, courage, and hope.

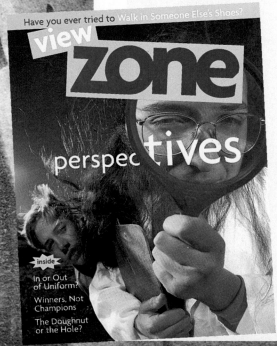

Theme Magazine

Do you prefer the doughnut or the hole? That is, do you look on the bright side or the dark side? The Theme Magazine *View Zone* may give you a fresh angle on these and other topics.

THE
ALL-AMERICAN
Slurp

by Lensey Namioka
from *America Street,*
edited by Anne Mazer

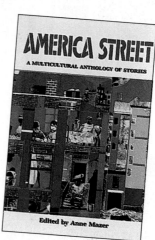

The first time our family was invited out to dinner in America, we disgraced ourselves while eating celery. We had emigrated to this country from China, and during our early days here we had a hard time with American table manners.

In China we never ate celery raw, or any other kind of vegetable raw. We always had to disinfect the vegetables in boiling water first. When we were presented with our first relish tray, the raw celery caught us unprepared.

We had been invited to dinner by our neighbors, the Gleasons. After arriving at the house, we shook hands with our hosts and packed ourselves into a sofa. As our family of four sat stiffly in a row, my younger brother and I stole glances at our parents for a clue as to what to do next.

Mrs. Gleason offered the relish tray to Mother. The tray looked pretty, with its tiny red radishes, curly sticks of carrots, and long, slender stalks of pale green celery. "Do try some of the celery, Mrs. Lin," she said. "It's from a local farmer, and it's sweet."

Mother picked up one of the green stalks, and Father followed suit. Then I picked up a stalk, and my brother did too. So there we sat, each with a stalk of celery in our right hand.

Mrs. Gleason kept smiling. "Would you like to try some of the dip, Mrs. Lin? It's my own recipe: sour cream and onion flakes, with a dash of Tabasco sauce."

Most Chinese don't care for dairy products, and in those days I wasn't even ready to drink fresh milk. Sour cream sounded perfectly revolting. Our family shook our heads in unison.

Mrs. Gleason went off with the relish tray to the other guests, and we carefully watched to see what they did. Everyone seemed to eat the raw vegetables quite happily.

Mother took a bite of her celery. *Crunch.* "It's not bad!" she whispered.

Father took a bite of his celery. *Crunch.* "Yes, it *is* good," he said, looking surprised.

I took a bite, and then my brother. *Crunch, crunch.* It was more than good; it was delicious. Raw celery has a slight sparkle, a zingy taste that you don't get in cooked celery. When Mrs. Gleason came around with the relish tray, we each took another stalk of celery, except my brother. He took two.

There was only one problem: long strings ran through the length of the stalk, and they got caught in my teeth. When I help my mother in the kitchen, I always pull the strings out before slicing celery.

I pulled the strings out of my stalk. *Z-z-zip, z-z-zip.* My brother followed suit. *Z-z-zip, z-z-zip.* To my left, my parents were taking care of their own stalks. *Z-z-zip, z-z-zip, z-z-zip.*

Suddenly I realized that there was dead silence except for our zipping. Looking up, I saw that the eyes of everyone in the room were on our family. Mr. and Mrs. Gleason, their daughter Meg, who was my friend, and their neighbors the Badels—they were all staring at us as we busily pulled the strings of our celery.

That wasn't the end of it. Mrs. Gleason announced that dinner was served and invited us to the dining table. It was lavishly covered with platters of food, but we couldn't see any chairs around the table. So we helpfully carried over some dining chairs and sat down. All the other guests just stood there.

Mrs. Gleason bent down and whispered to us, "This is a buffet dinner. You help yourselves to some food and eat it in the living room."

Our family beat a retreat back to the sofa as if chased by enemy soldiers. For the rest of the evening, too mortified to go back to the dining table, I nursed a bit of potato salad on my plate.

Next day Meg and I got on the school bus together. I wasn't sure how she would feel about me after the spectacle our family made at the party. But she was just the same as usual, and the only reference she made to the party was, "Hope you and your folks got enough to eat last night. You certainly didn't take very much. Mom never tries to figure out how much food to prepare. She just puts everything on the table and hopes for the best."

I began to relax. The Gleasons' dinner party wasn't so different from a Chinese meal after all. My mother also puts everything on the table and hopes for the best.

Meg was the first friend I had made after we came to America. I eventually got acquainted with a few other kids in school, but Meg was still the only real friend I had.

My brother didn't have any problems making friends. He spent all his time with some boys who were teaching him baseball, and in no time he could speak English much faster than I could—not better, but faster.

I worried more about making mistakes, and I spoke carefully, making sure I could say everything right before opening my mouth. At least I had a better accent than my parents, who never really got rid of their Chinese accent, even years later. My parents had both studied English in school before coming to America, but what they had studied was mostly written English, not spoken.

Father's approach to English was a scientific one. Since Chinese verbs have no tense, he was fascinated by the way English verbs changed form according to whether they were in the present, past imperfect, perfect, pluperfect, future, or future perfect tense. He was always making diagrams of verbs and their inflections, and he looked for opportunities to show off his mastery of the pluperfect and future perfect tenses, his two favorites. "I shall have finished my project by Monday," he would say smugly.

Mother's approach was to memorize lists of polite phrases that would cover all possible social situations. She was constantly muttering things like "I'm fine, thank you. And you?" Once she accidentally stepped on someone's foot, and hurriedly blurted,

"Oh, that's quite all right!" Embarrassed by her slip, she re-solved to do better next time. So when someone stepped on *her* foot, she cried, "You're welcome!"

In our own different ways, we made progress in learning English. But I had another worry, and that was my appearance. My brother didn't have to worry, since Mother bought him blue jeans for school, and he dressed like all the other boys. But she insisted that girls had to wear skirts. By the time she saw that Meg and the other girls were wearing jeans, it was too late. My school clothes were bought already, and we didn't have money left to buy new outfits for me. We had too many other things to buy first, like furniture, pots, and pans.

The first time I visited Meg's house, she took me upstairs to her room, and I wound up trying on her clothes. We were pretty much the same size, since Meg was shorter and thinner than average. Maybe that's how we became friends in the first place. Wearing Meg's jeans and T-shirt, I looked at myself in the mirror. I could almost pass for an American—from the back, anyway. At least the kids in school wouldn't stop and stare at me in the hallways, which was what they did when they saw me in my white blouse and navy blue skirt that went a couple of inches below the knees.

When Meg came to my house, I invited her to try on my Chinese dresses, the ones with a high collar and slits up the sides. Meg's eyes were bright as she looked at herself in the mir-ror. She struck several sultry poses, and we nearly fell over laughing.

The dinner party at the Gleasons' didn't stop my growing friendship with Meg. Things were getting better for me in other ways too. Mother finally bought me some jeans at the end of the month, when Father got his paycheck. She wasn't in any hurry about buying them at first, until I worked on her. This is what I did. Since we didn't have a car in those days, I often ran down to the neighborhood store to pick up things for her. The groceries cost less at a big supermarket, but the closest one was many blocks away. One day, when she ran out of flour, I offered to borrow a bike from our neighbor's son and buy a ten-pound bag of flour at the big supermarket. I mounted the boy's bike and waved to Mother. "I'll be back in five minutes!"

Before I started pedaling, I heard her voice behind me. "You can't go out in public like that! People can see all the way up to your thighs!"

"I'm sorry," I said innocently. "I thought you were in a hurry to get the flour." For dinner we were going to

have pot-stickers (fried Chinese dumplings), and we needed a lot of flour.

"Couldn't you borrow a girl's bicycle?" complained Mother. "That way your skirt won't be pushed up."

"There aren't too many of those around," I said. "Almost all the girls wear jeans while riding a bike, so they don't see any point buying a girl's bike."

We didn't eat pot-stickers that evening, and Mother was thoughtful. Next day we took the bus downtown and she bought me a pair of jeans. In the same week, my brother made the baseball team of his junior high school, Father started taking driving lessons, and Mother discovered rummage sales. We soon got all the furniture we needed, plus a dart board and a 1,000-piece jigsaw puzzle (fourteen hours later, we discovered that it was a 999-piece jigsaw puzzle). There was hope that the Lins might become a normal American family after all.

Then came our dinner at the Lakeview restaurant.

The Lakeview was an expensive restaurant, one of those places where a headwaiter dressed in tails conducted you to your seat, and the only light came from candles and flaming desserts. In one corner of the room a lady harpist played tinkling melodies.

Father wanted to celebrate, because he had just been promoted. He worked for an electronics company, and after his English started improving, his superiors decided to appoint him to a position more suited to his training. The promotion not only brought a higher salary but was also a tremendous boost to his pride.

Up to then we had eaten only in Chinese restaurants. Although my brother and I were becoming fond of hamburgers, my parents didn't care much for western food, other than chow mein.

But this was a special occasion, and Father asked his coworkers to recommend a really elegant restaurant. So there we were at the Lakeview, stumbling after the headwaiter in the murky dining room.

At our table we were handed our menus, and they were so big that to read mine I almost had to stand up again. But why bother? It was mostly in French, anyway.

Father, being an engineer, was always systematic. He took out a pocket French dictionary. "They told me that most of the items would be in French, so I came prepared." He even had a pocket flashlight, the size of a marking pen. While Mother held the flashlight over the menu, he looked up the items that were in French.

"*Pâté en croûte,*" he muttered. "Let's see . . . *pâté* is paste . . . *croûte* is crust . . . hmm . . . a paste in crust."

The waiter stood looking patient. I squirmed and died at least fifty times.

At long last Father gave up. "Why don't we just order four complete dinners at random?" he suggested.

"Isn't that risky?" asked Mother. "The French eat some rather peculiar things, I've heard."

"A Chinese can eat anything a Frenchman can eat," Father declared.

The soup arrived in a plate. How do you get soup up from a plate? I glanced at the other diners, but the ones at the nearby tables were not on their soup course, while the more distant ones were invisible in the darkness.

Fortunately my parents had studied books on western etiquette before they came to America. "Tilt your plate," whispered my mother. "It's easier to spoon the soup up that way."

She was right. Tilting the plate did the trick. But the etiquette book didn't say anything about what you did after the soup reached your lips. As any respectable

Chinese knows, the correct way to eat your soup is to slurp. This helps to cool the liquid and prevent you from burning your lips. It also shows your appreciation.

We showed our appreciation. *Shloop*, went my father. *Shloop*, went my mother. *Shloop*, *shloop*, went my brother, who was the hungriest.

The lady harpist stopped playing to take a rest. And in the silence, our family's consumption of soup suddenly seemed unnaturally loud. You know how it sounds on a rocky beach when the tide goes out and the water drains from all those little pools? They go *shloop, shloop, shloop.* That was the Lin family, eating soup.

At the next table a waiter was pouring wine. When a large *shloop* reached him, he froze. The bottle continued to pour, and red wine flooded the tabletop and into the lap of a customer. Even the customer didn't notice anything at first, being also hypnotized by the *shloop, shloop, shloop.*

It was too much. "I need to go to the toilet," I mumbled, jumping to my feet. A waiter, sensing my urgency, quickly directed me to the ladies' room.

I splashed cold water on my burning face, and as I dried myself with a paper towel, I stared into the mirror. In this perfumed ladies' room, with its pink-and-silver wallpaper and marbled sinks, I looked completely out of place. What was I doing here? What was our family doing in the Lakeview restaurant? In America?

The door to the ladies' room opened. A woman came in and glanced curiously at me. I retreated into one of the toilet cubicles and latched the door.

Time passed—maybe half an hour, maybe an hour. Then I heard the door open again, and my mother's voice. "Are you in there? You're not sick, are you?"

There was real concern in her voice. A girl can't leave her family just because they slurp their soup. Besides, the toilet cubicle had a few drawbacks as a permanent residence. "I'm all right," I said, undoing the latch.

Mother didn't tell me how the rest of the dinner went, and I didn't want to know. In the weeks following, I managed to push the whole thing into the back of my mind, where it jumped out at me only a few times a day. Even now, I turn hot all over when I think of the Lakeview restaurant.

But by the time we had been in this country for three months, our family was definitely making progress toward becoming Americanized. I remember my parents' first PTA meeting. Father wore a neat suit and tie, and Mother put on her first pair of high heels. She stumbled only once. They met my homeroom teacher and beamed as she told them that I would make honor roll soon at the rate I was going. Of course Chinese etiquette forced Father to say that I was a very stupid girl and Mother to protest that the teacher was showing favoritism toward me. But I could tell they were both very proud.

The day came when my parents announced that they wanted to give a dinner party. We had invited Chinese friends to eat with us before, but this dinner was going to be different. In addition to a Chinese-American family, we were going to invite the Gleasons.

"Gee, I can hardly wait to have dinner at your house," Meg said to me. "I just love Chinese food."

That was a relief. Mother was a good cook, but I wasn't sure if people who ate sour cream would also eat chicken gizzards stewed in soy sauce.

Mother decided not to take a chance with chicken gizzards. Since we had western guests, she set the table with large dinner plates, which we never used in Chinese meals. In fact we didn't use individual plates at all, but picked up food from the platters in the middle of the table and brought it directly to our rice bowls. Following the practice of Chinese-American restaurants, Mother also placed large serving spoons on the platters.

The dinner started well. Mrs. Gleason exclaimed at the beautifully arranged dishes of food: the colorful candied fruit in the sweet-and-sour pork dish, the noodle-thin shreds of chicken meat stir-fried with tiny peas, and the glistening pink prawns in a ginger sauce.

At first I was too busy enjoying my food to notice how the guests were doing. But soon I remembered my duties. Sometimes guests were too polite to help themselves and you had to serve them with more food.

I glanced at Meg, to see if she needed more food, and my eyes nearly popped out at the sight of her plate. It was piled with food: the sweet-and-sour meat pushed right against the chicken shreds, and the chicken sauce ran into the prawns. She had been taking food from a second dish before she finished eating her helping from the first!

Horrified, I turned to look at Mrs. Gleason. She was dumping rice out of her bowl and putting it on her dinner plate. Then she ladled prawns and gravy on top of the rice and mixed everything together, the way you mix sand, gravel, and cement to make concrete.

I couldn't bear to look any longer, and I turned to Mr. Gleason. He was chasing a pea around his plate. Several times he got it to the edge, but when he tried to pick it up with his chopsticks, it rolled back toward the center of the plate again. Finally he put down his chopsticks and picked up the pea with his fingers. He really did! A grown man!

All of us, our family and the Chinese guests, stopped eating to watch the activities of the Gleasons. I wanted to giggle. Then I caught my mother's eyes on me. She frowned and shook her head slightly, and I understood the message: the Gleasons were not used to Chinese ways, and they were just coping the best they could. For some reason I thought of celery strings.

When the main courses were finished, Mother brought out a platter of fruit. "I hope you weren't expecting a sweet dessert," she said. "Since the Chinese don't eat dessert, I didn't think to prepare any."

"Oh, I couldn't possibly eat dessert!" cried Mrs. Gleason. "I'm simply stuffed!"

Meg had different ideas. When the table was cleared, she announced that she and I were going for a walk. "I don't know about you, but I feel like dessert," she told me, when we were outside. "Come on, there's a Dairy Queen down the street. I could use a big chocolate milkshake!"

Although I didn't really want anything more to eat, I insisted on paying for the milkshakes. After all, I was still hostess.

Meg got her large chocolate milkshake and I had a small one. Even so, she was finishing hers while I was only half done. Toward the end she pulled hard on her straws and went *shloop, shloop.*

"Do you always slurp when you eat a milkshake?" I asked, before I could stop myself.

Meg grinned. "Sure. All Americans slurp."

◗N RESPONSE

A Letter to China

Put yourself in Mrs. Lin's shoes. What have you observed about Americans during your time here? Write a letter to relatives in China showing your reaction to the way Americans eat, dress, and behave.

Make Yourself at Home

Both the Lins and the Gleasons may have felt uncomfortable having dinner at one another's home. In a group, look through the story for examples of foods or manners unfamiliar to the visiting family. Tell what you would have done at each dinner to make your guests feel more at home.

AUTHOR AT WORK

Lensey Namioka was born in Beijing, China. Her family came to the United States when she was still a child. Some of Ms. Namioka's stories are based on her own experiences as an immigrant. Other stories are based on the experiences of her children and their friends as first-generation Asian Americans.

About her writing Ms. Namioka says, "For my writings I draw on my Chinese cultural heritage and on my husband's Japanese cultural heritage. My involvement with Japan started before my marriage, since my mother spent many years in Japan. My long years of training in mathematics had little influence on my writing, except for an urge to economy."

Ms. Namioka attended Radcliffe College and the University of California at Berkeley, where she received her master's degree. Ms. Namioka has two grown daughters and lives in Seattle, Washington, with her husband.

Louis Braille

BRINGING WORDS TO LIGHT

from *Remarkable Children* by Dennis Brindell Fradin

On the morning of February 15, 1819, Louis Braille said good-bye to his mother and then walked with his father to the stagecoach station. He couldn't know it at the time, but, except for periodic visits, he was never to make his home in Coupvray again. Four hours later Louis and his father arrived at their destination, the National Institute for the Young Blind on St. Victor Street in Paris. After speaking to several of the school's officials, Simon Braille parted from his ten-year-old son and returned to Coupvray.

The first few days, Louis wished he had never asked to go to the school. He couldn't find his way from his bunk to the bathroom or from the classroom to the dormitory, and often he either tripped or got lost. He had come from a very loving home, and he was upset by the antics of the other students, many of whom liked to fight in the dormitory and play tricks on one another. To make things worse, when the blind students were taken outside for walks, children would call them names and sometimes even throw things at them.

Slowly, however, Louis eased into the routine of the school. He learned to count the steps between his bed and the bathroom, and from the dormitory to the cafeteria. He made several friends among the students, and was soon exchanging jokes with them, helping them with their work, and even getting into occasional fights. But the best part about the school was the fact that his mind was greatly stimulated.

a
b
c
d
e
f
g
h
i
j
k
l
m
n
o
p
q
r
s
t
u
v
w
x
y
z

a ⠁
b ⠃
c ⠉
d ⠙
e ⠑
f ⠋
g ⠛
h ⠓
i ⠊
j ⠚
k ⠅
l ⠇
m ⠍
n ⠝
o ⠕
p ⠏
q ⠟
r ⠗
s ⠎
t ⠞
u ⠥
v ⠧
w ⠺
x ⠭
y ⠽
z ⠵

Not only was he being taught many subjects, including how to play the piano and the organ, for the first time in his life Louis was able to read. Valentin Haüy, the school's founder, had devised an ingenious reading method for his students. He had arranged for books with embossed, or raised, letters to be printed. By feeling the letters, the blind young people could make out the words.

First, Louis was taught to recognize the written alphabet and also the sounds that the letters made. Once he could do that, he began reading the books. Although people had read to Louis in the past, reading by himself was a wonderful new experience. He could pause to think about the author's words if he wanted, reread the best parts, and skip the boring parts.

Like many young people who have just begun to read, Louis Braille developed a hunger for books. Unfortunately, there was nothing for him to read once he'd finished the school's few embossed books. It was difficult to print the books by the Haüy method. Each letter had to be many times larger than the usual printed letter. Because of the large size of the letters, a book had to be divided into about twenty separate parts, each weighing about twenty pounds. This meant that a single book might weigh four hundred pounds! Another problem was that, despite the large size of the letters, it wasn't always easy for the students to tell an *h* from an *n*, or an *i* from an *l*. This made for very slow reading.

Louis's hunger for reading materials inspired him to think about better ways of creating books for the blind. Even at the age of eleven, it seemed to him that the key was to find a simple code for the letters. During the next several years he tried to think of ways that this could be done.

Louis began to work late every night, testing various methods for achieving his goal. He tried codes made of mathematical symbols and ones that used foreign words. During his vacations, Louis would return to Coupvray and go into his father's shop just as he'd done as a little boy. While Simon Braille worked away making saddles, Louis would cut shapes out of the leather and try to think of how shapes could be used to express letters.

Each method Louis thought of had drawbacks, however. Some were as complex as Haüy's letter-embossing method and would require huge volumes. With simpler methods it was often difficult to determine what the symbols were, meaning that the reader would have to spend a lot of time deciphering each word.

Just as Louis Braille was beginning to despair, he heard of a French army captain named Charles Barbier, who had invented a method for sending messages in the dark. Barbier's system, called "night writing," consisted of dots and dashes raised on paper. By touching the dots and dashes, the soldiers could decipher the message without using a light. Night after night, Louis Braille worked at creating a writing system for the blind based on dots and dashes. In 1824 he finally worked out the basics of what became the *braille system*. Louis Braille, whose method has since helped tens of thousands of blind people read, was only fifteen years old when he invented his system.

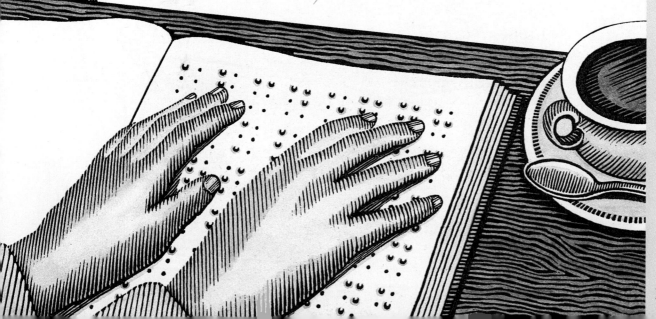

a
b
c
d
e
f
g
h
i
j
k
l
m
n
o
p
q
r
s
t
u
v
w
x
y
z

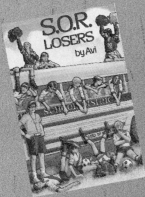

LOSERS TAKE ALL

from *S.O.R. Losers* by Avi

AWARD WINNER

South Orange River Middle School has a long tradition of success in sports. Every student must play one team sport each year. Ed Sitrow and several other boys escaped the requirement in sixth grade, but this year there is a soccer team just for them. Ed became goalie and later, team captain.

Led by their history teacher, Mr. Lester, the Special Seventh-Grade Soccer Team has lost all of its games so far. The school community is more concerned about its record than the team. Pep talks from everyone echo the same advice: if you believe in yourself, you'll win. As the team approaches its fifth match, against rival Pennington, pressure mounts for players to develop a winning attitude.

The game against Pennington was, well, interesting. Great weather. Crisp and bright. It almost made me want to be there. Sure enough, there were a bunch of people who came to watch. Ms. Appleton brought the whole rest of my class. Some parents too. Mr. Sullivan was there. So was Mr. Tillman. I think he had on new beads for the occasion.

Mr. Lester had us over by a corner where, after we pretended to get ready, he gave us his talk.

"Now, gentlemen, Pennington isn't such a great team. They've won a few and lost a few. More like you guys."

"We didn't win any," Porter reminded him.

Mr. Lester looked toward the sidelines. "Today you will," he said.

"How do you know?" asked Dorman.

"I feel it."

"Where?" Radosh wondered.

"And what about tomorrow?" Lifsom wanted to know.

"Gentlemen," said Mr. Lester, "we can really turn the season around if you want. Why not win for those nice people who have come to cheer?"

"Let them do it for themselves," whispered Saltz.

"Now," concluded Mr. Lester, "come out fighting and keep on fighting." He made that pathetic fist of his.

Right from the start, we tried. Honest. We got together in a circle, touched hands and started to roar, except just when we began, Eliscue sneezed. So instead of screaming, "Fight!" what came out was: "Fi . . ." *Sneeze!* "God bless you." "God bless you." "Thanks."

Not what I'd call a mean team.

As for the game. Well . . . there were one or two things. The big moment was when we scored a goal. Really. It was the only score (for our side) so far that season.

I'd like to tell you that Porter brought it smartly down the right line, snapped a crisp clothesline shot to Lifsom, who brilliantly headed it back to Hays, who smashed it by the helpless, prostrate goalie . . . except it didn't happen that way.

As much as I could see of it, the goal came about when Lifsom was trying to get the ball out of our territory. Well, that time he actually got his foot on it. The ball even started to go in the right direction. An improvement.

But then one of their guys intercepted, dropping the ball along his body. Then he began running it back. Our side moved into automatic full retreat.

But somehow, their guy tripped. The ball got away. Dorman saw the ball free and got it moving deep into their turf. I could see how excited he was by the notion that he was actually on the move with not much between him and their goal except their goalie because of what he did. What he did was stop and watch.

Macht came up and—not wanting to waste a shot—we didn't get too many—stole the ball from Dorman (who might have fallen asleep for all he moved) and gave a boot. Only Macht topped the ball. The ball just squirted forward. And Macht fell down.

What happened next? Their goalie cracked up, laughed so much that he let that little dribbler of a ball keep coming.

Meanwhile, Radosh came up from the left and gave the ball a thump, again, right at their goalkeeper.

Their goalie punched it right back. It hit Hays on the head and bounced into their goal.

Mind, I didn't say Hays headed the ball in, I said the ball hit him on the head and bounced in. In fact, Hays was so dizzy from the shot that he was actually walking around in circles for a few minutes.

It figured: we finally score a goal and the guy who scored it never did know what happened.

From the reaction of the people on the sidelines—our people—you would have thought we had just won the World Series. They went wild.

Actually, I was much more interested in the way Hays was wobbling all over, like a wasted duck. *That* was interesting.

As for the other high point, it involved me. It wasn't so complicated, but since it was me, I had the best view, sort of.

It came about because during the third period my shoe became untied. Normally, I'd wait for a lull in the action to re-tie it. However, there were no lulls, and as time went on I was sure my shoe was going to fall off. I had to do something. Over I bent to tie it. Only then the shoelace broke. That meant more work. And concentration.

What happened next was this terrible thud against my backside. It sent me head first into the net one way, and the ball another way, also into the net.

Buddy Saltz helped me untangle myself from the net. "It's probably not a bad idea to face the field," he suggested.

"Do you want to play goal?" I snapped.

"Not tall enough," he reminded me.

Final score: 18–1.

In the locker room there were some guys from our other teams. Of course they had to know what happened to us. We told them.

At first there were the usual jokes, and then this guy, Roberts, who was captain of the eighth-grade first-string team, stood on a bench and yelled for quiet.

We all listened.

"Look here," he said, looking right at us. As usual we were bunched together for self protection. "The joke's over," shouted Roberts. "When are you jerks going to get your act together? You're making *us* look stupid!"

Fortunately, Mr. Lester came in just then. There might have been a riot. Anyway, Mr. Lester shooed us all over into a corner to give us some kindly pointers. Not that anyone listened. It had all gotten too frustrating.

Then Mr. Tillman burst in. "Listen up, you guys," he said to us. We gave him our attention. He would have taken it anyway. There was an angry glint in his eyes that suggested trouble.

"I think I've learned my lesson," he said. "I admit it. I tried to sweet-talk you guys into feeling better about yourselves. That was wrong. What you need to be told is how rotten you looked out there today. I've never seen worse. Not around here. And you need to hear something else. I've checked. In the history of South Orange River Middle School sports, no team, I repeat, *no team*, has ever lost *all* its games.

"Do you guys want to go down in history as the worst team? Do you?"

There was absolute, stunned silence.

"Do you?" He insisted on an answer.

"Odds on that we can," said Macht.

Mr. Tillman turned savagely. "That's a defeatist attitude, Macht. Can it!" and he stalked out.

Mr. Lester looked embarrassed. "I know you try," he said softly. "I appreciate that. But I think it would be good to win one game. Next we play Parkville. Our last game. And I think I should tell you something. Parkville hasn't won a game all season either."

With those words of encouragement he left us.

"My gosh," said Barish, "another team as bad as us."

"Awesome," said Dorman.

"We'll be playing for 'Worst in the Universe,'" said Radosh.

There was almost—not quite—a thrill of excitement.

I was sitting in class trying to follow the math teacher who was working out a problem on the board. Looking down I discovered a carefully folded piece of paper on my desk with my name on it. A passed note.

I looked at Saltz. He shrugged.

Propping up my math book to hide my hands, I carefully unfolded the note. It read:

> *Meet me after lunch by*
> *the downstairs dump bins.*
> *Lucy*

Astonished, I slammed my elbow into Saltz and palmed the note to him. He looked at it and *he* turned all red.

I tried to squirm around to look at Lucy but all I got was the math teacher saying, "Ed, keep your eyes up here, will you? You need to know this. It might even help your team score goals."

Big yuks.

Anyway, all during the first part of lunch hour Saltz and I had a serious discussion about Lucy Neblet. As we stuffed sandwiches and Twinkies in our mouths, as well as sucking up milk through straws, the talk went something like this:

Saltz began by asking, "What do you think?"

"I don't know. I am working on that history project with her."

"What's that supposed to mean?"

"Doesn't mean anything."

"What's the project about?"

"Mohawk Indians."

"Did you ever see her sister?"

"Whose sister?"

"Lucy's."

"Yeah."

"Well?"

"Well what?"

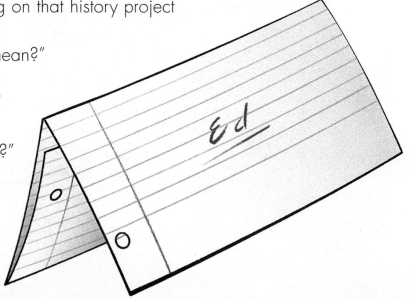

"Just, well."
"That's all you think about."
"I wasn't thinking about anything."
"Yes you were."
"How do you know?"
"I just do."
"I wasn't."
"Then how come you asked?"
"Just wanted to know."
"So nosey."
"You like her?"
"Who?"
"You know."
"No, I don't."
"Do too."
"What's it to you?"
"Curious."
"Why, do you?"
"Me, what?"
"I just said."
"No way."
"You used to."
"So what?"
"Then, who?"
"Me to know and you to find out."
"You're crazy."
"So you do like her."
"Maybe."
"Think she likes you?"
"Don't know."

"Someone once told me if she winks at you that means she does."

"Who told you?"

"What's the difference?"

"I'm going."

"Tell me what she said."

"She hasn't said anything yet."

"Watch her eyes."

"See ya."

"See ya."

I got out of the lunch room by telling the teacher on duty that I had to go to the boy's room. Instead I went downstairs, my heart beating, my head thinking, "This is it," except, I had no idea what "it" was.

At the back of the stairwell were these big garbage bins. The place stank. It was sort of dark and mysterious. But there was Lucy, perky and pretty.

"Hi," I said.

"Hi," she returned.

That was all until I said, "What's happening?"

"You're captain of the special soccer team, aren't you?" She was whispering, as if we were about to pass secrets to the Russians.

"Yeah," I said to her question. Don't ask me why, but I whispered too.

"Well," she continued, "I just thought I'd tell you . . ." She stopped.

"Tell me what?"

Her eyes were cast down. "I'm sorry you're losing."

"What?"

She looked up. No winking yet. "I'm just very sorry that you're losing." Then she blinked *both* eyes.

Something inside of me started to boil. "Why?" I said for the millionth time. "Why?"

"Why what?"

"Why are you sorry?"

"I just am," she said, startled by my reaction. "You must feel so badly."

"Well," I said, "I'm glad we're losing." By then I was almost shouting.

She looked at me as if I was crazy.

"Because if everyone else in this whole school wants to win," I kept on, "we're the eleven most unusual people in the whole building. And I like it that way!" Turning, I started for the steps, yelling, "Let's hear it for losers!"

For all I know she just stayed there by the garbage bins. It was the end of a beautiful romance.

I should have guessed what was going to happen next when this kid from the school newspaper interviewed me. It went this way.

NEWSPAPER: How does it feel to lose every game?

ME: I never played on a team that won, so I can't compare. But it's . . . interesting.

NEWSPAPER: How many teams have you been on?

ME: Just this one.

NEWSPAPER: Do you want to win?

ME: Wouldn't mind knowing what it feels like. For the novelty.

NEWSPAPER: Have you figured out why you lose all the time?

ME: They score more goals.

NEWSPAPER: Have you seen any improvement?

ME: I've been too busy.

NEWSPAPER: Busy with what?

ME: Trying to stop their goals. Ha-ha.

NEWSPAPER: From the scores, it doesn't seem like you've been too successful with that.

ME: You can imagine what the scores would have been if I wasn't there. Actually, I'm the tallest.

NEWSPAPER: What's that have to do with it?

ME: Ask Mr. Lester.

NEWSPAPER: No S.O.R. team has ever lost all its games in one season. How do you feel about that record?

ME: I read somewhere that records are made to be broken.

NEWSPAPER: But how will you feel?

ME: Same as I do now.

NEWSPAPER: How's that?

ME: Fine.

NEWSPAPER: Give us a prediction. Will you win or lose your last game?

ME: As captain, I can promise only one thing.

NEWSPAPER: What's that?
ME: I don't want to be there to see what happens.

Naturally, they printed all that. Next thing I knew some kids decided to hold a pep rally.

"What for?" asked Radosh.

"To fill us full of pep, I suppose."

"What's pep?"

Hays looked it up. "Dash," he read.

Saltz shook his head.

"What's dash?" asked Porter.

"Sounds like a deodorant soap," said Eliscue.

And then Ms. Appleton called me aside. "Ed," she said, sort of whispering (I guess she was embarrassed to be seen talking to any of us), "people are asking, 'Do they *want* to lose?'"

"Who's asking?"

"It came up at the last teachers' meeting. Mr. Tillman thinks you might be encouraging a defeatist attitude in the school. And Mr. Lester . . ."

"What about him?"

"He doesn't know."

It figured. "Ms. Appleton," I said, "why do people care so much if we win or lose?"

"It's your . . . attitude," she said. "It's so unusual. We're not used to . . . well . . . not winning sometimes. Or . . . or not caring if you lose."

"Think there's something the matter with us?" I wanted to know.

"No," she said, but when you say "no" the way she did, slowly, there's lots of time to sneak in a good hint of "yes." "I don't think you *mean* to lose."

"That's not what I asked."

"It's important to win," she said.

"Why? We're good at other things. Why can't we stick with that?"

But all she said was, "Try harder."

I went back to my seat. "I'm getting nervous," I mumbled.

"About time," said Saltz.

"Maybe we should defect."

"Where to?"

"There must be some country that doesn't have sports."

Then, of course, when my family sat down for dinner that night it went on.

"In two days you'll have your last game, won't you," my ma said. It was false cheerful, as if I had a terminal illness and she wanted to pretend it was only a head cold.

"Yeah," I said.

"You're going to win," my father announced.

"How do you know?" I snapped.

"I sense it."

"Didn't know you could tell the future."

"Don't be so smart," he returned. "I'm trying to be supportive."

"I'm sick of support!" I yelled and left the room.

Twenty minutes later I got a call. Saltz.

"Guess what?" he said.

"I give up."

"Two things. My father offered me a bribe."

"To lose the game?"

"No, to win it. A new bike."

"Wow. What did you say?"

"I told him I was too honest to win a game."

"What was the second thing?"

"I found out that at lunch tomorrow they are doing that pep rally, and worse. They're going to call up the whole team."

I sighed. "Why are they doing all this?" I asked.

"Nobody loves a loser," said Saltz.

"Why?" I asked him, just as I had asked everybody else.

"Beats me. Like everybody else does." He hung up.

I went into my room and flung myself on my bed and stared up at the ceiling. A short time later my father came into the room. "Come on, kid," he said. "I was just trying to be a pal."

"Why can't people let us lose in peace?"

"People think you feel bad."

"We feel *fine!*"

"Come on. We won't talk about it any more. Eat your dinner."

I went.

Next day, when I walked into the school eating area for lunch there was the usual madhouse. But there was also a big banner across the front part of the room:

MAKE THE LOSERS WINNERS
KEEP UP THE GOOD NAME OF S.O.R.

I wanted to start a food fight right then and there.

I'm not going through the whole bit. But halfway through the lunch period, the president of the School

Council, of all people, went to a microphone and called for attention. Then she made a speech.

"We just want to say to the Special Seventh-Grade Soccer Team that we're all behind you."

"It's in front of us where we need people," whispered Saltz. "Blocking."

The president went on. "Would you come up and take a bow." One by one she called our names. Each time one of us went up, looking like cringing but grinning worms, there was some general craziness, hooting, foot stomping, and an occasional milk carton shooting through the air.

The president said: "I'd like the team captain, Ed Sitrow, to say a few words."

What could I do? Trapped, I cleared my throat. Four times. "Ah, well . . . we . . . ah . . . sure . . . hope to get there . . . and . . . you know . . . I suppose . . . play and . . . you know!"

MAKE THE LOSERS WINNERS
KEEP UP THE GOOD NAME OF S.O.R.

The whole room stood up to cheer. They even began the school chant.

"Give me an S! Give me an O . . ."

After that we went back to our seats. I was madder than ever. And as I sat there, maybe two hundred and fifty kids filed by, thumping me hard on the back, shoulder, neck and head, yelling, "Good luck! Good luck!" They couldn't fool me. I knew what they were doing: beating me.

"Saltz," I said when they were gone and I was merely numb, "I'm calling an emergency meeting of the team."

Like thieves, we met behind the school, out of sight. I looked around. I could see everybody was feeling rotten.

"I'm sick and tired of people telling me we have to win," said Root.

"I think my folks are getting ready to disown me," said Hays. "My brother and sister too."

"Why can't they just let us lose?" asked Macht.

"Yeah," said Barish, "because we're not going to win."

"We might," Lifsom offered. "Parkville is supposed to be the pits too."

"Yeah," said Radosh, "but we're beneath the pits."

"Right," agreed Porter.

For a moment it looked like everyone was going to start to cry.

"I'd just like to do my math," said Macht. "I like that."

There it was. Something clicked. "Hays," I said, "you're good at music, right."

"Yeah, well, sure—rock 'n' roll."

"Okay. And Macht, what's the lowest score you've pulled in math so far?"

"A-plus."

"Last year?"

"Same."

"Lifsom," I went on, getting excited, "how's your painting coming?"

"I just finished something real neat and . . ."

"That's it," I cut in, because that kid can go on forever about his painting. "Every one of us is good at something. Right? Maybe more than one thing. The point is, *other* things."

"Sure," said Barish.

"Except," put in Saltz, "sports."

We were quiet for a moment. Then I saw what had been coming to me: "That's *their* problem. I mean, we are good, good at *lots* of things. Why can't we just plain stink in some places? That's got to be normal."

"Let's hear it for normal," chanted Dorman.

"Doesn't bother me to lose at sports," I said. "At least, it didn't bother me until I let other people make me bothered."

"What about the school record?" asked Porter. "You know, no team ever losing for a whole season. Want to be famous for that?"

"Listen," I said, "did we want to be on this team?"

"No!" they all shouted.

"I can see some of it," I said. "You know, doing something different. But I don't like sports. I'm not good at it. I don't enjoy it. So I say, so what? I mean if Saltz here writes a stinko poem—and he does all the time—do they yell at him? When was the last time Mr. Tillman came around and said, 'Saltz, I *believe* in your being a poet!'"

"Never," said Saltz.

"Yeah," said Radosh. "How come sports is so important?"

"You know," said Dorman, "maybe a loser makes people think of things *they* lost. Like Mr. Tillman not getting into pro football. Us losing makes him remember that."

"Us winning, he forgets," cut in Eliscue.

"Right," I agreed. "He needs us to win for *him*, not for us. Maybe it's the same for others."

"Yeah, but how are you going to convince them of that?" said Barish.

"By not caring if we lose," I said.

"Only one thing," put in Saltz. "They say this Parkville team is pretty bad too. What happens if we, you know, by mistake, win?"

That set us back for a moment.

"I think," suggested Hays after a moment, "that if we just go on out there, relax, and do our best, and not worry so much, we'll lose."

There was general agreement on that point.

"Do you know what I heard?" said Eliscue.

"What?"

"I didn't want to say it before, but since the game's a home game, they're talking about letting the whole school out to cheer us on to a win."

"You're kidding."

He shook his head.

There was a long, deep silence.

"Probably think," said Saltz, "that we'd be ashamed to lose in front of everybody."

I took a quick count. "You afraid to lose?" I asked Saltz.

"No way."

"Hays?"

"No."

"Porter?"

"Nope."

And so on. I felt encouraged. It was a complete vote of no confidence.

⬤ IN RESPONSE

Sound Off About Sports

Imagine you are Ed Sitrow being interviewed after your team's vote of no confidence. How would you explain your team's position about winning or losing? With a partner, take turns role-playing an interview for the school paper.

Take a New Perspective

Ed Sitrow said, "Doesn't bother me to lose at sports. At least, it didn't bother me until I let other people make me bothered." In a group, discuss whether the Lin girl ("The All-American Slurp") might have made a similar statement about slurping her soup. Use examples from the selection to support your point of view.

Avi

★ Award-winning Author

Avi, whose full name is Avi Wortis, writes books for children and young adults, using many genres and story-telling techniques. He often requires the main characters—as well as the readers—of his novels to question their world.

When he talks about writing, Avi says, "I think that each person has a way of looking at the world. I'll bet your dentist, upon meeting someone, notices teeth. The clothing designer will measure your cut, taste, and budget. . . . In just the same fashion, you can learn to look at the world from a novelist's point of view."

Avi adds that writing also requires reading a great deal and thinking like a writer. His ideas for novels are the result of considering various thoughts, observations, and moods from a writer's perspective. "My primary perception of the world is that of story." Because Avi loves to read, he has taught himself to think about people, situations, and events in terms of how they can be used in stories. "This means I am never without ideas," he says.

Avi was born and raised in New York City. For more than twenty-five years, Avi has combined the careers of a librarian and a writer. Avi is the father of two teenage sons—both soccer players.

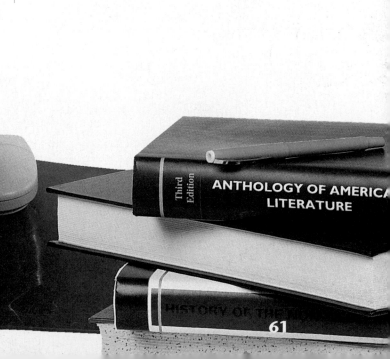

The MOUSE and the Elephant

retold by Barbara K. Walker

Once a small proud mouse lived in a corner of the forest. While other mice scurried about, afraid of their own shadows, he sat idly twirling his whiskers. From time to time, he stamped upon the earth and then put his ear to the ground and listened. Do you know why? He wished to see whether the earth trembled!

He laughed at the notion that anyone else could be as great and powerful as he was. One day his uncle said wisely, "Watch yourself, young one. The elephant has heard about your showing off and he is very angry."

"The elephant!" scoffed the little one, who had never seen an elephant. "Who is he? I'll show him who is master of this forest!"

His uncle, old and experienced, smiled behind his paw. "There is something to be said for size. But you must see for yourself, I suppose."

"I shall teach that elephant a lesson," declared the small one. And off he set. He walked and he walked, till he came upon a lizard.

"Hey, you," called the mouse. "Are you the elephant?"

"No, no, not I," answered the lizard. "I am only a lizard."

"In that case, you may count yourself lucky," said the mouse. "If you had been the elephant, I would have broken you to bits."

The lizard, who had seen the elephant, shook with laughter. When the mouse heard the lizard laugh, he stamped his paw with rage. As it chanced, at that moment there came a great clap of thunder. The lizard, thinking the mouse had made all that noise, scuttled away under a bush. Puffing out his chest with pride, the mouse walked on.

In a little while he saw a cockroach. "Ho, there!" he called. "Are you the elephant?"

"No, no, not I," answered the cockroach. "I am only a cockroach."

"In that case, you may count yourself lucky," said the mouse. "If you had been the elephant, I would have broken you to bits."

The cockroach, who had seen the elephant, shrugged his

shoulders. When the mouse saw the cockroach shrug his shoulders, he glared angrily. Just as he glared, there came a flash of lightning. The cockroach, frightened, scurried away. And the mouse, puffing out his chest even more, walked on.

A little farther on, he saw a dog. "See how slowly and sadly he walks," said the mouse to himself. "It is the elephant, and he must have heard that I was coming or he would not look so sad. Ho, there, elephant!" he called out.

"Elephant!" the dog exclaimed. "I am not the elephant. I am only a dog." And he smiled clear across his face.

"Oh, you may safely smile," said the mouse. "But if you had been the elephant, I would have broken you to bits."

Just as the dog was about to answer, a man called to him. "That is my master," said he. "For all I know, he is master of the whole world."

"Take that back!" shouted the mouse. "*I* am master of the whole world." But the dog had run off,

and there was no one to hear his boast.

Still angry, the mouse went on. Suddenly he came to what looked as big as a mountain. It was gray. It stood on four legs as large as tree trunks. It had two tails, one in front and one in back. It had two great ears. Yes, it was the elephant.

"Hey, you!" called the mouse. "Are you the elephant?"

The elephant looked from bush to tree to rock and finally he saw a small dot. It was the mouse. He bent his head down so he could hear what the mouse was saying.

"Who do you think you are?" asked the mouse boldly. "Look at me. I am the master of this forest. What do you think of that?"

The elephant, aiming his trunk at the speck on the ground, gushed forth all the water he had sucked up for his bath. *Whoosh!* The mouse was thrown ears over heels down the path with the sudden flood. He lay there for a moment, half dead from shock, and next door to drowned, besides.

When he came to his senses again, the elephant was gone. "What a storm that was!" exclaimed the mouse. "And it's a lucky thing for that elephant. If the sky hadn't opened up with a cloudburst, I would have broken the elephant to bits."

Home he went, singing to himself. When he arrived, there was his uncle waiting by the path to greet him. "And did you tell the elephant who was master of this forest?" asked his uncle, smiling behind his paw.

"I had just told him who was master of the forest when *Whoosh!* all the water in the sky came down in such a cloudburst that we were washed apart from one another. For all I know, he was drowned. I never saw him again. Better for him that he drowned rather than be broken to bits!"

Down he sat in his old corner. And if the elephant has not come along since to dispute him, he is still telling the same story.

Night Visions

People have different perspectives on the world, depending on where they live. These paintings show different portrayals of night. How do the views of night shown here relate to your perspective?

Painting by Vincent van Gogh (Dutch), *Starry Night,* **1889**

Vincent van Gogh, *The Starry Night,* 1889, oil on canvas, 29" x 36 1/4." The Museum of Modern Art, New York. Acquired through the Lillie P. Bliss Bequest. Photograph ©1996 The Museum of Modern Art, New York

The artist of each of these paintings used paint to describe a night in a particular place. How would you translate their descriptions into words?

Painting by Georgia O'Keeffe (United States), *Radiator Building—Night, New York,* **1927**

Describe what might be happening in the painting on the left. What is the man at the center doing? How do you know?

Painting by Pablita Velarde (United States), *Old Father the Story Teller,* **1960**

BENI SEBALLOS

from *It's Our World, Too!*
by Phillip Hoose

AWARD WINNER

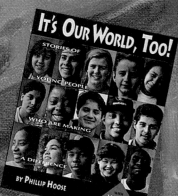

IT'S OUR WORLD, Too!

STORIES OF YOUNG PEOPLE WHO ARE MAKING A DIFFERENCE

BY PHILLIP HOOSE

One day when she was fifteen, Beni Seballos stepped onto a plane with ten of her aunts, uncles, cousins, nieces, and nephews and said good-bye to everything she loved. Soon her home, her friends, and her school in the Philippines were far behind her.

When they arrived in Los Angeles, they drove to a small house. There they would stay with her aunt and grandparents until they could find enough money to buy a home of their own.

The fourteen of them tried their best to be cheerful. For Beni, the hardest part was trying to get along with her grandmother. She was a stern, quiet woman, used to the respect that elders commanded in the Philippines. Beni was noisy and opinionated. Her grandmother always seemed to disapprove of her. Each day Beni would ask her grandmother if she could help with dinner, and the answer was always no. That "no" filled the kitchen, leaving no space for Beni. She always left the room in anger, wondering how long she could take living there.

Racida High School was no better. She didn't know anybody at first. She made the basketball team but rarely got in the games. "Academic Decathlon was even worse," Beni recalls. "A team of kids from Racida High tried to answer questions faster than a team from another school. It wasn't about learning.... I hated it."

The one thing she really liked was a volunteer organization called Youth Community Services, or YCS. After hearing about it at school, Beni went on a weekend field trip to plant trees in a farm area. There was no feeling of competition here. Everyone was working together. She volunteered for YCS at a blood bank, at a recycling center, and with a program that helped keep young kids off drugs. At last, she was having fun in the United States.

Her parents didn't understand. To them, volunteering just kept her away from home. She wasn't even getting school credit for it. When Beni put on her

jacket to go to a YCS event, her grandmother would
glare, and her mother would say, softly but pointedly,
"Oh, you're going off again, aren't you, Beni?"

During the summer break, a YCS counselor urged
Beni to volunteer at a senior citizens center. The staff
needed volunteers to help take care of old people who
had Alzheimer's and Parkinson's diseases. Think of all
you could learn, the counselor kept saying.

Beni wasn't so sure. She found herself wondering
what a sixteen-year-old could really have in common
with someone who was seventy-five or eighty. She
hated to admit it to herself, but old people sounded
boring. Even worse, what if they all treated her the
way her grandmother did?

But maybe the counselor was right. After all, she
thought, you learn most by doing what you understand
least. Beni signed up for four days a week, five hours
a day, and then walked to the library to find out about
Alzheimer's and Parkinson's diseases.

A medical encyclopedia said that both diseases affect the brain's ability to function. Alzheimer's patients gradually lose their memories, and Parkinson's patients gradually lose control of their muscles. After reading less than a page, Beni closed the book, unable to go on. "I was terrified," she remembers. "I could see myself having to force-feed these drooling people. I'd have to pick them up off the ground all the time. I thought they'd be vegetables.

"I practically ran out of the library. I was ready to quit before I had ever met a single patient. By the time I got home, I was wondering, 'What did I get myself into?'"

The first day, Beni introduced herself to the center's supervisor, Kathleen, and the six other volunteers, all in their forties and fifties. They were friendly, but she wondered if they really believed a teenager could handle the work.

Kathleen explained that the volunteers were supposed to feed the patients, take them for walks, and help give them their medicine. She went over each patient's medicine and diet. She kept looking at Beni and saying, "Don't worry, you'll do fine."

Then Kathleen opened the door, and they all walked out into the hallway, where about fifteen patients and their relatives were waiting. Some patients were in wheelchairs. Others were in walkers. A few leaned on canes.

Beni hung back and watched as the other volunteers rushed forward to greet the patients. Was she supposed to help them into their wheelchairs? How did you do it, anyway? What if she dropped someone? "I could see some of the patients' relatives looking at me. I felt them thinking, She's just a kid. She doesn't look like she knows what she's doing."

She followed the crowd into a big room, where the volunteers were supposed to serve the patients coffee and doughnuts. Beni's mind went blank. She couldn't remember who was supposed to have only half a doughnut and who wasn't supposed to get a doughnut at all. Kathleen was nowhere in sight. Beni fought back tears. This was terrible. It was the Alzheimer's patients who were supposed to have memory problems, not her.

After coffee, Kathleen was reading a newspaper article to a group of patients when one of them interrupted. He pointed to Beni. "You're a young person," he said. "What do you think about this?" Beni was startled. An older person actually wanted her opinion? This was certainly different from home. Well, actually she *did* have an opinion on the topic of the article, and so she gave it. They listened carefully and discussed it. This part isn't so bad, Beni thought.

She went home that night exhausted and determined to do better tomorrow. As always, her grandmother was in the kitchen. They went through the usual routine again, with Beni offering to help and her grandmother refusing her. Beni walked out fuming. She had to get out of there.

The next morning, Beni went to the center early and memorized the patients' names. When the patients arrived, she sat down beside a frail woman named Lil with a sparse crown of thin white hair. Beni peeled an orange for her and filled up her cup of coffee halfway with a single lump of sugar, just as Lil's chart said. As she was working, Beni told Lil about what it had been like to move from the Philippines.

Lil began to talk, too. She said she had spent much of her life raising five wonderful children.

"Where are they now?" Beni asked.

"Who?"

"Your children."

"What?"

"Your children. You were saying you have five children."

Lil wrung the hem of her dress in her hands, looking frantically around the room. "What do you mean? I-I-I can't remember." She seemed to be growing more desperate by the second. Beni quickly changed the subject to her own college plans, and gradually Lil relaxed. It was Beni's first real contact with Alzheimer's disease. It taught her that she had to listen and be flexible, alert to each patient's needs. Patients wouldn't always be able to stick to the same subject for very long.

Later that week, Beni was leading a patient named Oscar outside for a game of shuffleboard when she heard the sharp scrape of metal behind her. His walker had become caught between two chairs. Trembling, he tried to shake loose. Beni knelt to pry the walker free, but it was no use. Oscar was growing enraged and started to shout. His face was turning red. Here it is, Beni thought, the emergency I can't handle. She sprinted into the kitchen to get help. Three volunteers and Kathy rushed out, and in a moment, they had him free. "You handled it well," Kathy said to Beni later. "Just get help."

As the summer went by, Beni faced many different kinds of challenges. A few patients tried to wander off. Some became angry because they couldn't remember when to take their medicine. One refused to go back inside after a walk.

After a few weeks at the center, Beni found herself thinking differently about the patients. She could no longer think of them as "old people" or "senior citizens," or "Alzheimer's patients" or even "patients." They had become individuals, like her, who just happened to be at a different stage of their lives. Like her, they all had their own interests and families, hopes and fears, opinions and problems.

She discovered that if she listened carefully, she could find something in common with almost everyone. Alex wrote poetry, just like Beni. Sometimes at the shuffleboard court, they recited their poems to each other. Beni and Oscar spoke Spanish together. Blackie told her World War II stories. Mary taught her a few words of Czech. Lil loved to talk about children.

By the end of the summer, it seemed to Beni that being young had been an advantage, not a handicap, at the center. "I was special to some of the Alzheimer's patients," she says. "I think maybe having me around helped them remember how they were when they were young themselves."

In September, Beni said a tearful good-bye to the patients and staff and took a week off before school started. She had some unfinished business.

All summer long, things had gotten worse and worse with her grandmother until finally she had moved out of her aunt's house in order to find some peace in her life. But she didn't feel at peace. She loved her grandmother, and she wanted to put things right between them.

For a while it had seemed strange that she could have fun with Lil or Oscar or Alex but not her own grandmother. Then it came to her: When things got tough with a patient at the center, she kept trying patiently until she found a way to get through. But when things got tough with her grandmother, she gave up.

So one afternoon, she walked over to her aunt's house, determined to treat her grandmother as she had learned to treat the people at the center.

As usual, Beni's grandmother was in the kitchen. "Hi," Beni said. "Is there anything I can do?" "No," said her grandmother. This time Beni didn't leave. She noticed a bowl of string beans on the counter and carried them to the kitchen table. She sat down, picked up a bean, and snapped off the end.

She began to tell her grandmother about her summer. Though her grandmother didn't say anything, Beni could sense that she was listening. After a while, her grandmother wiped her hands on a towel, pulled up a chair, and sat down at the other end of the table. She picked up a bean and snapped the top off. A half hour later, there was a big pile of beans between them—and the beginning of a friendship.

Beni says that friendship was maybe the greatest gift of the summer. It couldn't have happened until she herself changed, and volunteering at the center was the key that opened doors within her. "The summer started working for me when I began to share myself with the patients, not just log time," she says. "Then it was fun. I know I did a good job at the center, but I probably got more out of it than the patients. I learned that caring is like a muscle. The more you exercise it, the more you *can* share."

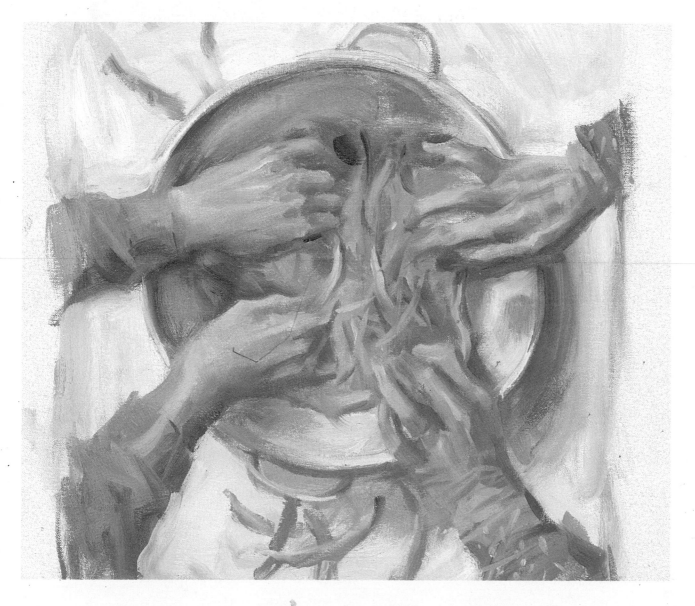

IN RESPONSE

Help Wanted

Prepare a help-wanted ad for a summer volunteer for the school newspaper. Choose examples from the story to tell what the volunteer is expected to do, what qualifications he or she needs, and what he or she will get from the experience.

Turning Point

In "The All-American Slurp" and in "Beni Seballos," the main character begins to see things from a different perspective. In a group, discuss each selection and find the point at which you think the change happens. Use examples to support your choice.

AUTHOR AT WORK

Like Beni Seballos, Phillip Hoose has tried to make a difference in the world. He once worked as a tenant organizer; he also helped found the Children's Music Network. Mr. Hoose hopes his stories inspire young people to work to make a difference in the world. He and his family live in Portland, Maine.

★ Award-winning Author

Another Book About . . .

Volunteering

Kids Who Make a Difference by Joyce M. Roché and Marie Rodriguez, MasterMedia, 1993

Library Link Want to learn more about how to make a difference? Beni Seballos's story, along with stories of other young people, appears in *It's Our World, Too!* The book, which the author calls "a guide to power for young people," includes tactics and resources you and your friends can use to start making a difference.

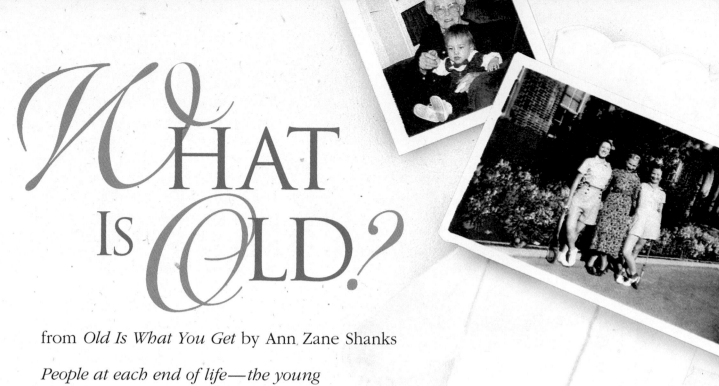

WHAT IS OLD?

from *Old Is What You Get* by Ann Zane Shanks

*People at each end of life—the young
and the old—have their own perspectives
on aging. The following quotes show a
variety of worries and fears, as well as
respect and optimism.*

When you feel like having
somebody around, like your
grandchildren and children.

JAN
Classroom interview

It's deeply frustrating to be old.
You can't do things you want
to. So you want to, but you
can't. And you have to see a
doctor much more.

AARON
Classroom interview

I think it's in your mind.

ANDRE
Classroom interview

Sixty is old. I mean, not *old* old.
But that's beginning to get old.

LUCY MERRILL, age 15

It's like being more of a *nothing* than a something. When I was six, I thought twenty was like, "Oh, my . . . that's old!" And now ninety is terribly old. Still, when I think of someone who's forty . . . It's what's old to you.

   If you're not dependent on somebody, you're not old.

MARK
Classroom interview

You're old when your mind gives out, when you can't think straight, and you can't change.

KATHY
Classroom interview

Some people might feel it's nice being old, because after all your frivolous years, you finally have a rest.

DAVID
Classroom interview

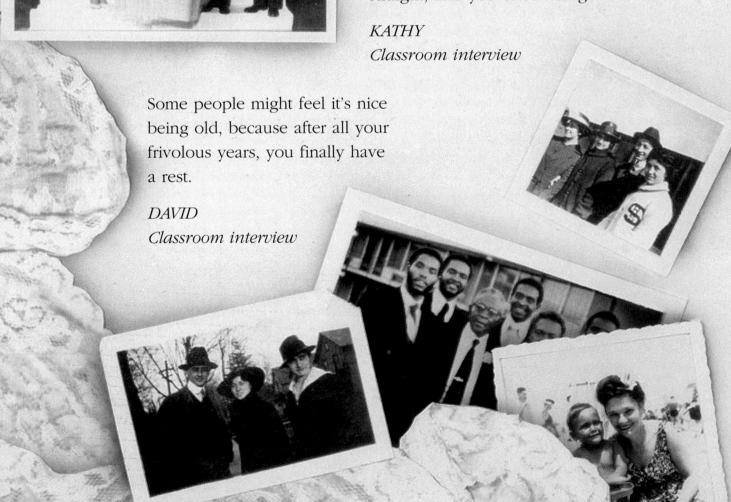

I'm not particularly interested in being old or whether other people are old or not. My life's concern has been for justice in society, and it just happened I got a job at seventy that showed me what old people are up against. Later I got into the Gray Panthers group through Maggie Kuhn, its founder, and wanted to continue the work she was doing. I like young people because they keep up with the changing world, and I, too, like to keep track of what's happening.

Two things are important when you're old: to have financial stability and to have good health. If you have too much pain, you can't do much. But I get angry when I think of those people who are perfectly well and competent who sit at Senior Citizen Centers and play Bingo. That gets me!

I've always been a defiant person. If I saw somebody in trouble, I tried to get after the person causing the situation and try to change it. I didn't take things lying down. I am an objector and always have been. I was the first married woman teacher in Detroit, Michigan. There was a rule that if you married and were a woman, you retired automatically. I didn't see any sense in that after I married, so I wrote to every member of the Board of Education and asked them what they were going to do about my marrying. I stayed.

You'd be surprised, but sometimes people are very kind to you when you're old. They do nice things for you. I've had two people at once on a bus get up and give me a seat. I can't occupy but one, although I look as though I could occupy two.

HOPE BAGGER, age 84

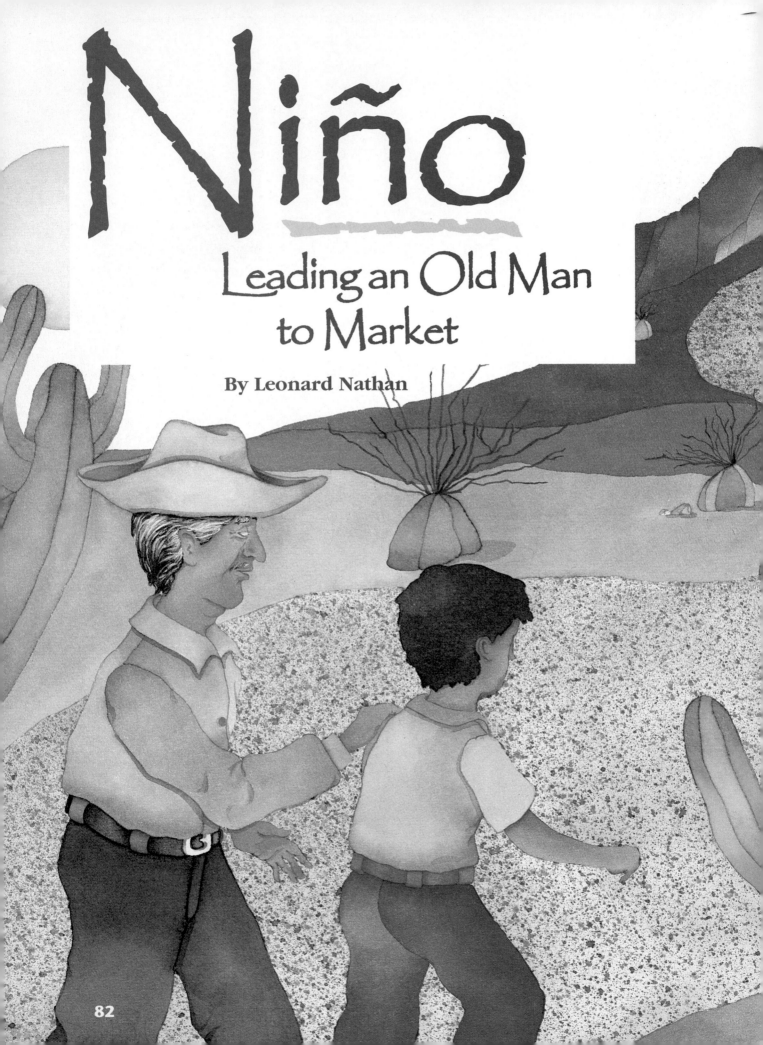

Niño

Leading an Old Man to Market

By Leonard Nathan

He is leading his grandfather under the sun to market.
Who needs to see? The hand is warm on his shoulder.
The sun tells a man whatever he has to know
And the eyes of the children take care of the rest.

This is a little procession, solemn and steady,
A way of seeing that has the right direction,
And needs the simplest of eyes; the hand is quite sure,
And the wealth of the sun takes care of the rest.

His children have children to spare for any errand
An old man must go on; like sun, they are warmly with him,
Though at night his wakeful hand may remember that seeing
Was going alone in any direction.

Time takes care of the rest. In the niño's eyes
He is leading his grandfather under the sun to market.
In the old man's mind he walks through warmth where he must.
They are going in one direction, and know it.

---

niño's (*NEE nyohz*) little boy's

84

PHOTOGRAPHY
AND OTHER LESSONS

from *RIO GRANDE STORIES*
by CAROLYN MEYER

R icky Begay focused the camera on his grandfather, who was hunched over his workbench.
Click went the shutter; *click, click,* two more
shots, just to be sure. Ricky moved the camera to a
different angle and took another reading with his
light meter. He refocused the lens for a close-up of the
old man's hands, veined and gnarled with age. *Tap tap
tap* went his grandfather's delicate hammer on the thin
silver disk.

The camera was ancient, bought at a pawnshop. It
was so old Ricky had to calculate everything: film speed,
amount of available light, shutter speed, size of lens opening. He had seen the automatics that did everything for
you. All you had to do was point those high-tech jobs and

snap the shutter, and the camera figured it all out. Ricky didn't like that kind. His Konica was more interesting and certainly more of a challenge.

Ricky's grandfather, Joe Bennett, wore his long gray hair in the traditional Navajo *chongo*,[1] pulled into a pony-tail that was twisted and looped back on itself and bound with a colorful ribbon. As always a couple of turquoise necklaces hung around his neck. The light over his work-bench glinted off his eyeglasses. Ricky adjusted the lamp so it wouldn't glare in the pictures. He had used most of a roll of black-and-white film already.

Ricky's idea was to tell the story of a piece of Navajo jewelry from the time his grandfather started working on it until it got sold, all in pictures. "It's a class project," Ricky had explained to him. "We're doing a book about our heritage. Being Indian and all."

His grandfather thought about that. "You going to do the whole book, Ricky?"

"No. Just one chapter."

"You could do a whole book about the Dineh. The People."

"Maybe someday I will."

"Too bad you couldn't take some pictures of the old *hogan*[2] where I learned," Grandfather said. "Then you'd have the story where it started."

This was where it started for Ricky, too. He had been born on the Navajo reservation up near Shiprock, in the

1 **chongo** (*CHOHN goh*)
2 **hogan** (*HOH gahn*)

86

northwest corner of New Mexico. His parents still lived there, and so did two older sisters. Ricky had come down to Albuquerque to live with his grandfather about six months earlier, after his grandmother got sick and died. He was supposed to keep his grandfather company in the little house he moved to after Grandmother died. The new house was so close to the railroad tracks that it sounded as though the trains were roaring right through it. But Grandfather couldn't stay in the old place because, like all Navajo, he was afraid of the dead, and there was the chance that Grandmother's ghost might still haunt their old house. The new house was noisy but safe.

Ricky didn't have the patience to sit at a workbench hour after hour, as Grandfather did, making bolo ties— silver-and-turquoise slides on leather strings. Bolos were popular at Old Town Plaza, where Joe Bennett sold his jewelry. Tourists liked them. Lots of white men wore them instead of a necktie. "Ladies wear them now, too," Grandfather said. "Got to be fashionable, I guess."

Ricky moved in for a close-up of a bolo. This one had a piece of polished turquoise set in an oval of silver stamped with a design around the edge. He watched his grandfather solder a narrow strip of silver to hold the bluish green stone on the silver disk.

"String a bunch of these together, like this," Grandfather said. He opened a drawer in his workbench and pulled out a handsome silver belt. "Concha belt, it's called. I made this one a long time ago. Your grandmother wore it on her velvet skirt. Looked real pretty." He stared at it and laid it aside. Ricky knew it must make his grandfather feel sad.

"They sell for a good bit of money. Kind of tourists I sell to usually don't want to pay that much, so I make the little things, too," Grandfather said.

He reached far back in the drawer. "Now here's something else you might like to make a picture of. Squash-blossom necklace. This crescent-shaped piece here in the middle is a *naja*.[3] They used to hang them on the browband of a headstall, the part of a bridle that fits over the horse's head. Then they started putting them on bead necklaces with these little silver squash blossoms in between the beads. My daddy made this necklace. I remember when he used to take it to the pawnshop at the trading post when he needed money, and it would stay there until he wanted to wear it to a dance or a sing or something special, and the trader let him borrow it. Afterward it would go back to the trading post. Everybody did that, I guess. Most people never had the money to get it out of pawn. That's how the best jewelry ended up in white people's collections."

3 **naja** (*NAH hah*)

Ricky hung the squash-blossom necklace around his grandfather's neck and took a photograph. Then he took pictures of other pieces of jewelry his grandfather had stashed around the little house, including a woman's squash-blossom necklace that Joe Bennett had made. More delicate than the man's, it had won a ribbon at Indian Market, but so far no one had bought it. It was too expensive.

"In the old days," Grandfather said after a while, "we used to make all kinds of things by sandcasting. I carved a copy of what I wanted to make out of wax and covered it with sand. Then I melted out the wax and poured melted silver into the space the wax left. And there it was— something beautiful. Buckles, bracelets, things like that. But not anymore. It costs too much, and people don't pay." He picked up his hammer again. *Tap tap tap.*

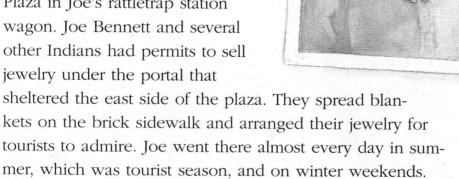

On the day after Thanksgiving, Grandfather packed up a few of his good pieces and a boxful of the less expensive items, and he and Ricky drove to Old Town Plaza in Joe's rattletrap station wagon. Joe Bennett and several other Indians had permits to sell jewelry under the portal that sheltered the east side of the plaza. They spread blankets on the brick sidewalk and arranged their jewelry for tourists to admire. Joe went there almost every day in summer, which was tourist season, and on winter weekends.

Winter was the slow time. It was cold and not so many tourists came. Most of the Indians stayed home to make jewelry for the big summer season. But Joe Bennett said it was a mistake to give it up entirely. Even in winter he spent time on the plaza on weekends, just in case. Sometimes Ricky went along to help.

Most of the Navajo vendors brought folding chairs to sit on while the tourists filed by slowly, staring down at the jewelry. Sometimes a customer would see something she liked and would stoop down to pick it up and examine it more closely. A lot of the Indians kept little hand mirrors so their customers could see how they looked in the jewelry. Joe arranged his merchandise with care, so that the expensive concha belts and the prize-winning squash-blossom necklace attracted attention, but

the cheaper bolos and earrings were in easy reach. He set
up little white cards with prices printed on them so customers wouldn't have to ask how much something cost.

Shivering and stamping his feet, Ricky wished he had
had this idea for the photographs when the weather was
warmer. He and Grandfather had bundled up in heavy
jackets and extra socks, for although the weather forecast
called for sunshine, the air was definitely chilly. A lot
of tourists had come to Albuquerque for the long Thanksgiving weekend, and according to Joe Bennett, the day
after Thanksgiving would be a big day.

Joe Bennett had been right. Large numbers of tourists
strolled around in a festive mood, soaking up the sunshine.
They crisscrossed the plaza, visited the historic San Felipe
de Neri Church, and wandered in and out of shops that

specialized in T-shirts and souvenirs. A horse and carriage waited on the west side of the plaza to take people for rides through the narrow side streets.

All morning Ricky sat with his grandfather next to their blanket, scanning the steady stream of tourists. Most of them just glanced at the jewelry and kept on going. Some stopped to look more closely, and a few actually bought something.

Some visitors assumed the Indians didn't speak English and talked loudly to make them understand. And Ricky overheard one elderly woman ask, "Do you take American money?"

"You get somebody like that almost every day," Grandfather said with a quiet chuckle when the woman had moved on, clutching her purse. "They don't know they're in the United States. They come to Albuquerque and think they left the country." The man on the blanket next to theirs said, "Maybe they have."

Around noon a man decked out in plaid pants and a bright yellow jacket strolled by. His wife wore a soft suede coat. The man carried an expensive camera slung over his shoulder. Ricky always tried to get a look at the cameras the tourists carried. Grandfather sat impassively, not looking at his customers, letting them decide on their own whether to stop or keep on going, whether to buy or just to look.

"Hey, Chief!" the man said loudly. "You interested in selling some of this stuff?"

Joe Bennett turned slowly to look at him and then turned away again, as though he hadn't heard.

"Hey, listen, Geronimo! You speak a little English, right? So you can talk to your customers once in a while?"

The man in the plaid pants leaned closer to Grandfather, his face only a couple of feet from Joe Bennett's proud profile.

Grandfather glanced at the man again. "You buy what you like," he said in his slow, flat voice.

The man's wife picked up the squash-blossom necklace, held it up to her neck, and turned for her husband to see. The man took it from her, examined it, and dropped it carelessly back on the blanket. "Your prices seem way too high. So let's do some bargaining here. I give a little, you give a little, maybe you've got yourself a deal. I'm offering you half what you're asking, okay?"

"No bargaining," Grandfather said. "Prices are fair."

"I go down to Juárez, and they bargain. You could learn something from the Mexicans." He turned to the other vendors on their blankets, searching for someone to agree with him. "Right?" he kept asking. "Am I right?"

But they were all Navajo; nobody responded or changed expression. They all stared at something off in the distance.

The man finally gave up. He grabbed his wife's arm and steered her away.

Grandfather's face remained as calm as stone. No one said a word.

Not all tourists were so bad, though. In fact, Ricky realized, some tourists were really nice. Three girls about his own age came out of a souvenir shop, their winter jackets unzipped to show off their identical T-shirts with hot-air balloons printed on them. They started to walk past the jewelry, but then they stopped and knelt down to try on some of Grandfather's bolos. *They are sisters,* he decided, *visiting from, ummm, maybe California. They look nice.* One of them glanced up and smiled at him. He wished he had the nerve to talk to the girls and ask if he could take their picture as they tried on some dangling turquoise and silver earrings.

Around noon Ricky and Joe Bennett ate the bologna sandwiches they had brought from home. Ricky had just made up his mind to take some pictures of Grandfather surrounded by his blanketful of jewelry when a family stopped to examine Joe Bennett's work. "We're from Texas," explained the bald-headed man in a fancy photographer's vest with a dozen pockets. "These are our children and grandchildren." He beamed proudly. "We're here to do our Christmas shopping." His wife pulled out a long list, and within a short time they had bought something for everyone on the list.

The Texans had a camera and asked permission to take a picture of Joe Bennett with his jewelry. Then one of the women noticed Ricky sitting by quietly and asked if he would mind taking a picture of their family using their camera.

"My husband will set everything for you," the woman said reassuringly.

Ricky didn't need to have anyone set it for him, but he didn't say anything. *What a beautiful camera,* Ricky thought, taking it carefully from the bald-headed man. He checked the focus while the family—grandparents, parents, and several small children—discussed how to arrange themselves, and then he took several shots while they were still trying to get posed. The little kids looked tired and grumpy. Ricky could see that they didn't want to be doing this, but then something caught their attention and Ricky captured their fleeting expressions of interest.

"Hey, you look right at home with that camera, young man," the bald-headed man said when the session was over. "Are you a photographer?"

Ricky nodded, tongue-tied.

"Maybe you let my grandson take a picture of you with his camera?" Ricky's grandfather asked suddenly. "School project," he added.

"Why, sure thing," the visitors said. "You just tell us what you want us to do."

Ricky got his camera out of its battered leather case. "Pick up something," he began, cleared his throat, and began again. "Would you please pick up something like you're going to buy it? Maybe the squash-blossom necklace?"

The grandmother knelt in front of the blanket and reached for the necklace. Ricky moved in and began clicking off the shots as the woman picked it up, examined it, tried it on, and smiled at her reflection in the hand mirror.

"Hope you're not out of film, son," said the grandfather, reaching into his hip pocket. "Might as well get a shot of this, too." Obediently, Ricky took a picture of him pulling out his wallet. "Got that?" he asked, winking at Ricky.

Ricky nodded.

"Looks like we're gonna take that necklace, too," the man said, handing a fistful of cash to Joe Bennett.

"You're buying it, Leonard?" the grandmother asked, and Ricky was quick enough to capture the look of surprised pleasure on her face.

"Early Christmas present," the grandfather explained gruffly. He fished a business card out of another compartment of his wallet. "Grateful if you'd send me some prints of those pictures," he said, handing the card to Ricky.

Ricky nodded again, completely speechless, and the customers moved away, waving and smiling. They had just made a lot of money, but his grandfather's expression hadn't changed at all. He merely nodded. The Navajo way.

Meanwhile, the man in the plaid pants and his wife were crossing the plaza. They stopped in the middle, near the gazebo, to discuss something. Ricky decided they were from New York. Someday he was going to visit and see the Empire State Building and the Statue of Liberty. He hoped not everyone from New York was like them.

"I don't like those people," Ricky said. "The man in the plaid pants. He talked to you like you're stupid."

"Like doesn't matter," Grandfather said slowly. After a long pause he went on, "Did I tell you about when I was a boy, not much older than you? I lied about my age and joined the Marines. They made me a code talker and sent me to the Pacific. And the white man who was assigned to work with me didn't like the idea of working with a dumb Indian. Then he found out I wasn't so dumb.

Once I saved his life. Once he saved my life. Didn't matter we didn't like each other. That's the way it was." He pointed. "Now, look."

The couple started walking toward them. The woman was smiling, her hand hooked in her husband's arm. Ricky stared at them, braced for more of the white man's rudeness. "We've been talking it over," the man said, "and I'd like to buy that necklace for my wife. That— what do you call it?—squash blossom. Now what's your best price?"

"Sold it," Grandfather said. "At full price," he added.

Ricky saw the woman's smile fade. "Don't you have another one?" she asked. It was the first Ricky had heard her say anything.

"No more." Wordlessly, Joe Bennett leaned forward and straightened the concha belt, just enough to call it to her attention. Then he gazed impassively off into the distance again.

The woman noticed the belt and picked it up. She studied the tooled design and the turquoise insets. Then she clasped it around her waist and turned to show it off to her husband. "Oh, George, look at this! It's exquisite!"

George sighed. He opened his mouth and closed it again. No bargaining, no arguing. He reached for his wallet and paid Joe Bennett for the belt, and the two New Yorkers strolled off, arm in arm.

Grandfather said nothing. Ricky said nothing. It was the Navajo way.

IN RESPONSE

Describe the Scene

Imagine that you were present in the Old Town Plaza and saw Grandfather with the tourists. Write a letter to a friend at home about it, describing Grandfather and telling what happened.

Form an Opinion

Suppose Ricky Begay had been interviewed for "What Is Old?" In your notebook or journal, write down what you think he would have said, based on his feelings about his grandfather.

Choose a Snapshot

If you could take photographs of four scenes from this story, which scenes would you choose? In your journal or on a piece of paper, sketch and write a description of the scenes you chose.

AUTHOR AT WORK

Even at a young age, Carolyn Meyer knew she would be a writer. Ms. Meyer loved to write and began writing even before the third grade. She says of her school days, "I couldn't do *anything,* like catching a ball or hitting it, or running fast enough to beat anyone anywhere."

Ms. Meyer has lived around the country and enjoys "finding how stimulating a new place—with its history to be explored and its culture to be experienced—can be."

Another Book by . . .

Carolyn Meyer

Where the Broken Heart Still Beats by Carolyn Meyer, Gulliver/Harcourt Brace, 1992

Library Link "Photography and Other Lessons" appears in *Rio Grande Stories,* a collection of stories by Carolyn Meyer about young people of many cultures.

ANCESTRY

written and illustrated
by Ashley Bryan

I splash in the ocean
My big brother watches me
We sing,
    "Wade in the water
      Wade in the water, children."

Mom and Dad
Teaching us spirituals
Reading us African tales
Singing songs
Telling stories
Reminding us
Of our ancestry

On the beach
Other children
Dig to China
I dig
To Africa

MY GRANDMA

by Letty Cottin Pogrebin

I used to be ashamed of my Grandma.

I know that's a terrible thing to say, but it was true until last Wednesday, so I have to admit it.

My Grandma lives in our basement.

She moved in about a year ago after Grandpa died. Mom and Dad put a Chinese screen in front of the water heater and stuck a blue rug on the floor, so it looks pretty nice for a basement. Grandma says she can be happy anywhere as long as she has a hard bed and her exercise bike.

My Grandma loves her exercise bike. She rides for twenty minutes every day and she's almost seventy. She makes me ride for ten minutes because she says I'm only half as strong as she is even if I'm sixty years younger.

"A sound mind needs a sound body," she says. But she talks funny so it comes out *a zound mind nids a zound body.*

My Grandma is from the Old Country. When I was little, I thought that was just a nice way of saying she was *old,* but it means she wasn't born here. She grew up speaking Yiddish and Polish and Hungarian and I forget what else, but whatever it was, it definitely makes her English sound weird. That's just *one* of the things I used to get embarrassed about.

At first I was glad she moved in because she's kind of fun to be with. She lets me braid her long gray hair, and she teaches me things like gin rummy and knitting and how to make those little pastries with nuts and sugar rolled up in them. She calls them *rugalach.*[1] I can't say it as well as she does so I call them ruggies.

I used to love Grandma's stories, too.

No matter what we're doing, she always slaps her forehead and says "Oy, that reminds me of a story."

---

1 **rugalach** (*ROO guh lahk*)

One time when we were baking, she remembered how she once churned butter so long it turned to cheese. "I was daytime dreaming," she said with a laugh.

And once we were sewing and my scissors wouldn't cut, and she told me about this guy who used to ride through the streets of her town with a special cart with a sharpener.

"He made a clang on his cowbell," she said, "and we ran out from our houses with our dull knives and scissors, and he sharpened them on a big stone wheel. Such sparks you never saw."

I told her that sounded pretty neat. I wish we had one of those guys in our neighborhood.

When there's a full moon outside, my Grandma always pulls down the window shades near my bed. She says it's bad luck if the moon shines on you when you sleep. I make fun of her superstitions but she always says, "You never know . . . you never know."

Mostly, my Grandma's stories are funny. But sometimes they're scary—so scary that I have to scrunch up my shoulders to cover my ears, even if I've heard them before.

For instance, there's the one about her aunt and uncle who lived in this poor little town with a winding brook and a wooden bridge. It sounds like she's starting a fairy tale but I know she's working up to the part about the pogroms.[2] That's when these soldiers called Cossacks attacked and burned Jewish people's houses. We're Jewish.

"If it wasn't for the pogroms," she says, "a lot of Jews who ran away to America would have stayed in Europe. Then they would have been killed by the Nazis. So maybe the pogroms were a blessing in disguise."

---

2 pogroms (*poh GRAHMZ*)

To me that's like saying, "Good thing we were hit by a two-ton bus or we might've been flattened by a ten-ton truck."

But to Grandma it's a happy ending. Grandma *loves* happy endings.

The trouble started when my friend Katy found Grandma's false teeth floating in a glass on the bathroom sink. I guess I was so used to seeing them that I didn't even notice them anymore. But Katy noticed. She shouted, "Yuuuck! Gross!" and started laughing hysterically, and pretending to talk to them and making them talk back. I had to get down on my knees and *beg* her to shut up so my grandmother wouldn't hear and get her feelings hurt.

After that happened, I started to realize there were a *million* things about Grandma that were embarrassing. Like the way she grabs my face in her palms and murmurs "*Shaine maidel*"[3] which means "beautiful girl" in Yiddish. What would Katy say if she saw *that!*

Or how Grandma always says her *B'rachas*[4] before she eats. *B'rachas* are Hebrew blessings that thank God for things. All I can say is my Grandma must really be hungry because what she eats isn't exactly worth a thank-you note. Chopped herring is gross enough but white bread soaking in warm milk could make a regular person throw up.

And that's just the problem. My friends are regular people. So when Katy or Jill or Angie are around, I have to worry about what Grandma's going to do next.

---

3 *Shaine maidel* (SHAY *nuh* MAY *dehl*)
4 *B'rachas* (BRAH *kahs*)

Once she took me and Jill out to Burger King, even though she doesn't eat there herself because they don't have kosher[5] meat. Instead of ordering our hamburgers well done, she told the person behind the counter "They'll have two Whoppers well-to-do." Jill burst out laughing, but I almost died.

Another thing I spend half my life explaining is why my Grandma wears a wig. It's not a designer wig either. It's like the hair on an old doll, sort of frizzy and brownish.

I have to explain that she doesn't wear it because her hair fell out and she doesn't wear it to change her hairdo. She wears it because the Jewish law she believes in says that after a woman gets married, she's not allowed to show her own hair to anyone but her husband.

"But he died," Katy said. "So what does he care now?"

Some things you just can't explain.

After a while, I started wishing I could hide my Grandma in a closet. It got so bad I even complained to my parents.

"You guys are at work all afternoon! You don't know what it's *like*. She barges in and talks nonstop. She tries to teach us thousand-year-old games that aren't even in English. And she looks like the Grandmother From Another Planet."

My parents said they understood how I felt, but I had to be careful not to make Grandma feel unwelcome in our house.

"She's had a very tough life," said my Dad.

"Try to make the best of it," said my Mom.

I was trying, *believe* me, I was trying.

---

5 kosher (*KOH shur*)

Then, like I told you, on Wednesday, something happened that changed everything. My teacher made an announcement that our school was going to be a part of a big Oral History Project. We were supposed to help find interesting old people and interview them about their lives so kids in the future will understand how things used to be.

I was trying to think if I knew anyone interesting when Angie nudged me from across the aisle.

"Volunteer your grandmother!" she whispered.

I was shocked.

"My Grandma??" I said.

"Yeah!" Angie said. "*She's* interesting!"

Interesting? That's the *last* thing I ever thought Angie would say about Grandma!

Well, okay, I said to myself. Why not? Talking is what my Grandma likes to do best. In fact, I've never been able to get her to stop.

So that's how I ended up here. The whole school is in the auditorium for a big assembly and I'm up here on the stage interviewing my own Grandma.

We have microphones clipped to our shirts and TV cameras pointed at us and a bunch of professors are standing off to the side in case I need help asking questions.

Which I don't.

After all this time, nobody knows my Grandma's stories better than I do. I just say the right thing to get her started.

Like when I say "Grandma, why did you leave the Old Country?" she goes right into how the Nazis took over her town.

I've heard all that before. But then she starts telling this incredible story that is brand new to me:

"My parents, they sold all their furniture to buy passage to America. In the meantime, they hid me in a broken-down barn under a pile of straw.

"Can you believe it?" Grandma says looking right at me. "When I was only a little older than you are now, I was running from the Nazis. Me and my parents and my grandparents got into a big old ship, and people were getting sick during the trip and some of them even died. But we had a happy ending when we saw the Statue of Liberty."

While my Grandma talks, I see all my friends and teachers are listening to her as if she's a great hero. And suddenly I feel so proud of my Grandma, I could burst.

I can hardly wait to ask her the next question.

"How did it feel when you saw the Statue of Liberty, Grandma?"

"Very nice," she says. "When that lady she held up her lamp for us to come in nice and safe, I *knew* everything would be okay. I *knew* it."

Next she talks about her life in America and I hear her saying something else that she never put in any of her stories before. She's telling us that she loved her family very much, but she has to admit one thing: that she used to be ashamed of her grandmother.

"For twenty years that woman was in this country, but she wouldn't learn English never," says my Grandma about her Grandma. "Such a shame she was to me in front of my American girlfriends."

I can't believe my ears. I feel a little stabbing pain in my heart. And right there on the stage I make a *B'racha* to thank God for never letting my Grandma know I was ashamed of her, too.

"Thank you for sharing your experiences—the happy ones and the painful ones," the principal is saying to Grandma. "We're so glad your granddaughter brought you to us today."

Everyone starts clapping really loud. I feel like laughing and crying at the same time. I feel like hugging my Grandma and saying I'm sorry and nominating her for the Grammy Award for Grandmothers.

But I just stand on the stage and listen to the applause, and I feel my Grandma grip my hand tight as we take our bows together.

Express **Yourself**

What can you learn when you look at things from another point of view? As the stories in Perspectives show, you can find out more about yourself, other people, and the world.

Quoting a Character

This theme opens with a quote: "Each person has a way of looking at the world." Which main characters share this attitude? With a partner, look through the stories and choose one character. How does this person think and feel about seeing the world from another perspective? Write what the character might say to describe his or her new point of view.

Compare the Changes

In "Beni Seballos," a teenage girl changes her attitude toward her grandmother. How does her change in attitude compare with that of the main character in "My Grandma"? Which person do you think learned more about her grandmother? Which learned more about herself? Discuss your answers in a small group. Did either story teach you something about yourself or your grandparents? Explain.

More Than One Way to Tell a Story

Writers know that there are many ways to tell a story.
In "Losers Take All," author Avi uses mostly dialogue.
In "Photography and Other Lessons," Carolyn Meyer
uses mostly description. How important is dialogue in
telling a story? How important is description? Discuss
your answers in a small group, and give examples
from the stories.

A New View

When you meet someone with a different point of view
from yours, you begin to think about yourself in a new
way. Look back at the stories and choose a character
who is very different from you. How might your own
perspective change if you became friends with this person? Write your thoughts in a paragraph.

Turn the Tables

"Beni Seballos," "Photography and Other Lessons,"
and "My Grandma" all show a young person interact-
ing with a grandparent. Each story is told from the
grandchild's perspective. Choose one of the three selections, and write what the grandparent might have
thought about the story's events.

More Books for You to Enjoy

A String in the Harp
by Nancy Bond, Atheneum, 1976

After his mother's death, Peter reluctantly moves to Wales. There he finds a key used to tune the harp of a sixth-century Celtic poet. Drawn to the mysterious key, Peter sets out on a mission that takes him back in time.

The Final Tide
by Norma Cole, Margaret K. McElderry Books, 1990

Geneva is caught between pleasing her parents and following her own dreams. Isn't it bad enough that the government dam will soon flood their farm and force her family to leave? Must it also be Geneva's responsibility to convince Granny to leave her home as the final tide approaches?

Uncle Shamus

by James Duffy, Charles Scribner's Sons, 1992

Akers and Marleena are intrigued by the blind ex-convict who moves into their shantytown. They begin running errands for him and soon are drawn into the adventure of their lives.

Grandparents: A Special Kind of Love

by Eda LeShan, illustrated by Tricia Taggart, Macmillan, 1984

Does your grandma or grandpa live far away? Do you have one grandparent or several? Whatever kinds of grandparents you have, this book provides helpful insights and advice on understanding grandparents.

If I Were in Charge of the World and Other Worries

by Judith Viorst, illustrated by Lynne Cherry, Atheneum, 1981

Whether silly, thoughtful, or sad, these poems will make you giggle and think. They may even make you look at life in a new way.

Uncovering the Past: Ancient Egypt

"See the words?
Read them."

—Deborah Nourse Lattimore
"The Winged Cat"

CONTENTS

Theme Trade Books

Pyramid
by David Macaulay

This informative book, based on current archaeological information, describes in detail how the pyramids were built. Readers learn how the stone blocks were selected, the foundations laid, the inner chambers planned, and the huge structures built.

Zekmet the Stone Carver
by Mary Stolz

When the pharaoh of Egypt commands his vizier to design a monument, Zekmet, a stone cutter, agrees to help. Inspired by an encounter with a lion in the desert, Zekmet designs what we now call the Sphinx—a crouching lion with the face of a pharaoh.

PYRAMID
DAVID MACAULAY

ZEKMET
THE STONE CARVER
A TALE OF ANCIENT EGYPT
BY
MARY STOLZ
ILLUSTRATED BY
DEBORAH NOURSE LATTIMORE

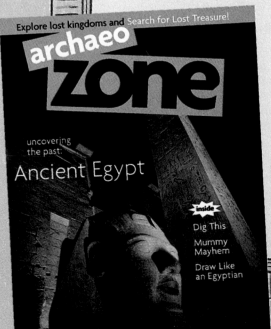

Explore lost kingdoms and Search for Lost Treasure!

archaeo zone

uncovering the past:
Ancient Egypt

inside
Dig This
Mummy Mayhem
Draw Like an Egyptian

Theme Magazine

How do archaeologists know where to dig? Can kids discover ancient civilizations? Where else besides Egypt have mummies been found? Read the Theme Magazine *Archaeo Zone* to find out.

A Walking Tour of the Pyramids

from *A Short Walk Around the Pyramids
& Through the World of Art*

This is a place called Saqqara.[1] It is on the edge of a great desert an hour's drive from Cairo.[2] You could reach it by camel, but that would take much longer. As you approach Saqqara, a line of walls and a strange pyramid rise from the sand like a golden mirage. But they are not a mirage. They are among the oldest works of art in the world. They were built more than 4,600 years ago by an Egyptian king with a wonderful imagination. His name was Zoser.[3]

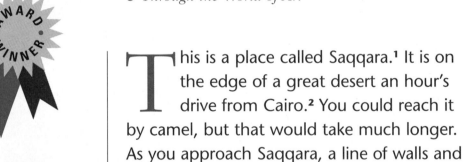

1 **Saqqara** (*sah KAHR ah*)
2 **Cairo** (*KY roh*) capital city of Egypt
3 **Zoser** (*ZOH suhr*)

TEXT AND PHOTOGRAPHS
BY PHILIP M. ISAACSON

The pyramid that came from Zoser's imagination—with help from his architect, Imhotep[4]—is called the Step Pyramid. It is made of pieces of stone stacked to form six huge steps. Its sides were once covered by a layer of white limestone that transformed it into a star, dazzling in the pure desert air. The Step Pyramid was the first pyramid ever built. Although it is such a simple, logical shape, no one before Zoser and Imhotep had ever thought of it, and when it was finished, those steps climbing high above the desert must have caused hearts to jump with surprise and fear. They still do.

4 Imhotep (*ihm HOH tehp*)

The Step Pyramid, which may have been King Zoser's tomb, inspired other Egyptian rulers to build even larger pyramids. At Giza,[5] a few miles north of Saqqara, sit three great pyramids, each named for the king—or Pharaoh—during whose reign it was built. No other buildings are so well known, yet the first sight of them sitting in their field is breathtaking. When you walk among them, you walk in a place made for giants. They seem too large to have been made by human beings, too perfect to have been formed by nature, and, when the sun is overhead, not solid enough to be attached to the sand.

5 **Giza** (*GEE zuh*)

In the minutes before sunrise, they are the color of faded roses, and when the last rays of the desert sun touch them, they turn to amber. But whatever the light, their broad proportions, the beauty of the limestone, and the care with which it is fitted into place create three unforgettable works of art.

What do we learn about art when we look at the pyramids?

First, when all of the things that go into a work—its components—complement one another, they create an object that has a certain spirit, and we can call that spirit *harmony.* The pyramids are harmonious because limestone, a warm, quiet material, is a cordial companion for a simple, logical, and pleasing shape. In fact, the stone and the shape are so comfortable with each other that the pyramids seem inevitable—as though they were bound to have exactly the form, color, and texture that they do have.

The pyramids also show us that simple things must be made with care. The fine workmanship that went into the building of the pyramids is a part of their beauty. Complicated shapes may conceal poor work—such shapes distract our eye—but in something as simple as a pyramid, there is no way to hide flaws. Because any flaw would mar its beauty, the craftsmanship must be perfect.

Look at a recent pyramid. It is made of glass and was finished in 1989. Designed by an American architect, I. M. Pei,[6] it is in the Cour Napoléon,[7] one of the great courtyards of the Louvre[8] Palace in Paris. The Louvre is a famous museum, and the pyramid is its new entrance. It is a pure crystal, bending the light of Paris into silver, pale blue, and yellow and multiplying itself in the pools around it. Any building less beautifully designed or made with less skill would have looked awkward in the company of the dignified old structures near it.

---

6 **I. M. Pei** (*pay*)

7 **Cour Napoléon** (*koor nah poh lay AHN*)

8 **Louvre** (*loov*)

Finally, pyramids show us that light helps to shape our feelings about art. As the sun moves above the desert, the pyramids seem to change. As they do, our feelings about them also change. In the early morning they sit squarely on the horizon, and we feel that they have become the kings after whom they are named; by midday they have become restless and change into silver-white clouds; and at dusk they settle down and regain their power.

The pyramids will always work their magic on us. Their forms, so simple and reasonable, and their great size lift us high above the ordinary moments in our lives.

The Secret Chamber

from *Into the Mummy's Tomb*
by Nicholas Reeves with Nan Froman

Lord Carnarvon, a wealthy Englishman interested in archaeology, and Howard Carter, an experienced archaeologist and Egyptologist, were both sure that the tomb of the boy king Tutankhamun[1] was hidden in the Valley of the Kings. After waiting for years for a permit to dig there, Carnarvon and Carter began their search of the valley in 1917. Hundreds of workers cleared tons of rock, using picks, hoes, and their bare hands. Five years passed without results. In 1922 Carter convinced Carnarvon to continue—for one more year. On the entire valley floor, only a single unexplored area remained. Within days, workers found one hidden step, then twelve steps, then a tomb door. Immediately, Carter sent two telegrams. One went to Carnarvon; the other went to Arthur Callender, an old friend whose help Carter needed with the excavation. Once again Carter had to wait.

"Hello, here we are," Lady Evelyn cried, waving from the window of the train as it pulled into Luxor station.

Two and a half weeks after Carter sent off his telegram, Carnarvon and his daughter had finally arrived in Egypt. Carter walked along the platform to greet them. At last, he thought, I'll be able to see what is on the other side of that plastered doorway.

Lord Carnarvon stepped from the train stiffly and leaned forward on his cane. "Well Carter, what have you found for us?" he asked.

"I'd like to show you at once, my lord, unless you're too tired."

"Nonsense. We're keen to visit the site, aren't we, Eve?" Carnarvon smiled at his daughter.

After what seemed an endless wait for the ferry, Carter, Carnarvon, and Lady Evelyn

(Inset, left to right) **Lady Evelyn, Lord Carnarvon, Howard Carter, and Arthur Callender stand at the top of the staircase** *(top)* **leading to the mysterious plastered doorway.**

crossed the Nile and then climbed on the donkeys which would take them to the Valley of the Kings. Arthur Callender had supervised the clearing of the steps and tomb entrance in time for their arrival.

"How exciting!" Lady Evelyn exclaimed a little nervously when she saw the cleanly-cut steps descending into the dark ground. In the falling light they examined the mysterious seals on the plastered door. It was too late in the day to continue the hard work of digging out the last few steps, so the little party agreed to meet at the site the next morning.

Carter and his friends were at the tomb entrance shortly after sunrise. The Egyptian workers were delighted to see Lord Carnarvon back in the valley and they smiled and waved when they saw him. Even Carter was

---

1 **Tutankhamun** *(toot ahnk AH muhn)*

impressed by how fast his team worked as they dug out the remaining steps and removed debris from around the plastered door. Everyone was anxious to see what lay behind it. Lord Carnarvon paced about smoking, while Carter directed the diggers.

At last Carter could see the whole doorway. He bent down once again to examine the ancient seals that had been uncovered in the morning's digging. Lord Carnarvon and Lady Evelyn stood just behind him. The seals at the bottom of the door were much less blurry, and Carter could read the name on several of them.

"Tutankhamun!" he read aloud in awe. Had he at last found the hidden tomb of the boy pharaoh?

"But look," Carter continued, his heart sinking, "part of the door has been opened and reclosed." He pointed to the top left-hand corner where there was a patch in the plaster. "Someone must have entered the tomb after it had been sealed."

"Ancient tomb robbers, no doubt," suggested Carnarvon grimly. "It looks as though it has been opened twice. Here's another patch in the plaster."

Carter didn't know what to think. He feared that the tomb had indeed been robbed, stripped of all its valuables.

Trying to conceal his fear, he sat down with his sketchpad and made careful drawings of the door and the seals on it while Lord Carnarvon took photographs. Then, block by block, they broke down the stone doorway. Behind the ancient wall stretched a sloping passage filled from floor to ceiling with limestone rubble. They could see that a tunnel had once been dug through this rubble, and that it too had refilled long ago. Carter was certain that this tunnel had been made by robbers on their way into the tomb.

It took the workers nearly two days to empty the passage. The strongest men shoveled the limestone chips into baskets. A long line of boys passed the heavy baskets along the corridor and up the steps where they were emptied outside the tomb entrance. Mixed in with the pieces of limestone were several fascinating objects.

(Above) Rubble from the filled-in corridor was carted away in basketfuls by a line of young boys. Buried in this rubble, Carter found a beautiful painted wooden model of the young pharaoh's head rising from a lotus flower like the Egyptian sun god (right).

Carter picked up one of these—the head of the young king rising out of a lotus flower made of painted wood. Perhaps it had been dropped by the thieves as they fled.

At the far end of the passage was a second plaster-covered doorway stamped with the priests' seals. Some of the seals bore the name of Tutankhamun. This door's top left-hand corner also showed signs of having been opened and then repaired. The opening would have been the perfect size for someone to squeeze through.

Carter chipped away at the plaster and stone with an iron rod until there was a small hole in the door. He inserted the rod. There seemed to be empty space beyond.

"Light the candle," he said. Lady Evelyn handed him a candle and, with trembling hands, he put it through the hole to test for foul gases. It was safe—the flame remained lit. Carter widened the hole a little and putting the candle back inside, he peered through. The candle flame flickered briefly as hot air escaped from the chamber. As it steadied, light penetrated the inky darkness of the room for the first time in over three thousand years. A few seconds passed, and then a few more.

"Can you see anything?" Lord Carnarvon asked anxiously.

His first brief glimpse into the dimly lit tomb was enough to show Howard Carter that he had found something no one else had seen for over three thousand years: the dazzling treasure-filled tomb of an Egyptian pharaoh, just as the ancient priests had left it.

"Yes," breathed Carter, unable to tear himself away from the peephole, "wonderful things!" Once his eyes had adjusted to the dim light, Carter was able to make sense of the mysterious shadows and shapes within the room. There were gilded wooden animals, statues and gold—everywhere he looked there was the gleam of gold!

Pulling himself away, Carter widened the hole so that they could all look through.

"Shall we go in?" he asked, already breaking apart more of the plaster.

A few minutes later Carnarvon, Carter, Lady Evelyn and Arthur Callender climbed through the hole and stepped carefully down into the room. They felt like intruders in someone else's home. A faint smell of sweet perfume and oil lingered inside the stuffy chamber. It looked as though someone had been there just a few days ago—here was a blackened lamp, and there on the floor was a garland of dried flowers. They looked so fresh that Carter had to remind himself they had been left there over three thousand years before.

At first no one could speak. The light from their candles moved crazily about as they tried to take in the wonders before them. Here were exquisitely carved chairs, regal beds and a glistening throne overlaid with gold. Over there were delicate alabaster vases and a brightly painted chest. Before them were three huge gilt couches, their sides carved into the shapes of strange animals. Lord Carnarvon ran his hand along the back of one, which seemed to be part crocodile and part lioness, with the head of a hippopotamus, its ferocious jaws open wide.

"The great goddess Ammut,[2]" Carter murmured, "who devours the souls of the wicked."

Lady Evelyn turned her light to the left and gasped. A pile of the broken bodies and wheels of several golden chariots seemed about to tumble on her. "It's as if there had been some horrible crash!"

When Carter entered the tomb, he found three gilded couches in the shapes of animals. The one shown here represents the goddess Ammut: part crocodile, part lioness, and part hippopotamus.

"There was no accident," said Carter. "Tomb robbers must have thrown them aside in their search for gold."

To their right, still standing guard at one end of the room, were two lifesized statues of a king. They held their maces and staffs before them forbiddingly. The gold of their skirts, sandals and headdresses gleamed, and from each forehead a sacred gold cobra reared up as if to strike.

Their minds whirling, the four agreed to continue exploring the next day.

---

2 Ammut (*AHM moot*)

In the morning, Callender set up electric lights in the chamber. In their glare, wonder quickly gave way to curiosity. Carter peeked into one of the chests—it was filled with ancient linen clothing of the finest quality and elegant sandals.

"Look, a snake!" cried Lady Evelyn with delight at the sight of a carving of a great gilded reptile peeping out from a black shrine.

Carnarvon was down on his knees, peering under one of the great couches. "Here's a hole in the wall—it seems to lead to another room." Carter joined him and through the hole they saw a smaller room cluttered with pottery wine jars, alabaster vessels, baskets of fruit, stools, chairs and bedsteads.

Carnarvon looked at Carter. "Why would these rooms be in such confusion?"

"Thieves again," Carter replied. "But they didn't get away with everything. What I'm wondering is why we haven't glimpsed a coffin or a mummy."

"Maybe this isn't Tutankhamun's tomb after all. Maybe it's just a cache of objects hidden away by the ancient priests," Callender suggested.

When Lord Carnarvon knelt under one of the animal couches, he spotted a hole in the wall leading to another chamber.

While the three men gathered around the hole in the wall, Lady Evelyn explored the first chamber. "This looks like the entrance to another room," she observed, running her fingers along the uneven surface of one wall. Between the two royal statues was another plastered area the size and shape of a doorway. Like the first two, a part of this doorway looked as though it had been opened and resealed. Carter's heart jumped.

"There must be more— what we've seen so far is just the beginning!" Carter needed time to think. He reeled at the prospect of the fabulous artifacts that might lie on the other side of the doorway, but it was too late to begin taking down the door that day.

They all climbed back into the passageway, and Carter and Callender reclosed the hole they had made. Carter instructed the watchmen on duty that night to guard the tomb with their lives, and then the four of them mounted their donkeys and rode out of the valley in a daze.

They talked about their discoveries late into the night.

"We've got to find out what's inside that third room," Carter said urgently. "Then we'll know whether or not we really have Tutankhamun's tomb."

After a moment's heavy silence, Carnarvon said, "I suppose there wouldn't be too much harm in a little investigation. But we'd have to keep it quiet—we don't want to give anything away to the newspapers yet. They won't pay to publish a story when everyone already knows how it ends!"

Carter nodded quickly, his eyes gleaming, and smiled at Callender. He was already planning their next visit to the tomb.

"I'm coming too," declared Lady Evelyn.

No one slept much that night. Their minds turned with all they had seen and all they might yet see in the sealed rooms. Long after the others had gone to bed, Carter sat up writing in his diary. For him, this had been "the day of days, the most wonderful that I have ever lived through, and certainly one whose like I can never hope to see again."

The next night four donkeys wound their way back up the valley. Their riders were quiet, speaking only now and then in hushed, hurried whispers. Reis Ahmed Gurgar[3] came forward to meet them as they neared the excavation site, shielding a lantern with his hand. "The guards have been dismissed," he told Carter. "I'll wait here for you." And then in a lower voice he added, "Be careful, Mr. Carter. This is a sacred place."

Moments later, Carter, Carnarvon, Lady Evelyn and Callender stole down the dark steps into the passageway. They entered the now familiar first room and Callender switched on the lights. "Eve, stand at the door and listen for anyone coming until we're through the wall," Carnarvon said.

Taking a chisel in his hand, Carter gently tapped at the resealed section at the bottom of the doorway. He felt the piercing gaze of the two royal statues as he worked. The plaster gave way quite easily, and soon he had made an opening large enough to squeeze through. Crouching down on all fours, Carter poked his head in and then inched his way forward. Carnarvon and Lady Evelyn followed.

"Hold on, wait a minute," the rather large Arthur Callender whispered hoarsely. "I don't think I can make it through such a small hole."

But the others didn't hear him. Once through the entrance, they faced what seemed to be a wall of gold! As Lord Carnarvon and Lady Evelyn shook the dust from their clothes, Carter made his way along this wall to the edge of the room. He realized that the small chamber was almost entirely filled by a large gilded shrine. "There's no doubt now. It's the burial chamber," he declared.

He noticed two ebony bolts holding the doors of the shrine shut and glancing at Carnarvon, who nodded back, Carter carefully pulled them. Nothing happened. He tried once again, then, slowly, the two huge doors swung open. Behind them was another gilded shrine draped with a brown linen shroud. The doors of the second shrine were tied shut just as the

---

3 **Reis Ahmed Gurgar** (*REE ys AH mehd GUR gahr*)

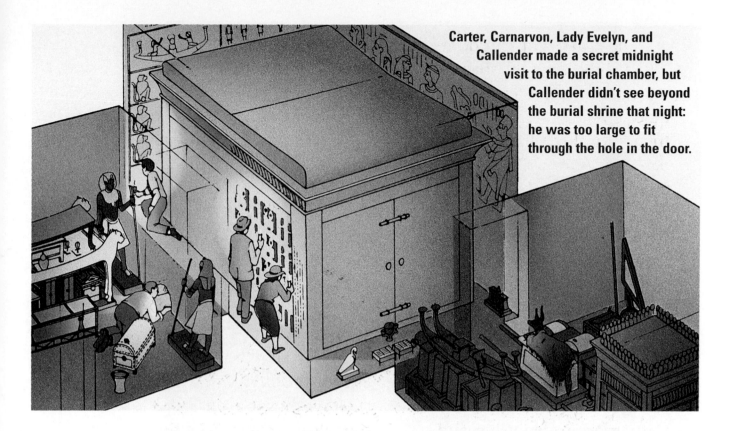

Carter, Carnarvon, Lady Evelyn, and Callender made a secret midnight visit to the burial chamber, but Callender didn't see beyond the burial shrine that night: he was too large to fit through the hole in the door.

priests had left them thousands of years before.

"We've got Tutankhamun—intact." Carter's voice broke as he looked around at Carnarvon and Lady Evelyn.

Their secret visit to the tomb had told Carter what he so desperately wanted to know—that the mummy of Tutankhamun still lay undisturbed within the burial chamber. One by one Carter, Carnarvon and Lady Evelyn squeezed back through the hole in the wall which Carter covered with a large basket lid. The official opening of the first chamber was due to take place the next morning. No one must know that they had already explored the tomb.

As the four explorers rode back down the valley, Carter pondered on all that he had seen. Ancient tomb robbers had clearly burrowed into the burial chamber, but they must not have had time to disturb the mummy. How would the mummy look after more than three thousand years? What riches would be buried with it? And why, he wondered, had the boy king been buried in such a small tomb?

In this scene from the golden wall of one of the burial shrines, Tutankhamun *(center)* has arrived in the world of the gods and is presented by Maat, the goddess of truth *(right)*, to Re-Harakhty *(left)*, the sun god who carries the disc of the sun on his head.

The next day Carter, Carnarvon and Lady Evelyn sat on the cool verandah of Carter's house trying to imagine how the ancient robberies had occurred.

It was clear that the outer doorway of the tomb had been opened and repaired twice—so there must have been two separate robberies. The fact that the repairs on the doorway had been stamped with the seals of the ancient priests seemed to indicate that all the plundering had been done within a short time of the king's burial.

"The robbers could have witnessed the funeral or even been among the burial party, who knows?" Carter said. "On the night of the robbery they probably met in the valley after dark. Then they would have had to drug or bribe the royal tomb guards. They must have worked very quickly, hammering at the blocked doorways, tearing the stone and plaster away with their hands until they had made an opening big enough to slip through. When those first robbers came, the passage leading to the tomb was empty, so it would have been easy for them to reach the first chamber."

"Of course. There were those bits of gold and the bronze arrowheads you found underneath the rocks in the corridor," said Lady Evelyn. "They must have been dropped by the first set of thieves on their way out and covered by rubble later."

"That's right," Carter continued. "The thieves probably searched in a frenzy for valuables that they could carry away with them—breaking pieces of gold off the furniture and the chariots which were too cumbersome to cart off. They seem to have taken linen and cosmetics as well."

"They left plenty of evidence. There's that cosmetic jar with fingerprints in the ointment—maybe one of them tested a little, just to see if it

was worth taking," Carnarvon laughed. "And there's also that white wooden box with dirty footprints on it. No doubt they belonged to an ancient thief."

"Yes," Carter agreed. "Perhaps the first set of robbers didn't get beyond the first and second chambers. Just before sunrise, the lookout probably called to them, and they would have hurried out of the tomb, staggering under the weight of their plunder.

"My theory is that once they discovered that the tomb had been robbed, the royal officials were in a hurry to put things back into order," he continued. "They filled the corridor with rubble to protect the tomb from more robberies. The second group of thieves would have had to dig a tunnel through all those rocks."

"So they had to work for their booty—just like us," Lady Evelyn said, smiling at her father. "It must have taken them ages."

"Once inside they explored the entire tomb," Carter said, caught up in his version of what might have happened. "It's clear from the mess those jewel boxes were in that they made off with a lot of what was left of the valuables.

"But at least one of those thieves met with some bad luck. Remember, we found eight gold rings wrapped in a scarf in one of the boxes in the first chamber. I suspect someone was caught in the act and tried to get rid of the evidence quickly. After the second robbery, the tomb seems to have been tidied up in a hurry before it was resealed."

"According to what I've been reading, if they were caught the robbers' fate would have been a grim one," Carnarvon said. "Apparently tomb robbers were impaled on a sharpened stake. They must have had nerves of steel to risk such a death."

"Let's just hope we don't have any unwelcome visitors," Carter frowned. "We have reliable guards, but I'll only rest easy when the steel bars are in place."

Once Carter knew that Tutankhamun's mummy lay undisturbed in the burial chamber, he wanted nothing more than to break the seal on the second shrine. He imagined over and over again the moment when he would lift the lid of the coffin and gaze upon the face of the pharaoh.

But he knew that before he could reach the mummy, a huge task lay ahead for the excavation team. Before exploring the other chambers of the tomb, Carter wanted to empty the first chamber, keeping precise records of everything he found. Clearing and studying one object at a time from the tomb was the best way to learn about the burial customs of the ancient Egyptians. He also hoped that by working in one chamber at a time, he could prevent precious objects from being accidentally damaged by the many people who would have to pass through the first chamber on their way to the rest of the tomb.

Carter and Arthur Callender stood in the first chamber surveying the heaps of treasure around them.

"There's so much work to do. I don't know of an archaeologist in the world who has ever had such a mammoth task ahead of him."

Howard Carter personally supervised the moving of each of the priceless artifacts from the tomb to the nearby laboratory.

Callender could see his friend was feeling the strain of the job and tried to calm him. "Well, what do we need first?"

"That's easy. What we really need is an instant excavation team—a conservation expert, specialists in reading hieroglyphs, draftsmen, a cataloguer, a photographer, guards. . . ."

Luck was with Howard Carter. He received a telegram from the curator of the Egyptian Department at New York's Metropolitan Museum of Art. The cable congratulated him on his fabulous discovery and offered to help him in any way possible. Carter lost no time in answering: DISCOVERY COLOSSAL AND NEED EVERY ASSISTANCE.

Within weeks Carter had a team of experts to help him. The tomb, which had lain in silence for thousands of years, became a noisy hub of activity.

The excavators' job was made especially difficult by the sweltering heat in the valley. Though it was winter in Egypt, temperatures would soar to 100°F (38°C). Carter, his temper already made short by the heat, found himself under pressure from journalists who clamored to get into the tomb. They were furious because Lord Carnarvon had signed a contract giving *The Times* of London the first opportunity to report on anything to do with the discovery. Even the Egyptian newspapers would have to wait to hear news of what was happening in their own country.

The site was plagued by tourists who arrived as early as the workers and gathered

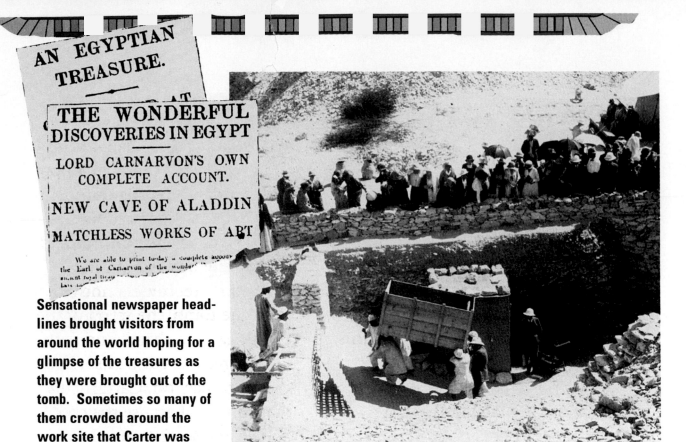

AN EGYPTIAN TREASURE.

THE WONDERFUL DISCOVERIES IN EGYPT

LORD CARNARVON'S OWN COMPLETE ACCOUNT.

NEW CAVE OF ALADDIN

MATCHLESS WORKS OF ART

We are able to print to-day a complete account by the Earl of Carnarvon of the wonderful ancient royal treasure discovered by...

Sensational newspaper headlines brought visitors from around the world hoping for a glimpse of the treasures as they were brought out of the tomb. Sometimes so many of them crowded around the work site that Carter was afraid they would all tumble into the tomb entrance.

around the entrance to the tomb all day. They could be as pesky as flies with their questions and demands for a guided tour. Some of them even claimed to be Carter's long-lost relatives in the hope that he would let them in.

Finally the team was ready to remove the first big object from the room—a wooden chest exquisitely painted with hunting and battle scenes.

"All right, Harry, I'm ready for you," Carter called out.

Harry Burton, the team's photographer, entered the chamber and took pictures of the chest where it sat.

Meanwhile, the draftsman drew a picture of it on his floor plan of the first chamber. Callender and Carter then gingerly lifted the chest onto a padded wooden stretcher and secured it with bandages. They carried it up the corridor and stairs where they were met by a guard.

As Carter and Callender emerged from the darkness of the tomb with their precious load, the sunlight shone brightly on the painted chest. There were loud whistles and squeals of delight from a crowd of tourists who had arrived hoping to catch a glimpse of the ancient treasures.

"Would you look at that paint job!" a man with a large camera said.

"Beautiful!" someone else exclaimed. "I wonder what's inside?"

But Carter and Callender had no time to stop and answer questions as they pushed their way through the crowd. They would have to repeat this time-consuming procedure for the hundreds of other objects in the first chamber before they could open the sacred shrines. And once spring came, it would be too hot to even set foot in the valley.

They carried the chest over to their lab which had been set up in an empty tomb nearby. There Carter and his assistant spent days carefully emptying the chest, which held a pair of rush sandals in perfect condition, a gilded headrest and royal robes of a size that would fit a young boy.

Soon after it was removed from the tomb, the wood of the chest began to shrink and parts of the precious painted surface started to peel off. Carter knew that this was because the cool, dry air in the lab was a shock after three thousand years in the warm, humid tomb. To prevent further damage, the chest was coated with wax. After it had been treated, it was

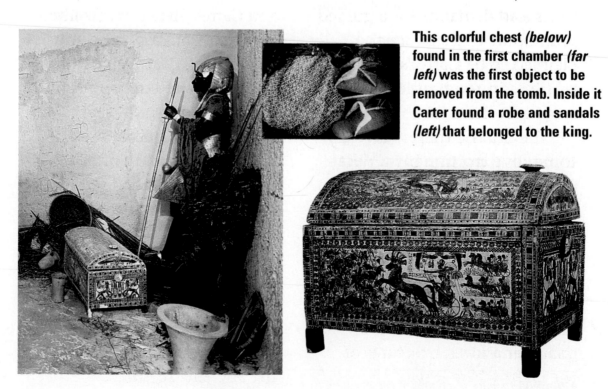

This colorful chest *(below)* found in the first chamber *(far left)* was the first object to be removed from the tomb. Inside it Carter found a robe and sandals *(left)* that belonged to the king.

photographed once again then packed for the journey to Cairo.

The clearing did not always go as smoothly as Carter had hoped. A pair of beaded sandals on the floor of the chamber looked like they were in perfect condition. But when Carter tried to pick one of them up, it crumbled to dust, leaving him holding a handful of beads. Horrified, Carter decided that some of the objects would have to be conserved on the spot. He poured melted wax on the other sandal, and once it had hardened he was able to pick it up quite easily.

Inevitably, there were some disappointments. What Carter had thought was a box of papyri[4]—ancient records written on reed paper which might clear up the mysteries of Tutankhamun's reign—turned out to be full of nothing but underwear for the young king.

The head of one of the statues that stood guard outside the burial chamber.

In January when Lord Carnarvon and Lady Evelyn returned to the valley, Carter took them directly to the lab. The smell of chemicals nearly knocked them over. Carnarvon was in high spirits, and while Lady Evelyn poured glasses of champagne for the hot, tired excavators, he looked over the treasures which had been recently cleaned and conserved. He clapped Carter on the back. "These things look even more beautiful than they did when we first set eyes on them. You've done a fabulous job, Carter!"

Carter smiled wanly, and politely waved away the glass that Lady Evelyn held out to him. "No, thank you. Too much to do."

A few weeks later everything had been cleared out of the first room except for the regal statues standing guard at the entrance to the burial chamber. Another official opening, this time of the burial chamber, was about to

---

4 papyri (*puh PY ry*), plural of *papyrus* (*puh PY ruhs*), a writing material made from a tall water plant found along the Nile River

take place. All of Luxor seemed to know about it—the name of Tutankhamun was on everyone's lips. Twenty guests had been invited including Egyptian royalty and foreign ambassadors, and chairs had been set up for them in the now nearly-empty first room.

"I must admit Carter, I'm a little nervous that someone's going to find out we've already been in there," Carnarvon confessed in hushed tones outside the tomb. It was just after two o'clock and the guests, lavishly dressed as if going to a party, had already gathered inside and were waiting for Lord Carnarvon and Howard Carter to give their speeches. A large crowd of uninvited guests and journalists had gathered around the stone wall outside the tomb.

"So am I. But Callender and I have built up that small platform hiding the place where we entered. And I'll start chipping away at the door from the top. Once we're inside everyone will be too excited to notice," Carter responded, straightening his shirt.

"I hope you're right," muttered Carnarvon, going down the stairs to the tomb. "If the newspapers find out we already know what's in there, it will take all the suspense away."

As the guests watched, Carter put on a pair of heavy gloves, picked up a crowbar and began to chip away at the plaster doorway leading to the burial chamber. Piece by piece he, Lord Carnarvon and their assistants removed the stones. The excitement and suspense in the room were almost unbearable.

Ten minutes later Carter had made a large hole. He peered in with a flashlight and saw once again the magnificent wall of gold. Then he set about widening the hole so that they could enter the chamber. The stones were heavy and it was a good two hours before the blocking could be removed.

At last Carter and Carnarvon stepped down through the opening. Their eyes met briefly as they remembered their first secret entry into the chamber a few months before.

When they reached the great doors of the shrine Carter drew back the ebony bolts revealing the doors to the second shrine with its seals intact.

This model of Tutankhamun was carved from a single piece of wood. It shows the king wrapped in a shroud and lying on a bed that resembles the funerary bed found in the tomb.

They bore the name of Tutankhamun. He touched the seals longingly—if only he could break them open now.

But then Carter felt a slight chill. They were intruders in the presence of the dead king. No one uttered a word for a minute or two. A large bouquet of flowers reminded them that the last people to stand inside this tomb had probably been the young king's friends and family, bidding him a last farewell.

Carnarvon said, "Come, Carter, we ought to let our guests have a look."

"Wait! Here's another chamber!" Carter exclaimed. The men made their way a little further along the wall until they reached a low doorway and then edged their way past the elegant black Anubis[5] dog guarding the entrance to the room. They had seen this fourth room on their secret visit to the burial chamber, but in the excitement of discovering the unopened shrines, hadn't taken the time to explore it.

Carter caught his breath when he saw a gilded shrine-shaped chest, delicately modeled with the figures of four guardian goddesses. It was the most beautiful monument he had ever seen in all his years as an archaeologist and it brought a lump to his throat.

This elegant statue of Anubis, the jackal god of embalming, with its gilt ears and eyes and silver toenails, guarded the entrance to the Treasury. According to ancient Egyptian myths, Anubis made the first mummy and by doing this showed how eternal life could be possible for everyone.

---

5 **Anubis** (*uh NOO bis*)

"This probably contains the king's embalmed internal organs—the liver, lungs, stomach and intestines," he said.

Carter lifted the lid of a wood casket. Inside was an ostrich feather fan with an ivory handle. "This is in perfect condition—it's as though the tomb were only closed yesterday," he marveled. The room was full of fascinating objects including a number of black shrines and chests. They were all sealed except for one in which Carter could see statues of Tutankhamun standing on the backs of black leopards. And scattered everywhere were model boats for the king to use in the afterlife. There were canoes for hunting hippos and birds as well as ceremonial vessels for making holy pilgrimages. Some of the boats had linen sails and rope rigging.

The men emerged from the burial chamber, their eyes shining. Two by two the guests were invited to climb through the opening and look at the wonders within.

As the excavation season drew to a close, the days became hotter and hotter and there were frequent dust storms in the valley. Carter was tense and exhausted, but still he pressed his team on. He wanted to clear as much of the tomb as possible before the unbearable heat of the Egyptian summer forced them to close it down.

One scorching day Carter left the site earlier than usual, returning to

At left is one of the many model boats Carter discovered stacked in the burial chamber of Tutankhamun's tomb.

his house for lunch. Shortly afterwards Lord Carnarvon arrived, eager to discuss his last meeting with the Egyptian authorities. "They are being impossible," he complained to Carter. "After all the money I've poured into this excavation they have the gall to tell me that all of the objects should stay here in Egypt."

"Well, perhaps they should, my lord, as national treasures."

"Come, Carter, not you too. I know you feel the same way about this as I do. I'm not insisting that I should take *all* the artifacts back to England with me, but a man should have something to show for his work."

"All I know is that if I were an Egyptian, I would hate to see any of the treasures leave my country," Carter continued stubbornly. "It would be a crime if the contents of the tomb were to be divided."

"But you know perfectly well that the whole lot would still be buried in the desert if it hadn't been for me," Carnarvon replied.

Carter, who had been pacing the room, turned on Carnarvon. "I do hope that my own small efforts haven't gotten in your way!"

Lord Carnarvon gripped his cane. He had seen Carter in a rage before, but it had never been directed at him. "What? Everyone knows how much credit you deserve. I think this heat is getting to us all, my good man," he said, trying to remain calm. "I know you don't mean what you're saying about giving the Egyptians everything. Perhaps we'd better discuss this another time."

Carter glared at Carnarvon, his face red with fury. "I meant exactly what I said," he shouted. "And I mean this too—get out of my house, and don't bother coming back again!" Carter stormed out of the room, slamming the door behind him.

A month later Carter received a letter from Lady Evelyn. Lord Carnarvon was seriously ill. He had been bitten by a mosquito, Lady Evelyn wrote, and had nicked the bite with his razor while shaving. Blood poisoning and fever had set in. After a few days her father had seemed to get better, but had then suffered a relapse and come down with pneumonia. Her mother, brother and the family doctor were on their way to Egypt.

Lord Carnarvon died a few days later on April 5, 1923. He did not live long enough to see the mummy of the pharaoh he had waited so many years to find.

Carter found this alabaster chalice inside the door of the Antechamber where it had been dropped by escaping thieves. He called it the "wishing cup" because the inscription on it contains a wish for Tutankhamun's eternal happiness.

Carter sat on the shaded verandah of his house thinking about Lord Carnarvon. He missed his friend a great deal, and bitterly regretted their final argument.

"Tea, Mr. Carter?" Abdul Ali asked, walking out onto the verandah with a laden tray in his hands.

"Thank you, Abdul."

"At the site they say Lord Carnarvon was struck by the mummy's curse," Abdul said as he poured. "He has been punished because he opened a sacred royal tomb."

"That's superstitious rubbish. There isn't any curse on the tomb."

"I'm not so sure," the servant replied. "They say the lights went out all over Cairo the night Lord Carnarvon died. And you yourself told me that his favorite dog howled and dropped dead in England at the same time."

"Those are coincidences, Abdul. Nothing but coincidences."

"And the cobra killing your canary, Mr. Carter? Was that a coincidence too?"

Carter stared off into the distance toward the Valley of the Kings. Abdul wasn't the only one who seemed convinced that they might all be touched by the mummy's curse. He shook off the thought. "Nonsense," he muttered to himself as he watched the last rays of the sun climb the pink cliffs, leaving the valley in deepest darkness.

IN RESPONSE

Spread the News

Imagine you are a newspaper reporter covering Carter and Carnarvon's discovery. Write a headline and a lead paragraph describing the pyramids you see on the way to the tomb. Be sure to answer the questions *who, what, where, when, why,* and *how.*

Draw the Clues

Carter and Carnarvon found clues that helped them decide that grave robbers had been in Tutankhamun's tomb. Draw or describe at least three of the clues the adventurers found.

AUTHORS AT WORK

Philip M. Isaacson, writer and photographer for "A Walking Tour of the Pyramids," delights in introducing architecture to young readers. Mr. Isaacson also wrote and photographed *Round Buildings, Square Buildings, & Buildings That Wiggle Like a Fish.*

As a teenager, Nicholas Reeves worked after school in a local museum. "On

rainy afternoons, the museum archaeologists would tell stories of their adventures in Egypt," he remembers. Nicholas Reeves decided that he, too, would make great discoveries.

Mr. Reeves became an archaeologist with a special interest in Egypt. In 1988 he found some objects from King

Tutankhamun's tomb at an auction! The grandson of Lord Carnarvon had found the objects hidden in the family's castle. Mr. Reeves agreed to catalog other objects found at the castle and used the information to help write *Into the Mummy's Tomb.*

Another Book by . . .

Nicholas Reeves

Howard Carter: Before Tutankhamun by Nicholas Reeves and John H. Taylor, Harry N. Abrams, 1993

Library Link This story was taken from *Into the Mummy's Tomb* by Nicholas Reeves. You might enjoy reading the entire book to learn more about Carter and Carnarvon's discovery.

Royal Treasures

Egyptians believed that the soul of a person lived on after his or her life on earth ended. Nearly four thousand years ago, unknown artists made these items for Tutankhamun to use in his next life.

Gold case, decorated with colored glass and semiprecious stones, about 1350 B.C.

Chair or throne of wood and gold, about 1347 B.C.

The case at left shows portraits of Tutankhamun, and the chair above is inscribed with his name. Many expensive, carefully crafted objects like these were found in Tutankhamun's tomb.

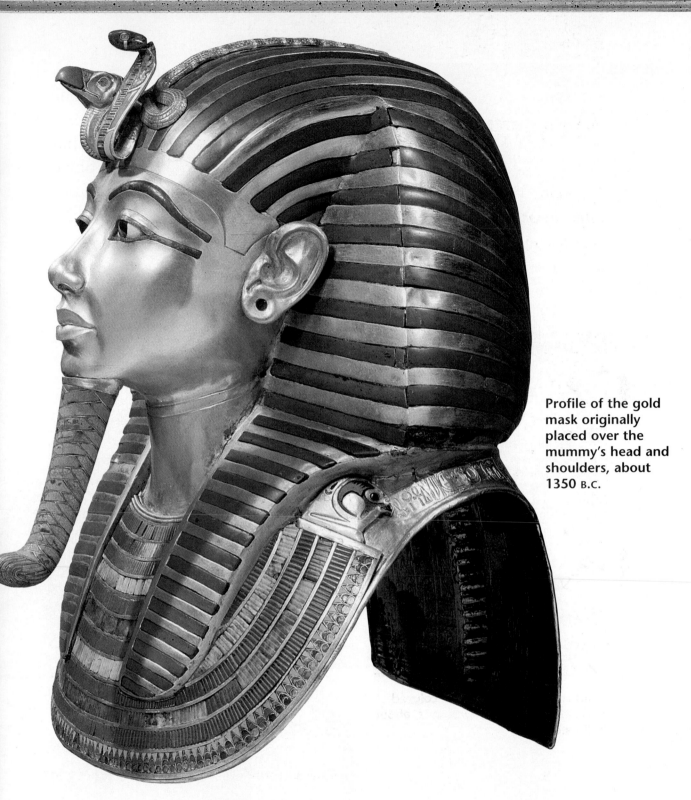

Profile of the gold mask originally placed over the mummy's head and shoulders, about 1350 B.C.

This mask is perhaps the most famous item from the tomb. The vulture and cobra symbolize that Tutankhamun ruled over Upper and Lower Egypt. Archaeologists believe that the face on this mask is probably a faithful portrait of the king, who died when he was about nineteen years old.

The necklace at the left represents the Egyptian sun god as a falcon. The fan below once held ostrich feathers. The scene on the fan shows Tutankhamun hunting ostriches. What do objects like these tell you about the king's power and his role in society?

Falcon necklace of gold set with glass and semiprecious stones, about 1350 B.C.

Fan of wood covered with thick gold foil, about 1350 B.C.

Game board of wood, gold, and ivory, about 1347 B.C.

How is the game board shown above different from a game board you might use? How would you feel if you owned a game board like this one? Would you use it every day?

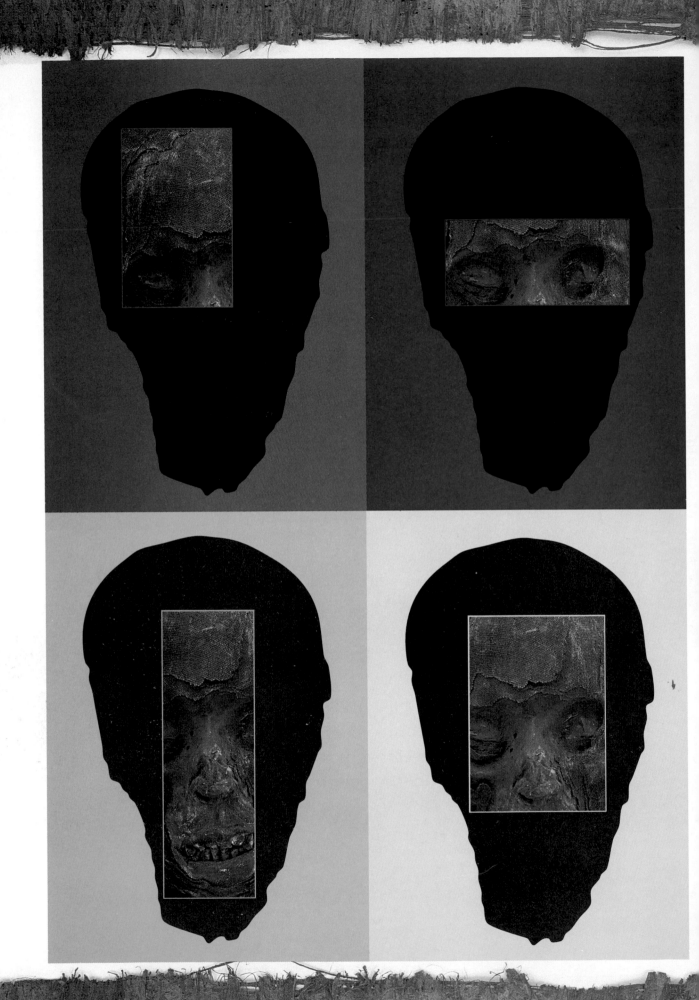

Revealing the Mysteries of MUMMIES

from *Mummies & Their Mysteries* by Charlotte Wilcox

What Is a Mummy?

1 f you are like most people, you probably picture a **mummy** wrapped in strips of ragged cloth, lying in the dusty corner of a museum or a dark passage in some Egyptian pyramid. The most famous ones are from Egypt, but mummies have been found all over the world. Some were buried with great care, but others became mummified because of natural conditions where they died.

A mummy is the body of a human or animal in which some of the soft tissues (skin, muscles, or organs) did not decay after death. This makes a mummy different from a skeleton or a fossil. A skeleton is only bones, with no soft tissues at all. A fossil keeps the shape of the human, animal, or plant, but the body itself has hardened into rock. Mummies are made naturally or by embalming, which is any process used to preserve a dead body.

While we are alive, our bodies fight off bacteria and fungi, but after death these germs and molds eat the body's tissues, causing decay. **Mummification** happens when bacteria and fungi cannot grow in the dead body. Most mummies, whether natural or embalmed, result when the body quickly dries out after death, because bacteria and fungi need water to live. Mummies can be dried in the sun, with chemicals, or with fire or smoke.

Drying isn't the only way to turn a body into a mummy. Taking away all air from around the body will stop decay, since bacteria and fungi need air as well as water to live. Quick, permanent freezing soon after death can produce mummies, because most bacteria cannot grow in below-freezing temperatures. Bodies can mummify if they are buried in soil containing chemicals that kill bacteria. Cool, dry air in some caves contains gases that kill bacteria and can make mummies naturally.

The skin and muscles of Egyptian mummies are hard and brittle because of resin used in embalming. Resin is a tree sap that works like glue — it is sticky when fresh, but becomes very hard when left out in the air. Even though they have become hard in many mummies, skin and muscles are called "soft tissues" because they were soft when the person was alive.

How We Got the Word *Mummy*

When the word *mummy* was first used in the English language in the early 1400s, it did not mean a body as it does now. Instead, it was the name of a medicine. Mummy comes from *mumiyah,* an Arabic word for **bitumen,** a sticky oil now used to make roads.

In the Middle Ages, people in Europe thought bitumen could cure diseases. They also thought ancient Egyptians had used bitumen in mummy wrappings. This, people felt, gave bitumen extra healing power. Around 600 or 700 years ago, Europeans began grinding up mummy wrappings and selling the powder as a medicine. People put **mummy powder** on wounds to help them heal and even ate it in hopes of curing stomach troubles!

At first, only the wrappings were made into medicine. Later, whole bodies—thousands of them—were ground into powder. As old mummies became harder to find, Egyptians started making fake mummies from bodies of people who had recently died. They stuffed the bodies with bitumen, wrapped them in linen, and dried them in the sun. When they were dry enough to look like real mummies, the bodies were sold to be ground into powder.

We now know that Egyptians used resin, not bitumen, in mummy wrappings. So the powder made from real mummies had no bitumen in it at all. Still, doctors all over Europe told patients to use mummy powder.

In the late 1500s, a doctor from France visited a factory that made fake mummies. When he learned that the Egyptians did not bother to find out how the people died, he was afraid. Fake mummies could carry diseases that could spread to people taking mummy powder as medicine. The Frenchman urged doctors to stop using mummy powder. Soon it was against the law to make fake mummies or to take mummies out of Egypt. This put the mummy makers out of business. People stopped using mummies for medicine, and by the 1600s the word came to mean what it does today—a preserved body.

Why Mummies Were Made

Most people all over the world, in every period of history, have believed in life after death. Ideas change with time and place, but most people feel their spirits will outlast their bodies. They often see death as the beginning of another life.

For these reasons, people treat dead bodies with respect, care, and sometimes even with fear. Turning bodies into mummies is one of many different ways of caring for the dead.

People have made mummies for at least 5,000 years. Many believed the body they had in this life might be needed in the next. People have imagined dead bodies could do all sorts of things—from walking and talking to putting curses on living people. These superstitions are not true, but people all over the world still show respect for the dead.

How to Look at Mummies

You may have mixed feelings about seeing a mummy. When you look at the photographs in this book—or when you see mummies in a museum—they will probably seem very different from living people. It may be hard to imagine that a mummy was once a child who grew, learned, and loved a family just as

In later Egyptian mummies, the wrappings sometimes formed unusual patterns.

you do. Anyone who wants to learn about mummies should keep two things in mind.

First, we must remember that a mummy was once a living person with thoughts and feelings much like ours. We respect what remains of that person's body, because it is similar to ours. Most religions ask that dead bodies be treated with dignity. Laughing or making jokes about the dead—even a mummy who died thousands of years ago—goes against the beliefs of many people throughout the world.

We must also remember that a mummy, though once really alive, is now *really dead*. A mummy can do absolutely nothing that a living body can do. It cannot see, hear, feel, or think. One thing a mummy can do is give us information about the past.

Mummies and Our Past

Preserving the body cannot bring life after death, but researchers are uncovering secrets mummies have kept for thousands of years. The secrets mummies hold can tell us how people lived, how environment affected their health, and how modern people have built on the knowledge of their ancestors. Mummies let us look at our past in a way no other form of history—stories, letters, art, photographs, or other artifacts—can.

Soft tissues—found in mummies but not in skeletons—tell us about family traits, diet, and disease. Lungs can show what was in the air in ancient times. Stomach, liver, and intestine tissue can show what people ate. Bacteria and other causes of disease stay in soft tissues, giving clues about how diseases are caused and spread.

When put together like pieces in a puzzle, these clues can help solve mysteries from the past. Let's take a look at some of these mysteries.

Coffins, boxes for burying dead bodies, have been used since ancient times. This Egyptian coffin is made of wood — which was probably expensive because not many trees grow in Egypt. The symbols painted on it are hieroglyphs, a form of picture writing used in ancient Egypt.

The Most Famous Mummies—Egypt

Egyptian mummies have been the subject of legends for thousands of years. It was once believed that ancient Egyptians used secret spells to preserve bodies. No Egyptian writings have ever been found telling exactly how Egyptians made mummies. But a Greek writer, Herodotus,[1] visited Egypt over 2,000 years ago and saw mummies being embalmed. Thanks to Herodotus and to modern research, the process the Egyptians used is no longer a mystery.

1 **Herodotus** (hih RAHD uh tuhs)

The oldest Egyptian mummies, from before 2500 B.C., were not embalmed at all. They became mummies naturally.

In early times, bodies were simply wrapped in cloth or leather and buried in the sand. Warm desert winds and hot sun heating the sand caused bodies to dry out very quickly, so they did not decay.

Even very early in their history, Egyptians believed in life after death. Pottery and jewelry were put in graves for the dead to use. Over time, this belief grew into a religion. As the Egyptian religion grew, so did the importance of taking care of the dead.

Egyptian kings, called **pharaohs,** were thought to be gods. When a pharaoh died, Egyptians thought his spirit turned into Osiris,[2] god-king of the dead. The dead pharaoh's son became ruler of Egypt in his place. Egyptians called their ruler Horus, god-king of the living.

In order for the pharaoh's spirit to live in the spirit world, Egyptians thought it had to have a body to rest in on earth. They thought that if the body looked something like the pharaoh did when he was alive, his spirit would recognize it.

During his life, a pharaoh made lavish preparations for the life he expected to live after death. He stored food, clothing, books, medicine, gold and jewels, weapons, furniture, and other things he enjoyed in life.

Egyptians believed that the spirits of the dead needed their own houses. At first this was done by building underground rooms, called tombs, where the body and other things were buried. Later pharaohs built rooms or houses over the tombs. As each pharaoh tried to outdo the ones before, the houses became larger and more beautiful.

The largest of all the tomb houses were the pyramids. Over 70 pharaohs built pyramids for themselves. The Great Pyramid, built by Pharaoh Khufu over 4,000 years ago, is

2 Osiris (oh SY rihs)

still the largest stone structure in the world. Until about a hundred years ago, it was also the world's tallest building.

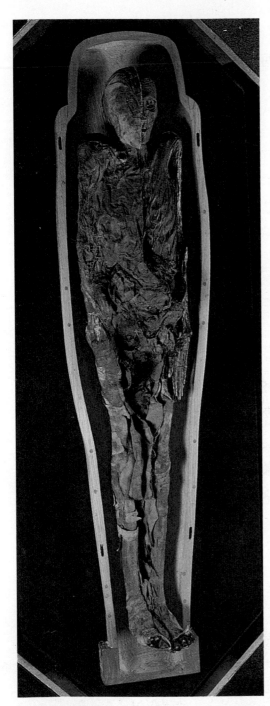

Egyptian mummies are famous all over the world. But Egypt is not the only place mummies have been found.

The Egyptian Funeral

Once the mummy was ready, the public part of the funeral took place. Special servants, called mourners, were hired to cry very loudly as the body was taken from the embalming tent to the tomb. Some pharaohs built special temples near their tombs. Religious ceremonies and sacrifices to Egyptian gods were held. Priests performed a ceremony they thought would help the mummy see, hear, eat, and drink again in the spirit world.

After the funeral, the tomb was closed and sealed. It was not to be disturbed. Unfortunately, some Egyptians didn't follow this rule. Workers built secret passages into some pyramids so they could rob them later. Some coffins had secret trap doors built into them for the same reason. Almost all the tombs of the pharaohs were robbed in ancient times. Grave robbers looking for treasure unwrapped many Egyptian mummies. When family members or caretakers found the damage, they had embalmers repair and rewrap the bodies.

As the practice of mummy embalming continued, bodies of royal wives, officials, and priests were also made into mummies, with the hope that they would join the pharaohs in the spirit world. Soon other wealthy Egyptians arranged to have their bodies mummified when they died.

Over time, almost all Egyptians who could afford it became mummies—more than 70 million mummies in about 3,000 years. The Egyptians stopped making mummies around the fourth century A.D. By that time, many Egyptians had become Christians, so they no longer believed mummification was necessary for life after death.

Animal Mummies

Ancient Egyptians believed many animals were sacred. Embalmers sold mummified animals to use as offerings in

Will the mummification of animals and people ever again be as popular as it was in ancient Egypt? That's one mystery these Egyptian animal mummies can't solve for us.

religious ceremonies. Mummified cats were buried near many shrines of the cat-goddess, Bastet.[3] Sacred crocodiles—kept in pools near temples of the crocodile-god, Sobek—were embalmed when they died. Bulls, beetles, dogs, bats, shrews, and even fish became mummies. Over a million bird mummies were buried in one cemetery alone.

The popularity of animal mummies may explain one mystery from Egypt's past—the disappearance of one kind of ancient ibis. This long-beaked water bird was special to the Egyptians because it returned to Egypt each year at the beginning of the growing season. Now the bird is extinct, probably because so many were killed by the ancient Egyptians to make mummies.

---

3 Bastet (bahs TEHT)

The ibis, a water bird, was special to the Egyptians. This ibis mummy has been unwrapped.

IN RESPONSE

Make a How-to Booklet

Imagine you are in charge of preparing the tomb for a pharaoh. Create a how-to booklet that explains and illustrates some steps for the pharaoh's burial.

Test Your Friends

With a partner, write five true or false statements describing how mummies are made. Exchange statements with another team to see if they can tell which statements are true.

AUTHOR AT WORK

Growing up on a farm in Minnesota, Charlotte Wilcox spent her spare time reading. Her love of reading and her desire to become an artist added up to a career as a writer of children's books.

Ms. Wilcox feels writing nonfiction for children resembles juggling three things at once. She translates technical information into everyday words, puts it into bite-size pieces, and checks that it makes sense to readers.

★ **Award-winning Author**

Other Books About . . .

Mummies

Mummies, Tombs, and Treasure: Secrets of Ancient Egypt by Lila Perl, illustrated with photographs and drawings by Erika Weihs, Clarion Books, 1987

Mummy by James Putnam, photographs by Peter Hayman, Alfred A. Knopf, 1993

Library Link This story was taken from *Mummies & Their Mysteries* by Charlotte Wilcox. You might enjoy reading the entire book to find out more about mummies.

DISCOVERING CULTURE
Through Art

Ancient Egyptians learned to "read" their artwork.

The statues and paintings created by ancient Egyptians are much more than decoration. Because most people in ancient Egypt could not read, artwork served as a way to teach them about their culture. Egyptian artists wanted their statues and paintings to reflect the characteristics of a certain god or goddess. In many instances, the artists used the qualities of a particular animal to teach people about a particular deity.

Jackal-headed Anubis oversaw the wrapping and mummification of bodies and then acted as a guide through the afterlife.

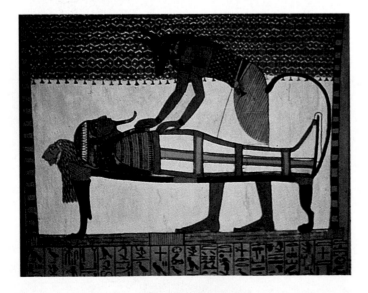

Osiris's white crown, crook, and flail are symbols of his authority.

For example, jackals feed on carrion, or decayed flesh, leading the Egyptians to connect the jackal with death. As artists tried to show Anubis,[1] guardian of the dead, they drew the god with the head of a jackal. When a person died, Anubis prepared the body for burial and guided the spirit to the Netherworld, or afterlife.

Each of the gods, in turn, could be represented by an animal. Egyptians may have thought along these lines: Thoth[2] was the god who invented writing. Egyptians wrote on papyrus. The ibis bird was often found in papyrus marshes. The head of an ibis, therefore, might be an ideal way to represent Thoth, the

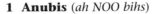

1 **Anubis** (*ah NOO bihs*)
2 **Thoth** (*thohth*)

god of writing. The sun god Horus[3] had the head of a hawk, perhaps because Egyptians believed hawks flew close to the sun.

Paintings and statues also show the gods and goddesses wearing crowns or headdresses and holding symbols of their authority. Many of these deities hold the ankh,[4] symbol of the sun, to show their connection to the source of all life.

Osiris, ruler of the Netherworld, wears the white crown of a pharaoh as a sign of his authority. He holds the crook and flail of a royal ruler. Isis, the wife of Osiris, is often shown wearing the sacred disk of the sun held between a cow's horns. She was the most powerful of all the goddesses and the protector of women and

children. Bastet, the cat goddess, was pictured with the regal head of an Egyptian cat. Ancient Egyptians regarded cats as sacred.

A statue of Bastet stands guard over a litter of kittens, showing that she protects the family.

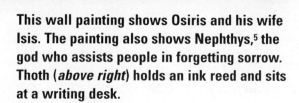

This wall painting shows Osiris and his wife Isis. The painting also shows Nephthys,[5] the god who assists people in forgetting sorrow. Thoth (*above right*) holds an ink reed and sits at a writing desk.

3 **Horus** (*HAWR uhs*)

4 **ankh** (*ahngk*)

5 **Nephthys** (*NEHF thihs*)

In Egypt most ancient there lived a serving girl named Merit who worked in the temple of the cat goddess Bastet. When she swept the halls in the heat of day, her friend Bast, a small cat, kept her company. At night, when Merit's work was done, they strolled out to sleep in cool comfort on the sandy banks of the Nile.

On just such a night, across the moonlit sky, the god Thoth sailed to the Netherworld, his home. Silently, as he traveled the starry stream, something fell from his neck down, far down, and landed between the sleeping girl and the cat.

The next morning Waha, Pharaoh's High Priest, spotted it. It was a gold amulet shaped like a heart, and there was nothing Waha loved more than gold. He carefully stepped over the sleeping girl and picked it up. Merit awoke but kept her eyes shut, because she recognized the voice of the powerful High Priest. His bad temper was well known.

"This is very royal indeed," Merit heard him say. "Should I take it to Pharaoh, or should I keep it?" As he turned to go, Waha tripped over Bast the cat, and the golden heart flew into the river.

"You! You rat-chasing lump of fur!" shouted Waha angrily. He seized Bast and flung her downstream.

Merit jumped up and rushed into the current to save Bast. But it was too late. The cat was lifeless in her arms.

"Pharaoh will judge you harshly for this!" cried Merit. "This poor cat belonged to the temple of the goddess Bastet."

"Go to Pharaoh, worm of a girl," retorted Waha. "See for yourself if a stupid cat matters at all."

Merit told Pharaoh what had happened, and the High Priest soon found himself called to the foot of the throne.

"A sacred cat was drowned," said Pharaoh. "Merit says you did it. You swear you did not. I cannot decide who is telling the truth."

"You have only to look into my heart to see that I am telling the truth," Waha said.

"Your words inspire my command," said Pharaoh. "Hear me! You must each take the magic spells from the Book of the Dead and travel to the Netherworld. When you arrive in the Hall of Judgment, the gods will decide who is telling the truth. If your heart weighs the same as Ma'at, the feather of Truth, you will have nothing to fear. But if your heart weighs more, it will be proof that you are lying, and the monster Ammit will devour you. Go and prepare!"

Now even though Waha was the High Priest, he did not own the necessary spells because he had sold them for gold. So he scribbled the few spells he remembered onto small wooden figures called *ushabtis*.[1] If the spells were the right ones, he could use them to open the twelve gates of the Netherworld. If the spells were wrong, he could always throw an *ushabti* to a hungry demon and still be safe.

---

1 ushabtis (*yoo SHAHB tees*), plural of *ushabti*, a small wooden figure

Merit returned to the temple of Bastet. She took the limp body of Bast, wrapped it in fine linen, and laid food and drink before it.

"Farewell, dear Bast," Merit said sadly. "Waha will find his way, and I, without any spells, will be lost and monsters will eat me."

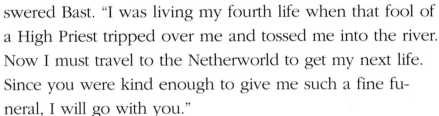

"*I* will not say farewell," said Bast.

"What!" exclaimed Merit. "You can speak?"

"My *ba*-soul speaks," answered Bast. "I was living my fourth life when that fool of a High Priest tripped over me and tossed me into the river. Now I must travel to the Netherworld to get my next life. Since you were kind enough to give me such a fine funeral, I will go with you."

"But I am too poor to buy spells from the Book of the Dead," said Merit. "How will we find the way?"

"The Book of the Dead is much more than just a handful of spells," purred Bast. "Spells are words. If you can read, we will find our way. Remember. Unless you keep your eyes ahead of you and read, all will be lost."

That evening as the sun blazed its path beyond the Western Horizon, Waha stood on the shore. Merit, with the invisible soul of Bast the cat on her shoulder, stood beside him. A gleaming boat appeared. On its deck stood the sun god, Horus, surrounded by the rays of the setting sun.

"Look carefully!" whispered Bast. "See the words? Read them and the boat will take us to the twelve gates of the Netherworld."

Merit saw hidden words appear, and she read them aloud.

"The mooring pin is like two ladies. They are Upper and Lower Egypt," she began. "The sails are bigger than Heaven. That is the goddess Nut. The oars are a hawk's fingers, and that is Horus. The breeze that holds up the sky is Shu. The ground is Geb, and the river is H'apy, the Nile."

"Come ride on my boat," said Horus, beckoning to Merit. "Now it is the Priest's turn."

Waha searched frantically in his sack. He finally brought out one *ushabti* and squinted at it.

"I have forgotten what this says," he muttered.

"Then feed the demon or be devoured," said Horus.

Waha threw a *ushabti* behind the boat to a demon, who gobbled it up with terrible gnashing teeth. Bast spread her wings around Merit's head so she would not look. Waha looked, and suddenly he remembered the heart amulet that had started the whole dispute. He stared into the water hoping to find it.

The boat stopped at the first of the twelve gates. Waha fished with his fingers behind the stern. Merit looked up. The great gate was staring at her.

"Name my parts and you may pass," it said.

Merit shook, hand to arm, knee to leg, as hungry monsters crowded around the boat, hoping she would make a mistake. She eyed the door carefully, and pictures appeared. Merit spoke:

"On the lintel is the great vulture who protects all Egypt. The side posts are legs and a cup, and on the door is a hand."

The door opened a crack, and then it stopped and looked at Waha. The High Priest dug around in his sack but could not find what he needed. Quickly he tossed

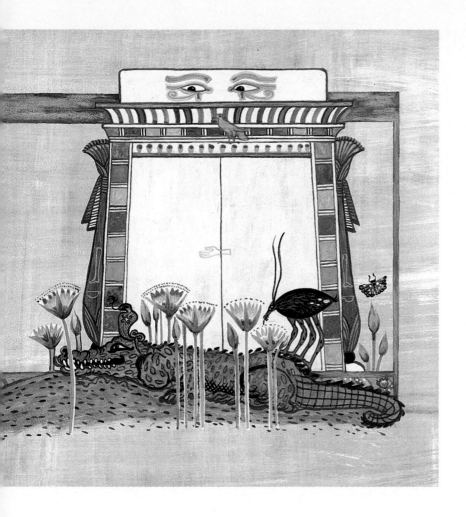

another *ushabti* behind the boat, and Merit heard the crunching of giant teeth. Waha leaned back and ran his fingers through the water in search of the amulet.

One by one Merit called out the names of the great doors, and one by one they opened. Waha made more and more mistakes and threw more and more of his *ushabtis* to the demons.

Finally, Waha became impatient. "Why must I make this dangerous journey just to rid myself of a stupid worm of a girl?" he thought. He leaned over in time to see the golden heart floating beside the boat. Quickly he plucked it from the water and thrust it into his sack. Now he had what he wanted. All he had to do was rid himself of Merit and go home.

The sun boat stopped at the entrance to the Hall of Judgment. On either side were swirling pits of fire. Just as Merit stepped out of the boat, Waha shoved her into the flames.

"Oh, no! Bast! Help me!" Merit cried.

"Stop! Think!" said Bast, spreading her wings around Merit's head. *"Read!"*

Through the flames, Merit could see on the doorway above her the words of the last spell:

"May this magic fire burn me if I am not good in my heart!"

As she spoke the words, the fires parted. Merit was saved.

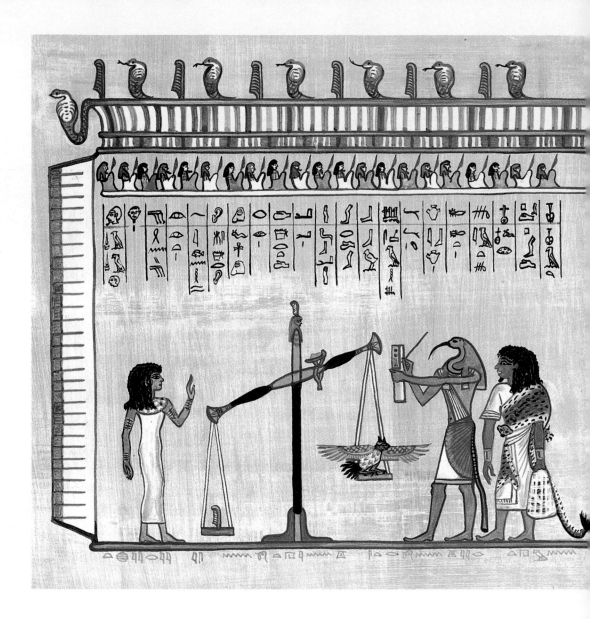

"Approach!" called a voice from the end of the Hall.

It was Anubis, the jackal-headed god of the dead. He stood beside the giant scales of Truth. Thoth stood on the other side, ready to record the results with ink reed and papyrus. Ammit crouched at the base of the scales grinding his teeth. Behind them all, staring in disbelief, was Waha.

"We know why you have come," said Anubis. "Since Merit passed the test of fire, she is now free. And Bast—

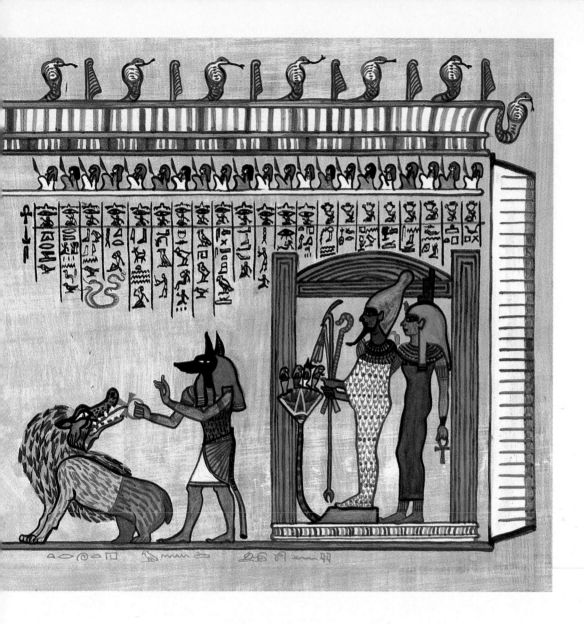

let your *ba*-soul and heart be weighed against the feather
of Truth and you may gain another life."

Bast flew to the scales. Since it was a soul and heart
with cat wings, it was lighter than the feather. The scale
tipped up.

"By Bes!" laughed Waha. "That's nothing! Why, I
have something here much better than that!"

Waha produced the golden heart amulet and gave it to Anubis to put on the scales. The heart, in its shining beauty, sank to the ground like the metal that it was.

"Guilty!" said Thoth. "Furthermore, I've been looking for this!"

Thoth picked up the heart and returned it to his neck. And before anyone could say "By Bes!" twice, Ammit had chewed and swallowed all of Waha, right down to his last *ushabti*.

As for Bast and Merit, they were taken on Horus's golden boat back to the riverbanks of the Nile. When Pharaoh saw them, he knew at once whose hearts were as good as gold. He rewarded Merit with a life of ease and plenty.

Bast even lived four more.

AFTERWORD

The ancient Egyptians loved life and believed that after people died, they lived again in a beautiful garden called The Field of Rushes. It had a river and marshes, fields, and fish and fowl. In fact, it looked just like Egypt itself. So eager were the ancient Egyptians to be sure that life after death was just like life itself, they had all their favorite things buried with them: clothes, food, perfumes, makeup, beds, chests of linens and jewels, and magic amulets to protect them from snakes and bugs. To do all the farming, cooking, and cleaning they included little wooden figures called *ushabtis* which often looked just like the dead person and did all the work so that he or she wouldn't have to. Even the dead person's body was supposed to stay as close as possible to its appearance in life. After death, the internal organs were removed and placed in special containers called canopic[2] jars. The body was piled high with natron[3] crystals, a kind of salt, and dried out until it looked a lot like leather. Then it was wrapped in fine linen, given a funeral complete with mourners, dancers and priests, and offerings of bread, beer and meat and fowl. (Since the new mummy couldn't really eat, the mourners did.) Then, with all of his or her possessions placed around the coffin, the deceased was sealed up in a tomb for eternity, life everlasting.

There was just one catch. The dead person had to go to the Netherworld, home of the gods and goddesses, to be judged worthy of a new life. A dead

---

2 **canopic** (*kuh NOH pihk*)
3 **natron** (*NAY trahn*)

person's *ba,* or winged soul, went before forty-two Judges and was asked questions such as, "Did you do any good deeds while you were alive? What were they?" If the soul answered correctly, then its heart was weighed on a scale against the feather *Ma'at* (Truth), and if the heart weighed less, the *ba* was free to go. But if the heart weighed more, a terrible demon called Ammit, part crocodile, lion, and hippopotamus, gobbled up the soul and the heart, and the person was gone forever.

Answers, spells, and confessions of good-deed-doing or confessions of wrongdoing were put together on papyrus rolls and buried with the deceased to help him on his way

through the Netherworld and its dangers. Spells from different dynasties were collected by Pharaohs; later by nobles and then commoners and were called The Books of the Dead. Egyptologists—scholars who study ancient Egypt—know them as the Amduat, The Coming Out by Day, The Book of Caverns, The Book of Breathings, The Book of the Two Ways, and others. Poor people were buried with a very few spells; the richer you were the more spells you could afford. But whether you were poor or rich, it was your heart that mattered, and the Judges of the Dead could see right through it to the truth. . . .

—*Deborah Nourse Lattimore*

IN RESPONSE

The King's Advisor

Imagine that you are advising the young King Tutankhamun on preparing for his next life. What does he need to do to ensure a pleasant afterlife? What are the dangers if he fails to prepare himself? Write advice using what you learned from "The Winged Cat" and other selections in this theme.

The Good Life

In a group, discuss what actions the Egyptians considered worthy. Support your opinions with examples from the story. How might knowing the story of "The Winged Cat" have helped Egyptians live a good life?

AUTHOR AT WORK

Even as a student, Deborah Nourse Lattimore was fascinated by the myths and stories of ancient civilizations. As she begins to write a story, she researches it at public and university libraries, checking all the details. Ms. Lattimore then creates lively, authentic art for the characters, setting, and costumes. Ms. Lattimore's goal is "to create a story with pictures that I hope will satisfy those two most critical audiences—scholars and children."

★ Award-winning Author

Other Books by . . .

Deborah Nourse Lattimore

The Flame of Peace: A Tale of the Aztecs by Deborah Nourse Lattimore, Harper & Row, 1987

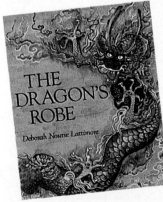

The Dragon's Robe by Deborah Nourse Lattimore, Harper & Row, 1990

Aïda

RETOLD BY
Leontyne Price

ILLUSTRATED BY
LEO AND DIANE DILLON

This tale, based on the opera Aïda, *tells the story of an Ethiopian princess who is torn between her love for her country and her love for an Egyptian soldier.*

Long ago, in the faraway land of Ethiopia, there lived a Princess named Aïda. She was fair as the sunrise and gentle as starlight touching a flower. Her father, the great King Amonasro, loved her dearly.

It was a time of terrible fear and danger in Ethiopia, for the kingdom was at war with its neighbor, Egypt. Both countries raided each other's lands, killing or enslaving their enemies.

For the safety of his people, King Amonasro set strict boundaries at the borders of his country, and no Ethiopian was allowed beyond them.

Aïda (ah EE duh)
1 Amonasro (AHM ahn ahs roh)

The Princess Aïda was young and, locked within
the palace, she grew restless. So, one morning, Aïda
and her trusted friends disobeyed the King's command.
They disguised themselves and slipped away from the
palace guards.

It was a glorious day of freedom, out in the gentle
breezes and lush green fields of their beautiful country.
But Aïda wandered farther than she should have. Off
on her own, enjoying the warm sun and fresh country

air, she did not hear her friends in the distance when they shouted, "Aïda! Beware! Come back!"

Once again, Egyptian soldiers had invaded Ethiopia, crossing the south edge of the River Nile. Now they marched toward Aïda.

When she finally did hear her friends' warning, it was too late. Soldiers seized her. Bound with ropes and chains, Aïda, the Royal Princess of Ethiopia, was carried off to Egypt as a slave.

Aïda had learned her royal lessons well. She revealed to no one that she was the daughter of King Amonasro of Ethiopia. But her beauty and noble bearing attracted great attention. So sparkling and unusual was she that the all-powerful Pharaoh, the ruler of Egypt, chose her from among thousands of captured slaves to be his gift—a personal handmaiden—to his only daughter, the Princess Amneris.[2]

It was easy for Aïda to perform the duties of a servant, for she remembered what her own handmaidens had done. The Egyptian Princess Amneris was fascinated, for Aïda was different from any slave she had ever seen. She wanted her new handmaiden to be her closest companion.

Even with the special privileges granted to one so close to the Royal Princess, Aïda felt nothing but despair. All her life she had been the beloved daughter of Ethiopia's King, and now she was a slave to her father's enemy. She knew there was no hope of seeing Ethiopia again.

---

2 **Amneris** (*AHM nuhr ihs*)

There was one source of light in her life, however. For Radames,[3] the handsome young captain of the Egyptian Army, had fallen in love with the gentle, beautiful slave the moment he saw her. She, too, had fallen for Radames, despite his position as an enemy of her homeland.

They met often, in secret, by the Temple of Isis, and in the joy of their moments together, Radames confided his dreams to Aïda.

"I will lead the Egyptian Army to victory," he told her, "and when I return, our countries will be united, and you will become my bride and reign as the Queen of your people. It will not be long, I promise."

The day finally came when the Pharaoh was to hold court and announce the new leader of the war against Ethiopia.

Amid the majestic columns of a great hall in the palace, Egypt's High Priest, Ramfis,[4] confided to Radames: "There are rumors that the Ethiopians plan to attack. Prepare yourself, for the Goddess Isis has chosen, and the great honor of leadership may be bestowed upon you."

All his life, Radames had dreamed of this day. If he became the new leader, he could return triumphant to free Aïda and marry her. "Ah, heavenly Aïda," he thought. "I could finally enthrone you in your native land."

Radames was deep in thought when Princess Amneris stepped from the shadows. She, too, was

---

3 **Radames** (*RAH dah mees*)
4 **Ramfis** (*RAHM fis*)

in love with the handsome leader, but she suspected he loved another.

Aïda suddenly appeared.

Oh, how Radames's eyes filled with passion! And when Amneris saw the look that passed between them, she was seized with suspicion and jealousy. Could Radames prefer a *slave* to the Princess of Egypt? It was intolerable! But her fury was interrupted by trumpets heralding the arrival of the Pharaoh.

A messenger came forward to give his report.

"Mighty Pharaoh, the Ethiopians have attacked. They are led by the fierce warrior King Amonasro, who has invaded Egypt!"

A thunder of anger broke out in court, and upon hearing her father's name, Aïda quietly cried out in fear.

The Pharaoh rose, and the crowd grew still.

"Radames will lead our army," he cried. "It is the decree of the Goddess Isis. Death to the Ethiopians! Victory to Egypt!" he shouted. "Return victorious, Radames!" he commanded.

"Return victorious! Return victorious!" the throng shouted, and Aïda, too, was stirred by the cry. In spite of herself, she also began to shout, "Return victorious! Return victorious!" as the court led the soldiers off to battle. Aïda was now left alone.

"Return victorious!" she called after Radames, but as her own voice echoed in the great hall, she suddenly realized she was asking for the death of her father, her mother, her friends, and all those she cherished. Yet how could she pray for the death of the man she loved?

Aïda was shocked. Her heart was torn between Radames and her loyalty to her father and Ethiopia. She fell to her knees and prayed.

"Oh, great gods of my youth!" she cried. "Pity me!"

That night, the halls of the temple rang as the priestesses chanted the sacred consecration song. The High Priest, Ramfis, led prayers to Phtha,[5] the creator of life and mightiest Egyptian god, as he gave the great hero the sacred sword of Egypt.

"Let the sword of Radames be the strength of our nation! Let his bravery in battle crush the Ethiopians! Protect our land," they prayed, "and make Radames the most magnificent warrior of all."

"Praise to Phtha! Praise to Phtha!" the Egyptians chanted, and the priestesses danced a sacred dance to please the great god and ensure death to their enemies.

With Radames gone, time passed slowly for Aïda. But soon the prayers of the priests were granted. A special day dawned for Egypt—a day of ceremony and grandeur, of pomp and pageantry. The Ethiopians had been defeated at last.

Amneris sat before her mirror. Surrounded by slaves and adorned in her most beautiful gown and jewels, she was pleased with her reflection. Surely today when Radames returned, he would be struck by her radiance. Yet despite her vanity, she secretly

5 **Phtha** (*thah*)

burned with jealousy to think that Aïda, a mere hand-maiden, might truly be loved by Radames.

So Amneris decided to test her privileged slave. And when gentle Aïda entered the royal chambers, Amneris sobbed, pretending great grief.

"Oh, Aïda, Aïda!" she cried in a shaking voice. "Egypt has lost its finest warrior. Radames has been killed in battle!"

Immediately Aïda wept with the pain of one whose heart has been broken forever. There was no longer any doubt in Amneris's mind.

"It is all a lie!" she shouted. "Radames was not killed. He lives!"

Aïda's tears of sorrow turned to tears of joy.

Overcome with fury, Amneris hurled Aïda to the floor. "How dare you, a lowly slave, love the same man loved by the Princess of Egypt?"

But Aïda, too, was a Princess. She rose proudly. She was about to tell Amneris the truth, but she stopped herself. Instead, with great difficulty, she asked to be forgiven.

"Have mercy on me," she begged. "Your power is unquestioned—you have all that a person could want. But what do I have to live for? My love of Radames, and that alone."

Aïda's plea only fueled Amneris's rage. She stormed out of the chamber, leaving Aïda to fear the worst.

Flags flew, and the entire city gathered to see the grand spectacle of the victory parade led by the Pharaoh, the Princess, and the High Priest.

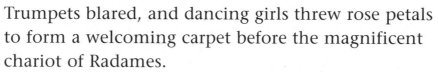

Trumpets blared, and dancing girls threw rose petals to form a welcoming carpet before the magnificent chariot of Radames.

The handsome warrior dismounted and knelt before the royal throne. When Amneris placed a laurel wreath on his head, the crowd was wild with joy.

"Hail to the conqueror!" they roared. "Hail to Radames!"

The Pharaoh proclaimed, "Radames, you are my greatest soldier. As a reward, whatever you wish shall be yours."

When Radames rose, he saw Aïda. Amneris saw the look of love on his face, and she was consumed with jealousy. Yet he dared not ask for Aïda's hand, not at that moment in public court.

"Mighty Pharaoh," he said instead, "I ask that you allow me to call forth our prisoners of war."

The Pharaoh granted Radames's request, and the Ethiopians were led into the square in chains. One tall, proud man stood out above the rest. Aïda gasped. It was her father!

The crowd was shocked to see her run and embrace him, but he whispered to her, "Do not betray that I am King."

Amonasro addressed the Pharaoh. "I am Aïda's father, and I have faithfully fought for my sovereign, who died in battle. I am prepared to die for him and my country, but I beseech you to have mercy on those who have been defeated."

With outstretched arms, Aïda joined the Ethiopians. "Let the prisoners go free," she begged Radames and the Pharaoh.

So moved by her appeal, the Egyptian people joined in, and their cries urged the Pharaoh to allow the captured soldiers to be released.

"No!" the High Priest, Ramfis, cried. "The Ethiopians are still a threat and should be put to death."

"Their freedom is my wish," Radames told the Pharaoh.

"Unchain the Ethiopians!" the Pharaoh ordered. "But you, Aïda's father, must remain my prisoner as a pledge of your people's good faith."

An even greater reward was now to be bestowed upon Egypt's greatest warrior. The Pharaoh led Amneris to Radames.

"My daughter will be your bride," he proclaimed, joining their hands. "One day, you shall be Pharaoh, and together you will rule."

Radames was horrified. He dared not refuse the Pharaoh. He bowed and pretended gratitude, but his heart was filled with sorrow. Amneris looked scornfully at her handmaiden.

Aïda wept in her father's arms as the triumphant Egyptian Princess held Radames's hand and led him to the palace.

"Do not lose faith," Amonasro whispered to his daughter. "Ethiopia will soon avenge our conquerors."

It was the eve of the great wedding, and a full moon shone on the dark waters of the River Nile beside the Temple of Isis. By boat, the High Priest,

Ramfis, brought Amneris to the Temple. There she was to pray that her marriage be blessed. Little did she know that Radames had sent a message to Aïda, who was waiting to meet him nearby.

Aïda sadly watched the moonlit river and longed with all her heart and soul to return to her beloved homeland. Suddenly she heard Radames approach. But when the man came closer, she was stunned to see that it was her father, King Amonasro.

"Listen carefully, Aïda," he said sternly. "My plan will bring both you and Radames back to Ethiopia. Our soldiers stand ready to attack when I signal. There is a secret, unguarded road, but only Radames knows it. It is your duty as the Princess of Ethiopia to make him reveal this path."

"Father!" she cried, "I *cannot* betray Radames!"

With anger and disdain, King Amonasro forced her to her knees. "You are no longer my daughter! You are nothing more than a lowly slave of the Egyptians and a betrayer of your country! Have you forgotten your loved ones who were slaughtered without mercy by these, your enemies?"

"You are wrong! I am *not* and will *never* be a slave to anyone. I am the Princess of Ethiopia, and I have never forgotten my royal blood. My duty to you and to my country will always be first in my heart!"

Even as she swore to obey his command, she cried inside for what her father and her dear country would cost her. Amonasro embraced her to give her courage, and he hid in the bushes to listen.

When Radames finally came, he was breathless with love. But Aïda turned on him scornfully.

"How could you betray me and marry Amneris as your reward?"

"Aïda, you have always been my love. My passion for you is deeper than the Nile, deeper than life itself," Radames told her.

"Then show me," Aïda demanded. "You have betrayed me. And if you truly love me, you will leave Egypt tonight and flee with me to Ethiopia. Only there will we find happiness and peace."

Radames was torn. The thought of leaving Egypt was unbearable, but the thought of living without Aïda was even more painful. At last, after much persuasion, he agreed to flee.

"The roads are heavily guarded by your soldiers. How will we escape?" she asked.

"All the roads are guarded except one," he told her. "The Gorges of Napata."

"The Gorges of Napata!" a voice rang out. Amonasro sprang from his hiding place. He was ready to attack with his army.

Radames could not believe it. "You, Aïda's father, are King of Ethiopia?" He was overcome. "I have sacrificed my country for my love of you!" he cried to Aïda.

"Come with us now," Amonasro told Radames. "You and Aïda will reign happily in Ethiopia."

But as the King took Radames's hand to lead him away, a shout rang out in the darkness. "Traitor!"

It was Amneris. She and the High Priest had come from the temple and had overheard the plot.

"Traitor!" she screamed again.

Amonasro leapt to kill Amneris with his dagger, but Radames ran between them to shield her.

"Go quickly!" he warned Aïda and Amonasro, and the King ran, dragging Aïda with him.

Radames stood before Amneris and the High Priest. He did not try to escape. Instead, he threw down his sword.

"I surrender!" he cried. "I am your prisoner!"

The treason of Radames shocked and infuriated all of Egypt. Guards locked him in the deepest dungeon in the palace. Soon his trial would begin, and he would be sentenced to a horrible death.

Amneris was in a state of grief. Her love for Radames had not diminished. Deep in her heart, she knew he had not meant to betray his country. Her own jealousy had made the mighty warrior a prisoner. She longed to beg her father, the Pharaoh, to release him, but she knew Radames still loved Aïda. She also knew soldiers had killed Amonasro, but Aïda had escaped and was still alive—somewhere.

In desperation, Amneris commanded the guards to bring Radames to her. She humbled herself and pleaded with him to forget Aïda.

"I will find a way to set you free, free to marry me and share the throne of Egypt," she said. "But you must never see Aïda again."

Radames refused. "You are Princess of Egypt, my country; and you have all that anyone could ask for. Yet I will always love Aïda, and there will never be room in my heart for anyone else."

The more Amneris begged him, the more strongly he refused.

When the priests came to take Radames, Amneris was in a rage of anger and jealousy, and she made no attempt to stop them. But when he left, she fell to the ground in tears, cringing as she heard the priests loudly accuse Radames of betrayal.

"Traitor! Traitor!" the High Priest, Ramfis, shouted again and again, but Radames never uttered a word to defend himself. Louder and louder the cruel accusations were hurled at him.

Amneris prayed to Isis and the other gods of Egypt to show mercy and save the man she loved, but the gods were silent.

The tribunal of priests pronounced Radames guilty of treason and sentenced him to be buried alive.

As the priests passed from the trial, Amneris flung herself before the High Priest. She insulted him and threatened revenge, but her cries were in vain.

"Radames, the traitor, will die," he said coldly.

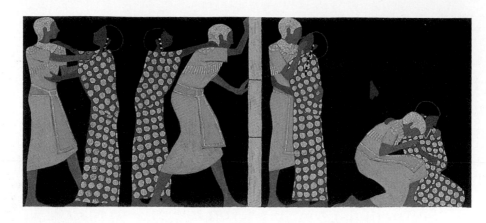

Only the priests and guards were allowed to watch Radames walk into the deepest vault below. They sealed the last opening, shutting out all light and the last breath of fresh air. Alone, waiting quietly for death, Radames thought only of Aïda. He would never see her sparkling eyes and gentle smile again.

Suddenly, in the darkness, he heard Aïda's voice. At first, Radames thought it was a dream. But no—she had escaped and was hiding in the vault, waiting for him.

"Aïda, my love, you are too young and too beautiful to die."

Radames pushed in vain, trying to open the vault.

But Aïda gently placed her arms around him. With a tender kiss, she told him to stop.

"Remember, we will never be separated again. For eternity, we will be together."

And with all the love in the world, they held each other close—so close—as if they would never part.

Above their tomb, dressed in black, Princess Amneris prayed to the gods to forgive her and to grant heavenly rest to Radames, her love.

The gods granted her wish, but not as she hoped. For as she prayed to the gods and wept, a peaceful death had come to the Ethiopian Princess Aïda and Radames, the greatest warrior of Egypt. Finally they were together—forever in each other's arms.

IN RESPONSE

Notes on Egypt

What have you learned about ancient Egypt from this theme? On an index card, write a heading like *Beliefs, Values, Customs,* or *Leaders.* Then write a sentence or two about that topic. Include examples from the selections.

Radames Returns

What would happen to Radames' spirit after death? Explain in writing what the ancient Egyptian who heard this tale might think. Base your answer on events in this story and what you have learned about Egyptian beliefs in other selections.

AUTHOR AT WORK

Leontyne Price was born and raised in Laurel, Mississippi. In some ways, she started her musical career at the age of nine, when she attended her first concert. By the time she reached eleven years of age, she was a local celebrity—earning money singing and playing the piano at weddings and funerals.

Ms. Price attended college in Ohio and went on to the Juilliard School of Music in New York. Ms. Price's formal studies of music led to her Paris stage debut in 1952. Her American debut followed four years later. As well as performing opera on stage, Ms. Price has recorded operas and spirituals. These recordings have brought her voice to worldwide audiences and have captured nineteen Grammy and three Emmy awards.

Speaking of Aïda, Ms. Price says, "Aïda has given me great inspiration onstage and off. Her deep devotion and love for her country and for her people—her nobility, strength, and courage—are all qualities I aspire to as a human being. I will never forget her."

Leo and Diane Dillon

Diane Dillon and Leo Dillon grew up in different worlds. Ms. Dillon grew up in Los Angeles, California, where her father was a teacher. Mr. Dillon grew up in Brooklyn, New York, where his father owned a small trucking business. But each loved to draw. Ms. Dillon remembers, "As a child, I drew all the time." Mr. Dillon reports that he still has the book that changed his life—*The Arabian Nights*. The pictures sparked his imagination and his desire to become an artist.

The Dillons met more than thirty years ago in art school. Although rivals at first, they now work as a single artist. They feel that drawing for children "is at once a responsibility, an honor, and a profound joy."

★ Award-winning Illustrators

Other Books Illustrated by . . .

Leo and Diane Dillon

Ashanti to Zulu: African Traditions by Margaret Musgrove, illustrated by Leo and Diane Dillon, Dial Press, 1976

The Hundred Penny Box by Sharon Bell Mathis, illustrated by Leo and Diane Dillon, The Viking Press, 1975

The People Could Fly: American Black Folktales retold by Virginia Hamilton, illustrated by Leo and Diane Dillon, Alfred A. Knopf, 1985

Over the years, the Dillons have developed a unique, cooperative way of completing illustrations. They talk about the story and visualize the images they'll use. As they work on the illustrations, they often pass the artwork back and forth between them. Once they are finished, Leo and Diane Dillon may not be certain who did what.

Express **Yourself**

In Uncovering the Past: Ancient Egypt, you explored the treasures, stories, and knowledge of the past. You also learned how these things influence the present. The characters you met along the way showed you how they have searched for lost civilizations and tried to solve ancient mysteries.

Now and Then

"The Winged Cat" and "Aïda" are both set in ancient Egypt. Does the time in which a story is set affect its plot? With a partner, list events from each story that would not occur in a story set in modern times. Next, list events from the stories that could happen today. Have you observed or experienced any of these events? Share them with your partner.

Fact or Fiction?

"The Winged Cat" is fiction and "The Secret Chamber" is historical fiction. Yet each contains facts. For each story, give three details that are fact and three that are fiction. How do you know, or how could you check?

Another Way to Write

"Revealing the Mysteries of Mummies" is an informational article. "Aïda" and "The Winged Cat" are stories. If you were going to write about the mysteries of the mummies, which kind of writing would you use? Why?

Press Conference

Howard Carter, Lord Carnarvon, and Lady Evelyn ("The Secret Chamber") needed to tell the press about their great discovery. With a group, role-play a press conference. What might reporters ask about the discovery and ancient Egyptian burials? Write questions based on "The Secret Chamber" and "Revealing the Mysteries of Mummies." Hold your press conference for the class.

Can't Know Enough

Sometimes the more you uncover about the past, the more you want to know. What questions do you have after reading this theme? For each selection, think of one question. What source would best answer each question? Write your questions and the research sources you would use. If you wish, you can look for answers later.

More Books for You to Enjoy

The Pharaohs' Curse

by Susan Dudley Gold, illustrated by Sandy Rabinowitz, Crestwood House, 1990

When archaeologists began to uncover the tombs of the pharaohs, sealed for centuries, many experienced strange sicknesses, accidents, and even death. Had they found treasure or trouble? Explore the legends and events surrounding the "curse" of the pharaohs in this intriguing book.

Digging to the Past: Excavations in Ancient Lands

by W. John Hackwell, Charles Scribner's Sons, 1986

Follow the excitement as an archaeological team uncovers fascinating information about the lives of ancient peoples. Learn how the roles of each participant contribute to a successful excavation. Discover why hunting for evidence of past lives can be a long, slow, yet rewarding adventure.

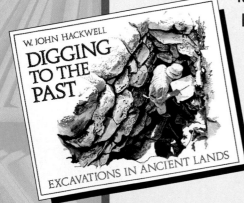

Hieroglyphs: The Writing of Ancient Egypt

by Norma Jean Katan with Barbara Mintz, Atheneum, 1981

Learn how to read the writings in a mummy's tomb! Write your name in ancient Egyptian! This book can show you these and other skills related to hieroglyphics.

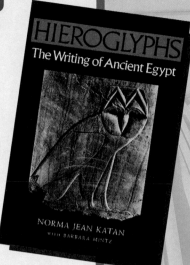

Tutankhamen's Gift

written and illustrated by Robert Sabuda, Atheneum, 1994

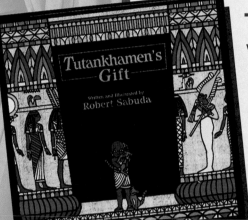

Beautifully illustrated, this is the story of how Tutankhamen, a shy and serious boy, became a king when he was only a child, and went on to become one of ancient Egypt's most popular leaders.

The Vandemark Mummy

by Cynthia Voigt, Atheneum, 1991

After their father is chosen to manage antiquities, twelve-year-old Phineas and his sister, Althea, become involved in a series of mysterious and dangerous events surrounding a two-thousand-year-old mummy.

Finding
Common Ground

"We had thought that
we were different
from each other, but
we had everything in
common."

—Arn Chorn
"Arn Chorn: Peacemaker"

209

CONTENTS

Theme Trade Books

The Night the Bells Rang

by Natalie Kinsey-Warnock
Young Mason hides from the high-school bully, Aden, and argues with his own brother, Ira. Yet Aden proves to be unusually kind. When Mason hears of Aden's death, he seeks common ground with Ira.

Bull Run

by Paul Fleischman
People from both sides explain their roles in one of the first battles of the Civil War. Soldiers, slaves, mothers, and sisters describe the glory and the horror of the Battle of Bull Run.

THE NIGHT
THE BELLS RANG
Natalie Kinsey-Warnock
ILLUSTRATED BY Leslie W. Bowman

BULL RUN
PAUL FLEISCHMAN
Woodcuts by David Frampton

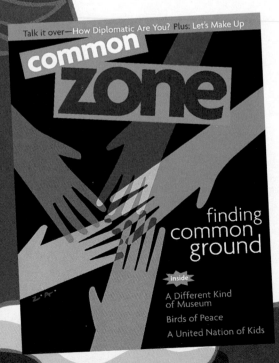

Talk it over—How Diplomatic Are You? Plus: Let's Make Up

common Zone

finding common ground

inside
A Different Kind of Museum
Birds of Peace
A United Nation of Kids

Theme Magazine

How diplomatic are you? How well can you deal with your little sister? What does a crane have to do with peace? Read the Theme Magazine *Common Zone* to find out.

Don't Let the Bedbugs Bite

by Ellen Conford

I admit that when my mother told me she was going to marry Tina Grossman's father, I did not take the news very well.

"You can't do this to me!"

"I'm not doing anything to you, Sally," my mother said. "I'm marrying a very nice man whom I love very much."

"And making Gruesome Grossman my sister! You know how many times she beat me up?"

"She never beat you up."

"Well, she threatened to. Twice a week. For three years."

"Sally, that was in fifth grade."

"And sixth grade," I said, "and seventh grade."

"She had problems," my mother admitted. "How would you feel if your mother left you to run off with a vacuum-cleaner salesman?"

"No worse than I feel now," I retorted. "At least I wouldn't have to worry about my stepsister murdering me in my sleep."

Gruesome Grossman, my stepsister. The thought was too horrible to contemplate. Sure, I knew my mother had been going out with Tina's father for a year. But they'd been trying to keep it a secret because they both teach at Locksley Hall High. My school.

My mother had sworn me to secrecy, and even though I was dying to tell my friends that she was dating their German teacher, I didn't. Even when my best friend, Selena, got a massive crush on him and wrote him thirty-seven love notes that she (fortunately) never mailed.

They didn't want to be teased and spied on. They didn't want to be the object of sordid teenage gossip and evil rumors. I could understand that. After all, I'm a teenager. I love sordid gossip and evil rumors.

But marriage? They were two middle-aged teachers with practically grown daughters. Why did they have to get married? Why couldn't they just go right on sneaking around, without forcing their children into this bizarre parody of a family?

I dropped into the nearest chair and glared at my mother. "Does Tina know about the impending nuptials?" I said "nuptials" with such disgust that my mother winced.

"No. Remember, she was in my history class when I started seeing Don. And then, when I had to flunk her, we thought . . ."

"See! Even her father's afraid of her. And she must *hate* you. Can't you tell this is never going to work?"

"It will work," my mother said firmly, "if we work at making it work."

I scowled at her. "Nobody could work that hard."

It's not that I resented my mother remarrying. I wasn't jealous about "sharing" her with someone else. In fact, for years after my father died, I tried to fix her up with men so I could have a daddy again.

The man who came to service the oil burner, the shoe salesman who fitted me at Wee Walk Inn, even the UPS driver who occasionally delivered a package to our house—I considered all of them potential father material.

Of course, I was eight years old at the time, and kept seeing all these old movies on TV where a little kid brings two people together who never realize they love each other until they both realize they love *her.*

But the little kid never ended up with a stepsister. Let alone a stepsister like Tina Grossman.

It was about this time that Tina—the Terror of Tyler Elementary School—began terrorizing me. Oh, she picked on other kids, too. I wasn't the only one who was afraid of her. But maybe I was the one who was most afraid of her. So naturally I was the kid she most enjoyed bullying.

I handed over lunch money, granola bars, homework, snap bracelets—even pencils with my name printed on them that my grandmother had given me for Christmas.

All she had to do was stand over me with her fists on her hips and say, "Gimme that!" At first I'd say no. Then she'd say, "Gimme that or I'll break your arm."

I generally decided that I needed my arm more than the lunch money, granola bar, or whatever it was she was trying to extort from me that day.

Maybe that's why I longed for a father so much. Maybe I thought he'd protect me from Tina. But I'd gotten over it. And eventually, Tina got tired of terrorizing me, and channeled her aggression into school sports, where she became the captain of the softball team, the volleyball team, and the basketball team. Possibly by threatening to break all the other players' arms if they didn't elect her captain.

Well, I was finally getting a father. Who was just as afraid of Tina as everyone else.

"When's the wedding?" I asked sourly. "And is there time to enroll me in boarding school before then?"

"July," my mother said.

"July?" I groaned. "That's only two months away. It's hardly enough time to write my will."

"I know it seems soon," my mother said. "That's why Don and I thought you girls ought to get better acquainted before then."

"We could hardly be worse acquainted," I said before I realized what she was getting at.

"So Saturday we're all going into the city together," she went on. "We have marvelous plans. First we'll go to a Yankee game."

"I hate baseball," I said.

"Then on to a nice restaurant for dinner," she continued.

"I'm on a diet."

"And after dinner we have tickets for *Oui,*[1] *Oui, Odette.*"

That shut me up. Momentarily. *Oui, Oui, Odette* was the hottest musical on Broadway.

"And then Tina will come back here to sleep over." She said it rapidly, as if hoping she could slip it by me. Unfortunately, I heard it.

"It will be a wonderful day," she promised.

"It will be a day that will live in infamy," I replied.

---

1 **oui** (*wee*) yes

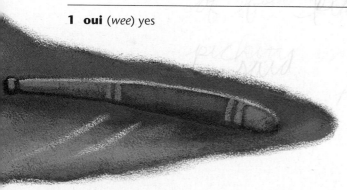

When Mr. Grossman came to pick us up Saturday morning, Tina was sullen and withdrawn. Obviously her father had told her about the wedding plans. Obviously she was as thrilled as I was about the prospect of joining our families.

She was wearing a white sleeveless T-shirt that displayed her overdeveloped biceps, and a denim skirt. For Tina this was practically formal wear. I couldn't remember ever seeing her in a skirt before.

She'd even tried to tame her long, frizzy black hair with gel or something. It wasn't as wild as it usually looked.

Tina and I immediately positioned ourselves as far apart as possible in the backseat of her father's car. She stared out the left window, silent. I stared out the right window. Silent.

My mother and Tina's father tried to get a conversation going.

"Beautiful weather for the ball game, isn't it?" he said.

"If you like baseball," I said.

"Tina loves baseball, don't you, Tina?" my mother said. "Your dad says you're a real Yankee fan."

"Yeah," said Tina.

Things went on like this until I actually began to feel a little guilty about not trying to be nice. I liked Mr. Grossman—whom I'd been calling Don for three months. I supposed it wasn't entirely his fault that Tina was such a creep.

So as we approached the Midtown Tunnel I admired the city skyline. "There's the Chrysler Building," I said. Its golden roof and spire gleamed in the sun. "Isn't it beautiful?" Just trying to be pleasant.

"Yeah," said Tina.

"It's my favorite building in New York," I said. "What's your favorite building?"

Finally she turned away from the window. She looked at me as if she thought I was nuts. "Favorite *building*?" She curled her lip in contempt.

I heard a sigh from the driver's seat.

We drove the rest of the way to Yankee Stadium without anybody trying to be nice to anybody else.

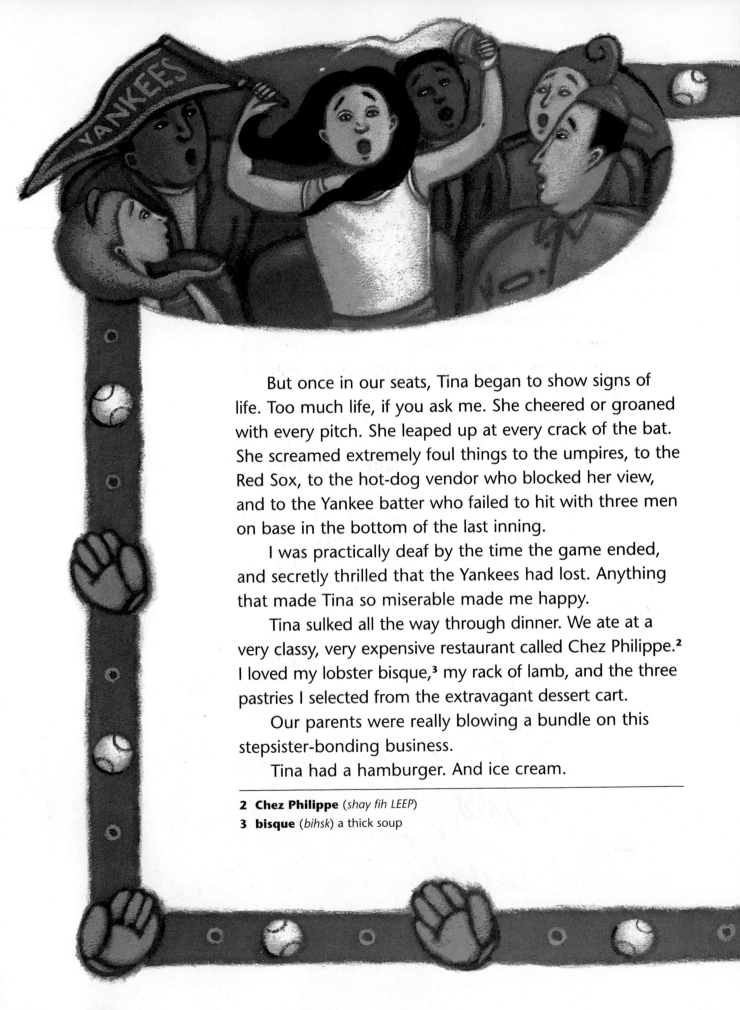

But once in our seats, Tina began to show signs of
life. Too much life, if you ask me. She cheered or groaned
with every pitch. She leaped up at every crack of the bat.
She screamed extremely foul things to the umpires, to the
Red Sox, to the hot-dog vendor who blocked her view,
and to the Yankee batter who failed to hit with three men
on base in the bottom of the last inning.

I was practically deaf by the time the game ended,
and secretly thrilled that the Yankees had lost. Anything
that made Tina so miserable made me happy.

Tina sulked all the way through dinner. We ate at a
very classy, very expensive restaurant called Chez Philippe.[2]
I loved my lobster bisque,[3] my rack of lamb, and the three
pastries I selected from the extravagant dessert cart.

Our parents were really blowing a bundle on this
stepsister-bonding business.

Tina had a hamburger. And ice cream.

---

2 **Chez Philippe** (*shay fih LEEP*)
3 **bisque** (*bihsk*) a thick soup

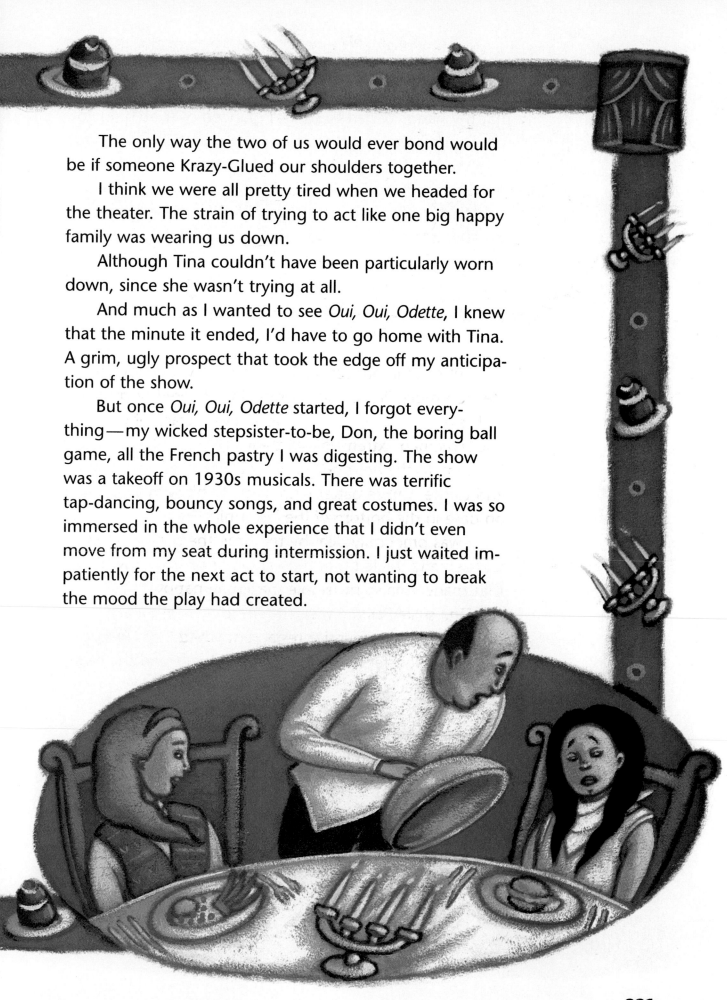

The only way the two of us would ever bond would be if someone Krazy-Glued our shoulders together.

I think we were all pretty tired when we headed for the theater. The strain of trying to act like one big happy family was wearing us down.

Although Tina couldn't have been particularly worn down, since she wasn't trying at all.

And much as I wanted to see *Oui, Oui, Odette*, I knew that the minute it ended, I'd have to go home with Tina. A grim, ugly prospect that took the edge off my anticipation of the show.

But once *Oui, Oui, Odette* started, I forgot everything—my wicked stepsister-to-be, Don, the boring ball game, all the French pastry I was digesting. The show was a takeoff on 1930s musicals. There was terrific tap-dancing, bouncy songs, and great costumes. I was so immersed in the whole experience that I didn't even move from my seat during intermission. I just waited impatiently for the next act to start, not wanting to break the mood the play had created.

At the curtain calls, I applauded so long and so hard that my hands began to sting. I glanced over at Tina. To my surprise, she was clapping as enthusiastically as I was.

"Wasn't that a great show?" I said as we walked to the parking garage.

"Yeah," Tina agreed. "It was." I was surprised that she added two more words than was absolutely necessary to reply.

I began to hum the tune to "Tap, *Tout le Monde,*⁴ Tap," the show's big production number. I was even more surprised when Tina started humming along with me.

---

4 tout le monde (*too luh* MAHND) everyone

But once in the car, she reverted to type. She sat all the way over on the other side of the seat again, and leaned her head against the window.

Don and my mother kept up an enthusiastic stream of chatter about what a wonderful day it had been.

I still had to get through the night.

I tried to tell myself that it was, after all, only one night—eight hours. We were both tired and would probably go right to sleep.

But of course, it wasn't only one night. It was the first night of the rest of my life. Or at least until I went to college. And although it seemed unlikely now that she would murder me in my sleep, what about having to deal with her the rest of the time? What about breakfasts and dinners and summers and trips and—*everything*?

I felt a very unpleasant tightness in my stomach—and it wasn't because of the three desserts.

There was a soft rumble from Tina's direction. I looked over at her. She was slumped against the window, snoring. Even sound asleep she looked tough.

When we got back to our house, Don declared that the day had been a rousing success.

"You girls ought to get right to bed," my mother urged. "Sally will show you where everything is, Tina."

Don hugged Tina and said he'd be back to pick her up in the morning. Tina got her sleeping bag and followed me up the stairs.

I felt like I was walking the Last Mile.

"The bathroom's there." I pointed. "You can use it first. My room's there."

"I don't see why we have to sleep in the same room," she said. Except for *Oui, Oui, Odette*, it was the only thing we agreed on all day. "I can put my sleeping bag anywhere."

"I don't see why, either," I said. "It's not like we're going to magically become friends overnight." Or ever. I was too tired to worry about insulting her. And she was probably too tired to punch me.

I got into my pajamas while she used the bathroom. She came back into my room wearing a green football jersey nightshirt, and unrolled her sleeping bag near my closet.

I spent a long time in the bathroom. I washed my face for five minutes and brushed my teeth till my gums nearly bled, hoping she'd be asleep by the time I got back to my room.

But she wasn't. She was lying in her sleeping bag, arms behind her head, staring at the ceiling.

"Well, good night," I said.

I climbed into bed and switched off the lamp on my night table. I punched my pillow a few times, pulled the sheet halfway up over my head, and scrunched around under the covers until I was comfortable. Or as comfortable as I could get with Gruesome Grossman sharing my room.

"Uh—Sally?"

I was startled. It was the first time she'd called me by name all day.

I pulled the sheet down from my nose. "What is it?"

"Sometimes I don't sleep too well away from home." Her voice was soft, tentative—almost childlike.

I didn't know what to say. I didn't know what she was getting at. Was there something I was supposed to do to help her sleep? And why did she sound so meek?

"I sometimes have trouble sleeping in a strange bed, too," I said. "Not that you're in a bed, but—"

"Your room is so dark," she said.

"It's nighttime," I reminded her. "It's supposed to be dark."

"My room isn't this dark."

"What, you sleep with a nightlight or something?" I blurted it out without realizing how insulting it sounded.

There was a long silence. Long enough for me to figure out that I'd stumbled onto the truth. Gruesome Grossman slept with a nightlight. Gruesome Grossman was afraid of the dark.

The shock was enough to get the adrenaline pumping through my system. Suddenly I wasn't sleepy anymore. I sat up and flicked on the lamp.

Tina was hunched up like a snail in her sleeping bag. I looked at her for a long time before speaking.

"I didn't think," I said finally, "that you were afraid of *anything*."

"I'm not afraid," she snapped. "I just don't like it too dark."

"Listen, everyone's afraid of *something*," I said. I nearly added, "I'm afraid of you." But I didn't.

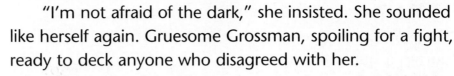

"I'm not afraid of the dark," she insisted. She sounded like herself again. Gruesome Grossman, spoiling for a fight, ready to deck anyone who disagreed with her.

"Okay, okay," I said. Not because I was afraid she'd deck me. But because I knew she must be feeling pretty embarrassed about this. And I found, to my surprise, that I had no desire to make her feel worse.

"Do you want me to leave the lamp on?" I asked.

She hesitated again. "But then you won't be able to sleep."

"Well," I agreed, "I do like it pretty dark." I thought for a moment. "I have an idea. There's a bulb in my closet."

I got out of bed and opened the closet door. The light came on. I closed the door halfway and got back into bed. I turned off the lamp.

"How's that?" I asked.

A narrow shaft of light illuminated the area around Tina's sleeping bag. If I turned toward the window and pulled the covers up to my nose again, it would hardly bother me.

"That's good," Tina said. She sounded relieved, as if she'd made it through a horror movie without having a heart attack.

"Thanks," she added.

"No problem," I said. "Good night."

She yawned deeply. "Good night," she said. "Sleep tight. Don't let the bedbugs bite."

IN RESPONSE

Write a Breakfast Dialogue

Picture Sally and Tina at breakfast the next morning. Sally starts a conversation about the day they spent together—the car ride, ball game, dinner, play, and sleepover. Will Tina be friendly? Write a dialogue.

See the Other Side

Tina has her side, too. With a partner, brainstorm a list of things Tina might say about having Sally as a stepsister.

AUTHOR AT WORK

As a girl, Ellen Conford loved books. In fact, she started writing books when she was in the third grade, although her first book wasn't published until much later. Ms. Conford writes about the problems and conflicts young people face. Often, her characters lack confidence or feel unloved. As the stories progress, something happens to the characters, and they begin to feel better about themselves. Ellen Conford knows that life can be hard for young people and hopes her books can help them laugh at their troubles.

★ Award-winning Author

Other Books by . . .

Ellen Conford

Can Do, Jenny Archer
by Ellen Conford, illustrated by Diane Palmisciano, Little, Brown, 1991

If This Is Love, I'll Take Spaghetti
by Ellen Conford, Scholastic, Inc., 1983

Library Link This story was taken from *I Love You, I Hate You, Get Lost* by Ellen Conford. You might enjoy reading the entire collection to find out how other teens solve their problems.

The Lion's Whisker

by Russell G. Davis and Brent K. Ashabranner

Bizunesh,[1] a woman of the African highlands, married Gudina,[2] a man of the lowlands. When Bizunesh went to the house of Gudina, she found that he had a son named Segab.[3] Segab was a very sad boy because his mother had died of the fever.

Bizunesh loved Segab very much and tried to be a true mother. She mended all of Segab's robes. She patched Segab's shoes. She always asked him which food he liked best. And she always tried to save the choicest pieces of meat from the stew for Segab. But he did not thank her. He did not even speak to her.

Bizunesh and her new son, Segab, were often alone together in the house of Gudina. Gudina was a merchant and

1 **Bizunesh** (*bih ZOO nihch*)
2 **Gudina** (*goo DEE nuh*)
3 **Segab** (*SAY gahb*)

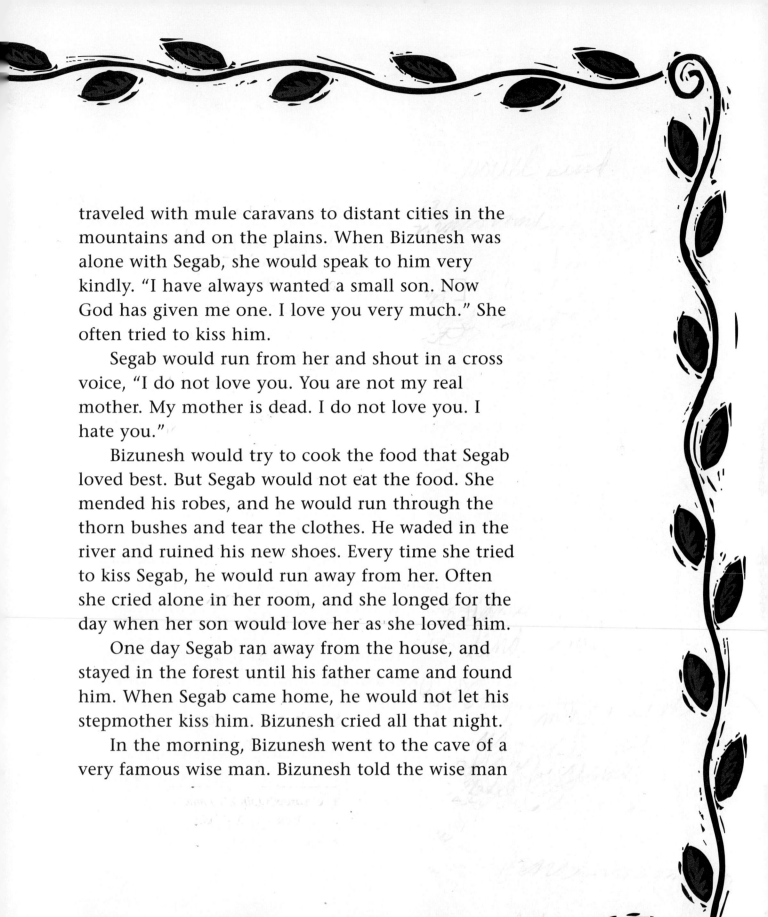

traveled with mule caravans to distant cities in the mountains and on the plains. When Bizunesh was alone with Segab, she would speak to him very kindly. "I have always wanted a small son. Now God has given me one. I love you very much." She often tried to kiss him.

Segab would run from her and shout in a cross voice, "I do not love you. You are not my real mother. My mother is dead. I do not love you. I hate you."

Bizunesh would try to cook the food that Segab loved best. But Segab would not eat the food. She mended his robes, and he would run through the thorn bushes and tear the clothes. He waded in the river and ruined his new shoes. Every time she tried to kiss Segab, he would run away from her. Often she cried alone in her room, and she longed for the day when her son would love her as she loved him.

One day Segab ran away from the house, and stayed in the forest until his father came and found him. When Segab came home, he would not let his stepmother kiss him. Bizunesh cried all that night.

In the morning, Bizunesh went to the cave of a very famous wise man. Bizunesh told the wise man

about her new son who did not love her. She said, "You must make me a magic love powder. Then Segab will love me, as he loved his own mother."

The wise man said, "To make such a powder I must have the chin whiskers of an old and ferocious lion who walks in the black-rock desert beyond the river. Bring the whiskers to me."

"How can I do that?" Bizunesh asked. "The lion will kill me."

"I cannot answer that," said the wise man. "I know about love powders. But I know little about lions. You must find a way."

Now Bizunesh loved Segab very much. She decided that she would try to get the chin whiskers, danger or not.

Bizunesh crossed the river to the black-rock desert and looked at the lion from afar. The lion was a fierce one. When he roared, Bizunesh was afraid, and she ran away home.

The next day Bizunesh came from her house carrying food. She placed the food on a rock a mile away from the lion and ran.

On the following day, Bizunesh brought food and left it only a half-mile from the lion. On the next day, Bizunesh left the food a quarter of a mile from the lion and watched him from a distance while he ate.

Finally, Bizunesh left the food only a hundred yards from the fierce lion. The lion saw her and growled in a friendly way. Bizunesh stayed while the lion ate the food. The next day she left the food fifty yards from the lion. Then one day Bizunesh went right up to the lion and fed him. She watched the lion's great jaw fly open! Crash shut! She heard the sound of his teeth tearing through the meat. She was very much frightened. But she loved Segab very much. She shut her eyes and reached out and snatched the whiskers from the lion's chin. The lion hardly noticed the small pain of losing three of his chin whiskers. Bizunesh ran away to the wise man's cave.

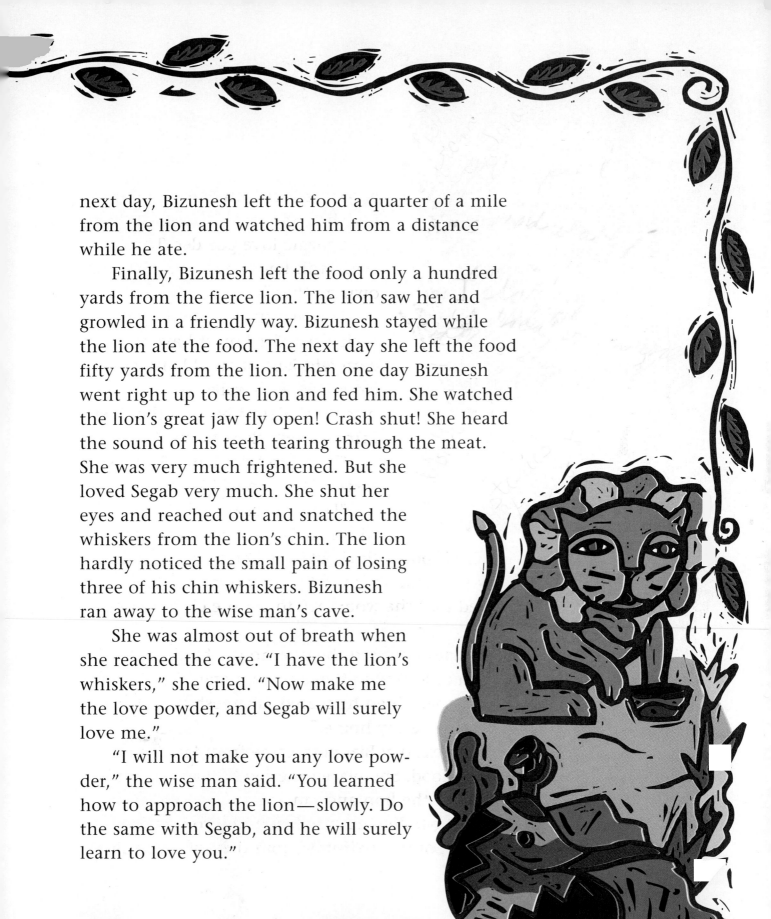

She was almost out of breath when she reached the cave. "I have the lion's whiskers," she cried. "Now make me the love powder, and Segab will surely love me."

"I will not make you any love powder," the wise man said. "You learned how to approach the lion—slowly. Do the same with Segab, and he will surely learn to love you."

The Meeting

by Eloise Greenfield

some nights they meet—

the people who live on

Neighborhood Street

get together to talk things out

work things out

and there's this brother who

always tries to pick a fight

says he's the only one who's right

his face gets ugly and he

starts to shout

he don't know what he's talking about

everybody just leans back and waits

and nods and smiles and says

"unh hunh, unh hunh" until

he sees that what they mean

is there's the door

and then he don't say

no more

from *The Outside Shot*

Shoot to Win

The electrifying sequel to Hoops!

The Outside Shot

Walter Dean Myers

by Walter Dean Myers

They give me this little piece of job. I was supposed to work in a hospital which was about a mile away from the campus. It was called University Hospital. A lot of the kids who were studying to be doctors and whatnot, they worked in the hospital. What I was supposed to do was to work in the physical therapy department. Leeds said there wasn't much to the job, but I had to do it if I wanted to get some money for extra expenses, 'cause the scholarship only covered books and tuition and stuff and just enough money to get by on.

I got the campus bus and went over to the hospital. I found the physical therapy department after asking about six people directions. They looked at me as if they had never seen a black guy before. Finally they sent me down to the end of the building that looked a little newer than the rest.

"Excuse me, I'm supposed to see Dr. Corbett."

The woman sitting behind the desk was kind of nice-looking. I thought I had seen her around the campus before but I wasn't too sure.

"You're Lonnie Jackson?" she asked. "The basketball player?"

"Yeah."

"I'm Ann Taylor." She stuck out her hand and I shook it. "It's really Annie Taylor, but I hate Annie, okay?"

"Hey, mama, it's your name."

"I hate mama, too."

"Yes, ma'am."

"Okay. Dr. Corbett isn't here right now, he's usually here in the mornings. It's my understanding that you're only going to be here six hours a week, right?"

"Right. Two days, three hours each day."

"Okay. Eddie Brignole comes twice a week, two and a half hours each time. I think you can work with him."

"*You* think?"

"Dr. Corbett isn't too enthusiastic about the athletes working with the kids, but we're too shorthanded to complain, really."

"Yeah, right."

"Let me tell you about Eddie. He's got one real problem, as far as we know. Sometimes with a kid you really can't tell what problems they have until they're more developed. Anyway, Eddie's nine and he's so withdrawn that at first we thought he was autistic, you know what I mean?"

"What does he do, draw and stuff like that?"

"Draw?" She had pretty eyes, man, and when she said that they got kind of wide and nice.

"No, he doesn't draw. He just sits around and does nothing most of the time. He won't play with the other kids or anything. Most of the time he just goes into the gym and sits by himself. What we do is just sit with him and talk to him. The staff psychiatrist seems to think that he looks forward to coming here even if he doesn't do anything and that it might help in the long run. Once in a while the athletes do get a rise from him, but not usually. So there you are."

"You said he'll be here soon?"

"Oh, one more little problem that you'll just love," Ann said. "Can I call you Lonnie?"

"Yeah."

"Eddie comes here with his mother. She sits in the gymnasium for the whole time. Whatever you do will be wrong as far as she is concerned. If she had the money she would take him to the—how does she put it now—'the best clinics in the world.' But she doesn't, so she's stuck with us, and we're stuck with her. She's not shy about telling you either."

"Okay," I said. "I guess I can handle it."

"I hope so. She's worn out two football players already."

I just sat around for a while and read and looked at a magazine until this kid Eddie was supposed to show up. After a while a woman about medium height with dark hair pulled away from her face with a comb and bobby pins at the back of her head came in. She wore a suede jacket with fur trim that fit her kind of nice. She probably could have looked a little better if she took care of herself. Ann motioned for me to come over. Well, this chick was sitting at the side of Ann's desk drumming her fingers like she was ticked off already.

"Mrs. Brignole, this is Lonnie Jackson." Ann's voice carried a smile with it. "He's going to be working with Eddie for a while."

"Hello." I stuck out my hand. She looked at it, and when she looked back at Ann she didn't make a move to shake my hand.

"Does he have experience working with young children?" she asked.

"Not at all," Ann said, smiling. "But I'm sure he'll do a wonderful job, Mrs. Brignole."

"If he has no experience, I don't want him working with Eddie," Mrs. Brignole said. "I insist upon having someone with some experience at least."

"Fine," Ann said. "We might get some experienced people in when the new budget is approved next spring. If and when we do, you'll be the first person we contact."

"I think . . . I think you're being impudent," Mrs. Brignole said.

"If you want to speak to Dr. Corbett, it's fine with me," Ann said. "He'll be in sometime tomorrow morning."

Mrs. Brignole took a deep breath and put her fingertips to her brow. Ann looked at her and then looked down at the desk. I started to say something like how I would try real hard, but Ann stopped me by raising her hand. I wasn't that interested in working with a handicapped kid in the first place.

"What am I supposed to do?" Mrs. Brignole spat each word out carefully. "Give my son over to any student who seems to have nothing to do?"

"I'm sorry, Mrs. Brignole," Ann said. "The only thing I can do is offer you what services we have. I don't want to sound uncaring, because I'm not, but you're going to have to take what we have to offer or wait until our budget is increased. Look, why don't you go and get Eddie, at least for today, and let him meet Lonnie."

Mrs. Brignole took a deep breath, stood, and walked out of the office.

"She don't seem too happy to see me," I said.

"She is not a happy woman," Ann answered.

"Look, is that it, she's just going now?"

"No, she has Eddie out in the car. She has this station wagon that looks like a World War Two tank. You know, the child has been like this for a long, long time. It's got to be hard on her, too, Lonnie. Dr. Corbett thinks it would help if she went through a little therapy herself, but she won't do it."

"She's a little wacky?" Lonnie asked.

"Probably not your out-and-out wack," Ann said. "But the home environment isn't right. A few hours here isn't going to help very much. But at least Eddie hasn't gotten worse."

"What do you do when he comes here? I mean, does he have a program?"

"No, he sits on the floor and he stays there for the whole time unless there's a chair set up—then he sits on that."

"He sits down wherever you put the chair?"

"Wherever you put it," Ann said.

"Hey, look, what am I supposed to be doing with the dude?"

"Well, let him sit down on the chair and you could talk to him and you can do jumping jacks, anything. He will just look at you. If he responds to anything, which I don't think he will, then you can try to play on that. The whole thing is to try to get some response and, you know, other than that, you're just babysitting."

"Yeah, okay. Look, I'm going to check on the gym."

I went into the gym. It was a little dinky gym. I saw where the chairs were stacked against the one wall and I got one. I set it up and put it at the side of the foul lane under one basket. I saw a basketball and I went and got that.

Just then a door opened and Mrs. Brignole came in with Eddie. He was a little kid. Not even five feet tall. He looked a lot like his mother, except for his hair. Her hair was dark brown and his was like a red, a deep, dark red. I stood beneath the basket, just sort of bouncing the ball off the backboard. I watched as Eddie came slowly toward the chair and sat in it. Mrs. Brignole leaned against the wall.

"Do you want to sit there or do you want to get up and play some ball?" I asked.

Nothing.

The cat's face wasn't like blank, which is what I thought that Ann meant. Instead he just had his head down, like, you know, beaten, pushed down. I threw the basketball through the hoop and I looked at Eddie. The boy's head was still down.

"Okay," I said. "Now you sitting in that chair because somebody told you that you got to sit in that chair, right?"

Nothing.

"Now you got to look at what I'm doing for the same reason you got to sit in that chair, because if you don't look at me, then I don't know if you know what I'm doing, see. And you and me are going to get along. You can't make believe I ain't here. That's the only thing I don't like. Now you look at me, man."

Nothing.

Eddie kept his head down.

"Hey, I'm not going to keep telling you. When I tell you to look at me, I'm serious, man. I'm really serious."

Nothing.

I put the ball under my arm and walked over to the dude and lifted his chin up. I moved my arm and he let his head fall down to his chest again. I lifted it up again, the expression was the same. Now, I mean, he looked like he was sad, so I lifted his head a little harder.

"Hey, man, I ain't playing with you, stop ignoring me, man."

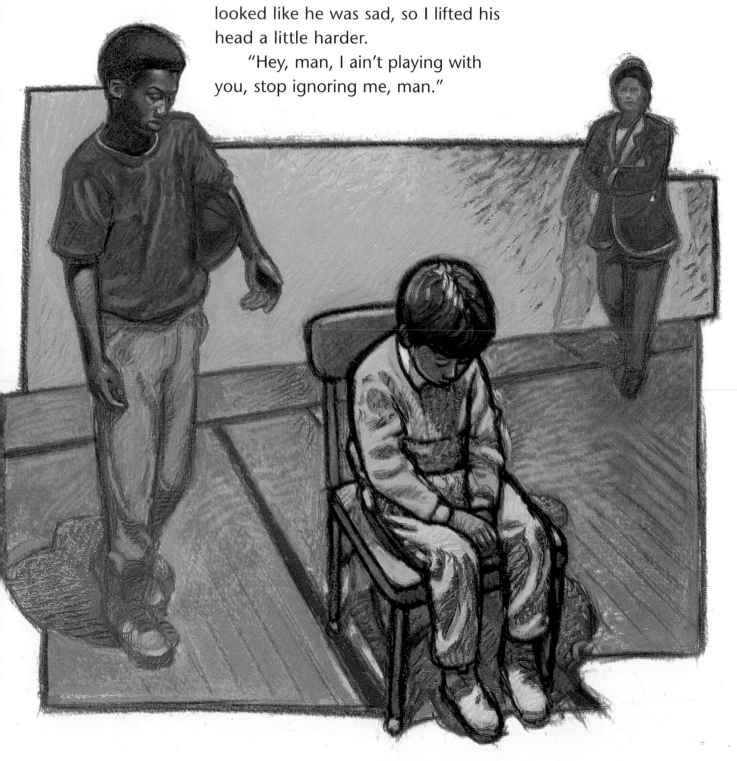

Out of the corner of my eye I could see his mama changing her position. I stood back and watched as my man's head dropped again and then I passed him the ball. It bounced lightly off his chest. I grabbed the ball and went up for a layup.

"Two nothing, my favor," I said. "Now it's your turn." I bounced the ball off of him again. "You missed an inbound pass, dude," I said, grabbing the ball. "I got it, I'll dribble around you, fake you out, and shoot. Yes! I got the ball in, that's four points for me and nothing for you. I'm going to wipe you up, turkey, you ain't no ballplayer."

I bounced the ball off Eddie's leg this time, grabbed it off the ground and started dribbling around him, faking left and faking right, then I leaned against Eddie's chair and turned around and put up a soft hook that touched nothing but net and fell through.

"All right. The kid is on his game," I said. "The television cameras are on me as I slaughter you, Eddieee. The score, nothing for you and six for meee."

I saw his mother take a step forward and stop. I see she is one of those protective mamas. I didn't care. I backed off a little bit and threw the ball to him, lightly.

"Here comes a pass to you." Bang. He didn't move and the ball rolled over to the side. I grabbed it.

"I got the rebound, now I'm going to dribble around you again and I'm going to fake you out. Here I come." I dribbled past him and laid the ball up again. "There, man. That's *ten* for me and nothing for you."

"Eight," came the voice from Eddie Brignole. "You only have eight."

"Okay, turkey," I said. "Eight. I thought I could beat you a little easier than that. I see you watching everything I do, huh. Okay, this time I'm not going to announce the game, man. I'm just going to go on and shoot the ball, man. 'Cause you got your head down and you won't be seeing what I be doing, man. Okay, here comes the ball to you." I threw him the ball. It bounced off of him again. I grabbed it and moved toward the basket, but this time I was watching him and he turned just as I threw the ball against the backboard. It fell through.

"Now I got ten, now I got ten!" Then I came back, threw him the ball again. I saw his hand move, he wanted to grab it. I just knew he wanted to grab that ball.

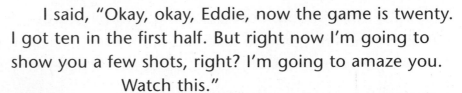

I said, "Okay, okay, Eddie, now the game is twenty. I got ten in the first half. But right now I'm going to show you a few shots, right? I'm going to amaze you. Watch this."

I moved back to the top of the key. I looked at him to see if he was looking at me. He wasn't looking right at me but he had lifted his head and I knew he could see me out of the corner of his eye. I put the ball on the floor one time and I threw up a soft jump shot. It arched easily through the air and bounced off the back rim. I looked over at Eddie and he smiled.

"Hey, man, don't be smiling at me. I mean, I could still beat you, even if I did miss that one shot."

It went on like that for about a half hour more. The dude was actually glad to see me miss and I didn't care. It was like a little game we were playing. He was sitting there watching me, hoping I would miss and I was watching him, seeing how he would react. Then I told him we would have a rest period and we would start the second half of our game, but this time I told him I wanted him to get up off that chair and try a shot. All you got to do is try one shot, just one shot and that's all, okay, one shot?

"Can you make one shot? Oh, I see you can't even make one shot, that's your problem, man."

He didn't say anything. I sort of picked him up in one arm, half lifted him, and walked him over to the basket. I knew he could walk okay. I put the basketball in his hands and lifted it, and I told him very softly in his ear, "Don't drop this ball when I give it to you, man.

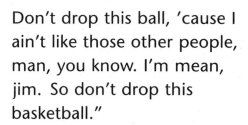

Don't drop this ball, 'cause I ain't like those other people, man, you know. I'm mean, jim. So don't drop this basketball."

I put it in his hand and he held it for a long moment.

"Go on shoot it, go on shoot it."

He threw the ball up, it hit the bottom of the rim and fell down. I grabbed it and I kept on playing like I had before when he was sitting down. I would grab it and dribble around him. He just stood there. I kept throwing him the ball but he would just let it bounce off his body.

I said, "Okay, man."

I figured I would see what this dude was really made of. I had an idea what he was made of when I saw the smile when I missed the shot and when he corrected me on the score. The dude didn't like losing. He didn't like losing, I knew.

I said, "Okay, Eddie, tell you what I'm going to do, man. Since I'm on the basketball team and you're not even on a basketball team, I guess you need a little break, so I'm going to give you a break. Here, I'm going to give you the basketball and walk all the way across the gym now. If you make a basket before I get back over to you, I'm going to give you ten points. Now hold this basketball, Eddie, HOLD THE BASKETBALL. I told you I'm mean, jim."

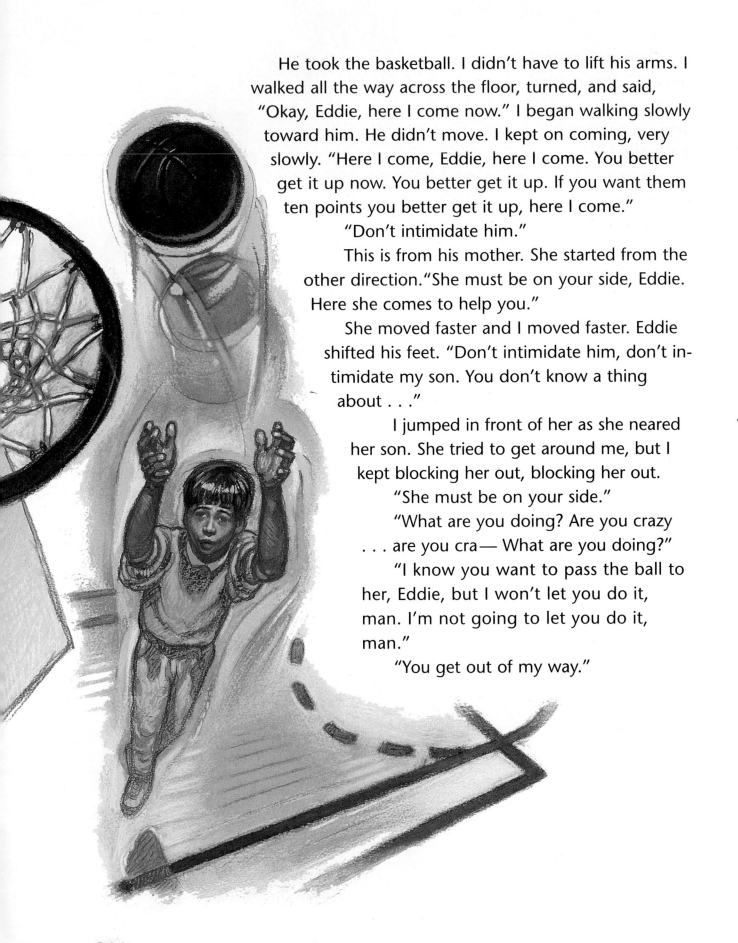

He took the basketball. I didn't have to lift his arms. I walked all the way across the floor, turned, and said, "Okay, Eddie, here I come now." I began walking slowly toward him. He didn't move. I kept on coming, very slowly. "Here I come, Eddie, here I come. You better get it up now. You better get it up. If you want them ten points you better get it up, here I come."

"Don't intimidate him."

This is from his mother. She started from the other direction. "She must be on your side, Eddie. Here she comes to help you."

She moved faster and I moved faster. Eddie shifted his feet. "Don't intimidate him, don't intimidate my son. You don't know a thing about . . ."

I jumped in front of her as she neared her son. She tried to get around me, but I kept blocking her out, blocking her out.

"She must be on your side."

"What are you doing? Are you crazy . . . are you cra— What are you doing?"

"I know you want to pass the ball to her, Eddie, but I won't let you do it, man. I'm not going to let you do it, man."

"You get out of my way."

Eddie turned and threw the ball up against the back-board. The ball rolled around the rim and I said a quick, quick prayer. "Lord, PLEASE, let it roll in."

The Lord did a cool thing, as the ball fell through the hoop.

Eddie looked up at the basket and then he glanced over at me.

"Good shot," I said. "You got a nice touch."

IN RESPONSE

An Electronic Note

Imagine Lonnie wants to persuade a friend on the basketball team to work at the hospital, too. Write a short note Lonnie might send by computer mail to that friend, telling about the experience with Eddie.

Be a News Reporter

A reporter from the school newspaper wants to write about the program at the hospital. With a partner, write several interview questions the reporter might have for Lonnie. Then, write answers Lonnie might give based on the selection.

Walter Dean Myers

★ **Award-winning Author**

Walter Dean Myers grew up in New York City, more specifically, in Harlem. Mr. Myers remembers, "The people I met there, the things I did, have left a permanent impression on me."

Even as a young child, Mr. Myers was interested in reading and writing. He learned to read at age four. "When I was a child, books were my secret friends. I never had to explain to them why I couldn't speak as clearly as the other children, or that I felt badly about not having money for things that other kids seemed to have, or that I wasn't very good at making human friends."

The teenagers in many of Mr. Myers's books must deal not only with the challenges of adolescence, but also with the obstacles of life in the inner city. His novels showcase the individual strengths and inner resources that allow the teens to cope and survive.

Mr. Myers finds writing for young people especially interesting: "I'm drawn to the eternal promise of childhood, and the flair of the young for capturing the essence of life."

Other Books by . . .

Walter Dean Myers

Young Martin's Promise
by Walter Dean Myers, Raintree, 1993

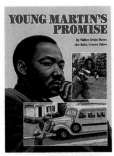

Now Is Your Time
by Walter Dean Myers, HarperCollins, 1991

New Basketball Teams Come to NY

... of children   the league's home. They
... have cleaned up the trash that cov-
... ered the court's floor and now
... games three or four

New Yor...
from W...
starte...
league...

old ...
lea...
fri...
gr...
h...

The Art of Unity

Unity can mean different things, depending on the people or ideas it involves. How does each of these pictures show a type of unity?

Describe what you see when you look at the painting below. Where might these people be? Why do you think they have gathered together?

Painting by Norman Rockwell (United States), *The Right to Know,* **1968**

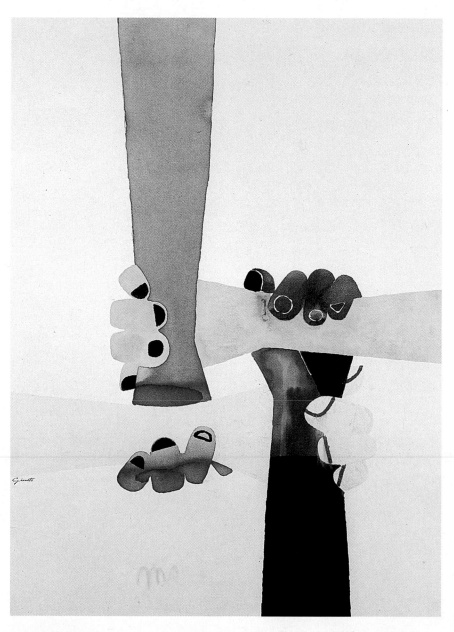

Painting by George Giusti (Italian), *"Civilization is a method of living an attitude of equal respect for all men."—Jane Addams, 1933* **(Great Ideas Series), 1955**

What are the hands doing? To whom do they belong? Does this painting show unity? Why or why not?

These girls are looking at a photograph together. How can shared experiences like this lead to a kind of unity?

Drawing by Isabel Bishop (United States), *The Snapshot,* **1936**

Painting by José Clemente Orozco (Mexican), *The Table of Brotherhood,* **1930–1931**

Painting by Allan Rohan Crite (United States),
School's Out, 1936

In the painting at the left, does the table separate the men or help bring them together? Why do you think so? What are the school children doing in the painting above? What clues tell you this?

THE REBELLION OF THE MAGICAL RABBITS

by Ariel Dorfman

When the wolves conquered the land of the rabbits, the first thing the leader of the pack did was to proclaim himself King. The second was to announce that the rabbits had ceased to exist. Now and forever it would be forbidden to even mention their name.

Just to be on the safe side, the new Wolf King went over every book in his realm with a big black pencil, crossing out words and tearing out pictures of cottontails until he was satisfied that not a trace of his enemies remained.

But an old gray fox who was his counselor brought bad news.

"The birds, Your Wolfiness, insist that they have seen some . . . some of those creatures. From on high."

"So how come I don't see anything from way up here, on my throne?" asked the Wolf.

"In times like these," answered the fox, "people have got to see to believe."

"Seeing is believing? Bring me that monkey who takes photos, the one who lives nearby. I'll teach those birds a lesson."

The monkey was old and weak.

"What can the Wolf of all Wolves want with me?" he asked, looking at his wife and daughter.

The little girl had an answer. "He must want you to take a picture of the rabbits, Dad."

"Quiet, quiet," said her mother. "Rabbits don't exist."

But the little monkey knew that rabbits did exist. It was true that, since the howling wolves had invaded the country, the rabbits no longer came to visit her as they had before. But in her dreams she continued hearing the green rain of their voices singing

nearby, reflecting in her head as if she were a pond under the moonlight, and when she awoke there was always a small gift beside her bed. Walls and closed doors were like water for the rabbits.

"That's why I sleep well," said the little girl. "That's why that General Wolf must need the photo. To keep nightmares away. You'll bring me a picture of them someday, won't you, Dad?"

The monkey felt fear crawl up and down his fur. "Send this little girl to her room," he told his wife, "until she understands that there are certain things we just don't talk about."

The King of the Wolves was not in the best of moods when the monkey came in. "You're late. And I'm in a hurry. I need photographs of each important act in my life. And all my acts, let me tell you, are supremely important. . . . Can you guess what we're going to do with those pictures? You can't? We're going to put one on every street, inside every bush, in every home. I'll be there, watching each citizen with my very own eyes. You'd better pity those who don't have the latest events of my life hung up on their walls. And you know who is going to distribute each picture? You don't know?"

The monkey was trembling so hard that no words came out.

"The birds, ugly monkey. Now they'll bite their own beaks before they twitter around with any nonsense about rabbits. And we'll tie an endless cord to their legs, so they can't escape. Understand?"

The monkey understood so well that his trembling paw immediately clicked the shutter of the camera, taking the first picture.

"Go," roared the Wolf, "and develop it. I want it on every wall in the kingdom."

But when the photographer returned some minutes later, he did not dare to enter the throne room, and asked one of the soldiers to call the counselor. Without a word, the monkey passed him the picture he had just taken.

The fox blinked once, and then blinked again. In a corner of the photo, far from the muscular, ferocious figure of the King—who had both arms up in the air as if he had just won a boxing championship—appeared what was without any doubt the beginning of an ear, the ear of someone who had insolently come to spy on the whole ceremony.

"You blind monkey!" fumed the fox. "How come you didn't notice that this . . . this thing was there? Can't you focus that camera of yours?"

"If it could get into the picture," the monkey answered, "it was because you and your guards let it get close."

"It won't happen again," the counselor promised. "Rub out that . . . ear before His Wolfishness finds out."

From his bag, the monkey took out a special liquid that he used to erase any detail that might bother a client. The intruding ear began to disappear as if it had never existed.

The King of the Wolves was pleased with the portrait and ordered it sent all over the realm. Two hours later he personally went on an inspection tour to make sure that not a window was without a picture of his large, gleaming, dangerous grin. "Not bad," he said, "but this photo is already getting old. People should see my latest deeds. Take another. Quick.

Show me scaring these pigeons—right away. And bring it to me immediately. You took too long last time."

But the monkey wasn't able to comply this time either. Once again he had the counselor called secretly.

"Again?" asked the fox. "It happened again?"

Except that now it was worse than an indiscreet ear. A whole corner of the new picture was filled with the unmistakable face of . . . yes, there was no denying it, of a rabbit winking an eye in open defiance of the nearby guards.

"We've got to tighten security," muttered the fox. "Meanwhile, erase that invader."

"Wonderful," shouted the King Wolf when finally he was given the picture. "Look at the frightened faces of the pigeons trying to escape. I want a million copies. I want them on milk cartons and on the coupons inside cereals. . . . Onward. Onward. Let's go and smash up a dam. Come on, monkey. Fame awaits us both."

The beavers had been working summer and winter for three years on a beautiful dam that would allow them to irrigate a distant valley.

The Wolf of Wolves climbed a tree. "I want you to shoot the precise moment when my feet crash into the middle of the dam, monkey. If you miss the shot, next time I'll fall on top of you and then I'll have to get myself another photographer. Are you ready?"

Not only was the monkey ready, so was the counselor. The fox was breathing down the old monkey's back, peering over his shoulder, watching, listening. Nothing could escape those vigilant, darting eyes. Not a fuzzy ear would dare to make its appearance.

So neither the monkey nor the fox could believe it when, a bit later, they saw at the bottom of the picture a rabbit lolling on his side as if he were relaxing at a picnic. Next to him, another rabbit had raised her paw and was boldly thumbing her nose.

"This is an epidemic," said the fox. "And let me tell you, our lives are in danger."

"Let's start erasing," the monkey said wearily.

"You erase. I'll get a squadron of buzzards and hawks. They see all animals, even the quick and the small."

His Wolfhood the King yelped with pleasure when he saw the picture. It portrayed him at the exact moment he was breaking the backbone of the beavers' dam. In the distance, families of beavers could be seen fleeing. There was not a single shadow of a rabbit.

"Send it out! A strong country is an educated country, a country that always is tuned in to the latest news. What are we going to do now for some fun?"

"We could rest," the monkey suggested, his paws peeling from the harsh erasing fluid.

The Wolf looked at him as if he were a stone.

"And who asked you for an opinion? I'm in charge here. That's why I was born with these teeth, and you'd better pray you never have to feel them crunching your bones. Onward. We are the future, the morrow, the dawn! We'll go on until there's no more light."

But in each new photo, the rabbits became more plentiful, audacious, and saucy. His Wolfinity the King destroyed sugar mills, shook squirrels out of their trees and hid their nuts, stripped ducks of their feathers, drove sheep off cliffs, drilled holes in the road so that horses would break their legs, unveiled new cages and old dungeons . . . and the more his frightening yellow eyes flickered, the more innumerable were the rabbits of every color that frolicked in the margins of the photographs. Even the clouds seemed full of fur and whiskers and cottontails.

"Hey, birdie," jeered the Supreme Wolf, grabbing a swallow about to fly off with a bag overflowing with pictures, "what tune are you singing now, featherhead? Who's that in the center of the picture, huh? Who's the King?"

The bird held his beak tight, so that not even a peep could come out.

"Lights, camera, action, monkey!" the Monarch demanded. "Call this: WOLF KING RECEIVES HOMAGE FROM A MESSENGER."

The monkey obeyed, but could hardly hide his despair. Though nobody ever saw the rebels when the photos were taken, they were always there when it was time to show them, nibbling lettuce at the very feet of the biggest and baddest of wolves.

"Exterminate them," hissed the fox, who had ordered a stronger, more acid liquid. "Don't leave even a twitch of a nose."

But the pictures were beginning to look defective. There were blank spaces everywhere. The monkey knew that the only solution was to convince His Wolfiness to sit up high on an elevated throne. Since rabbits live underground, they wouldn't be able to wiggle their way into the frame of the photograph.

The King, fortunately, was delighted with the idea. "I'll look more impressive up here. And I can keep an eye on those birds. What a surprise for my subjects when they find my new picture at breakfast, right? So get here early, monkey, do you hear?"

When the exhausted monkey dragged himself home, his fingers hurting from the terrible liquid, the latest photograph of the King had just been plastered on the front door of his house. Just at that moment, a soldier was leaving.

"No cause for alarm, Mr. Monkey," the soldier laughed. "Just a routine inspection to see if anybody is sabotaging His Wolfhood's pictures."

The monkey rushed inside. "Our daughter? Is she all right? Did she say anything?"

"I'm fine, Dad," the little girl said. "Those wolves are gone, aren't they? And you brought me that special photo—you know, the one I asked you for?"

The monkey felt as if from all four walls, from all four pictures on the four walls, the eight eyes of the Biggest of Wolves were watching each word he might say.

"Let your father rest," said her mother. "The only pictures he's taken are the ones we've put up in the house, like good citizens."

But the next morning, the monkey was awakened by his child's kiss. She put her lips near his ears and whispered something so softly that only he could hear it: "Thank you. It's the best present you could ever give me. You're a magical dad."

"Thanks? Thanks for what?"

She motioned almost imperceptibly toward the wall from which the photo of the Wolf King ruled. Her father opened his eyes wide. In one of the corners of that picture, like the sun rising over the mountains, he could just glimpse, in the act of making their gradual but glorious appearance, a pair of, yes, of course, a pair of soft, pink, pointed ears.

The monkey jumped out of bed. The liquid he had applied did not work permanently. The rabbits had needed the whole night to sneak back into the pictures, but somehow they had managed it.

"I think they knew I was scared," the little girl murmured, "and came to see me while I slept."

Her father dressed in less time than it takes a chill to run up a spine and scurried to the palace without stopping for

breakfast. Was this happening only at their house or could the same invasion have taken place everywhere in the kingdom? If so, how could the rabbits be removed from so many portraits?

His Wolfiness was still in bed, but the counselor was already pacing about, biting the tip of his tail. "It's a plague," he said, "but, fortunately, it is already under control. The offending pictures have been burned. As for you . . ."

"I swear that I—"

"Not a word from you," interrupted the fox. "It's lucky those creatures don't exist. Imagine the damage they'd cause if they really existed. But enough talk. What we need now is a new

photo to replace the ones that are contaminated."

They rushed to the new throne, which was now set up on top of four colossal wooden legs, out of reach of the spreading virus of the mischievous ears.

"I want two shots," His Wolfhood demanded, "one of me ascending my throne and another of me sitting on it, enjoying the fresh air. And send them abroad too, so those silly foreign papers will stop attacking me."

This time, when the photos were developed, there was no trouble. Not so much as a carrot of a sign of a rabbit.

"Didn't I tell you? Didn't I tell you they don't exist?" The counselor was jubilant. "It was just a matter of your focusing the camera properly."

For the next few days, there were no more unpleasant surprises. The Wolf of Wolves felt happy, high above the heads of the multitude. He let his lieutenants run things while he posed for pictures giving commands, delivering speeches, signing laws. He examined the shots carefully, however. "Congratulations," he said. "You're being more careful, monkey. It seems you're learning your trade just by being near me. I don't see any more of those whitish spots that spoiled my first pictures."

But one morning, the monkey was again awakened by his daughter's voice. "They're back, Dad," she whispered in his ears. "Those pictures you took sure are magical."

In one set of photos, at the foot of the towering throne, a small army of rabbits was biting, chewing, and splintering the wooden legs. Their teeth worked patiently, and they stopped their work only now and again to wave to the spectators.

The counselor was waiting. The monkey could see his fur ruffling and swelling like a swarm of bees.

"How many this time?" the monkey asked.

"The photos are being taken care of," the fox said grimly. "But the birds have got wind of what happened, and now they're telling everyone that those . . . those awful animals exist. And

His Wolfinity is beginning to suspect something. 'Why are those birds so happy, so shrill?' he asks. I told him they're just a bunch of featherbrains, full of hot air."

"What did he answer?" asked the monkey.

The King had announced that balloons are full of hot air too and that they could be popped. If those birds didn't keep quiet, he would make them disappear.

But the counselor had another idea: The Wolf of All Wolves should tie a recording of one of his latest speeches around the necks of the birds. They would have to carry not only the photos, but also the King's words, all over his kingdom. Nobody would be able to hear any of their songs.

"Hearing is believing," trumpeted His Wolfiness. "We'll give them a taste of some hymns, some military marches, some lessons in history, economics, and ethics."

The old monkey's life became unbearable. Not even the recorded howls of the King and his chorus of warlike beasts could stop the timid appearance, in the next photo, of an inquisitive nose, a pair of furry ears, some white whiskers, and something hungry gnawing away at the legs of the throne.

The fox replaced the chief officer of the royal guard with a boa constrictor straight from the jungle of a neighboring country. He put small, hundred-eyed spiders in strategic places through- out the Wolfdom. One day he ordered half the population to shave off their shiny fur so that no spy could hide in it. To punish the cows, accused of uttering subversive moos, he commanded that their milk be soured. And finally, he raised the volume of the King's broad- casts. But in spite of

these efforts, there began to be heard a persistent, rowdy, merry sound, the clicking of thousands of tiny teeth, the burbling of an underground stream.

The monkey felt dizzy.

The rhythm was maddening. During the night, the legs of the throne, spindlier by the minute, were reinforced grudgingly by woodpeckers who would have much preferred to take the throne apart. The monkey had to rely on every photographic trick of the trade, now erasing, now trimming with scissors, disguising ears so they looked like shadows and shadows so they looked like wallpaper. He even began using old portraits of the King, trying to make them seem like recent ones.

Until one night, when it was very late, the old monkey was

awakened by an angry hand that shook him from his slumber. It was the counselor, flanked by a fierce escort of soldiers. The Lord Wolf had sent for him.

The whole house was up by now. The little girl watched her father begin dressing.

"Say hello to His Foxcellency," said the monkey.

"Dad," she said, and it was astonishing that she did not speak in a low, fearful voice anymore, as if the armed guards were not even there, "today you've got to bring me that picture I asked for."

"A picture?" The counselor showed interest. "A picture of what, of whom?"

The child continued to ignore him. "Today you'll bring me a photo of the rabbits, right, Dad? For my wall?"

The mother monkey touched the girl's head as if she had fever. "Hasn't your father told you that rabbits don't exist? Haven't we shut you up in your room for telling lies?"

"They exist," the girl announced. "Everybody knows they exist."

"Just as I suspected," said the counselor. "Let's go."

The Wolfiest of Wolves was waiting for them atop his throne. Around each leg, hundreds of guards and snakes kept watch.

"Monkey, you are a traitor," thundered the King. "Your photos are being used by people who say that strange and malicious creatures—who are nonexistent as everyone knows—are conspiring this very night to overthrow my rule. They say my throne trembles and my dynasty will topple. Is there any evidence that my throne trembles? Does anybody dare say so?" And he yowled like a hundred jet fighters in the air. "We'll start by making a recording of that sound. And you, you monkey, you're going to help me stamp out these rumors. Touching is believing. You are going to make me a wide-angle, three-dimensional picture that will cover all walls. In color. Because I am going to crown myself Emperor of the Wolves, the Supreme Wolferor. And if a single wretched rabbit

shows its snout, I will make you eat the photos, one by one, a million of them, and then I'll eat you and not only you, but your wife and your daughter, and all the monkeys in this country. Now. Take that picture."

The monkey stuck his quaking head under the black cloth behind his camera and focused on the throne. He let out a little moan. Up till then, the rabbits had appeared only later, when the picture was developed. But here they were now, directly in front of his lens, ungovernable and carefree, gnawing away, biting not only the wood of the throne, but also the swords of the astonished guards and the very rattles of the rattlesnakes.

"What's the matter?" bellowed the future Wolferor, who was not looking downward so his profile would be perfect for posterity.

The monkey moved the camera nearer the throne, hoping the rabbit army would not come out in the picture. The rabbits moved faster than he did. They were clambering up the legs, one on top of the other as if they were monkeys or birds. The soldiers tried to frighten them away in silence, unwilling to attract the attention of the King, but the invaders were too agile. The Wolves kept bumping into one another and hitting each other over the head. The monkey realized that a contingent of birds had arrived from above, winging freely through the air, without a cord tied to them or a recording.

"Hurry up!" ordered the Wolf of all Wolves.

The monkey closed his eyes very tightly. It was better not to witness what was going to happen.

At the very moment he clicked the shutter, he heard a deafening noise. He knew what he was going to see when he opened his eyes, but still could not believe it: Like an old elm tree rotten to the core, the throne had come crashing to the ground along with the King of Wolves, guards, snakes, counselor, and all. The monkey blinked. There at the foot of his tripod lay the Biggest, Baddest, the Most Boastful Wolf in the Universe. His ribs were broken, his black fur was torn by the fall, his

yellow eyes were reddened, and he was wailing in pain.

"Monkey," squeaked the would-be Wolferor of the World, "this picture . . . you have my permission not to publish it."

At that moment, all the lights in the palace went out. The monkey was paralyzed. He did not know where to go. Then, as if someone in the darkness were suddenly shining a light on a pathway, he knew what he must do. He grabbed his camera and his bag, and clutching them to his chest like a treasure, he fled.

His daughter was waiting for him at the door of the house.

"Wait," he said to her. "Wait. I've brought you something." And without another word, he raced into his darkroom to develop the last picture as quickly as possible.

When he came out a few minutes later, his daughter and wife were standing on chairs, taking down the pictures of the Wolf King.

"Here," the old monkey said to his daughter, blinking in the bright light. "Here, this is the picture you've been asking for all this time. I've finally brought you your present."

"Thanks, Dad," the little girl said. "But I don't need it anymore."

She pointed around the room and toward the street and across the fields where the sun was beginning to rise.

The world was full of rabbits.

IN RESPONSE

Story as a Symbol

"The Rebellion of the Magical Rabbits" is an allegory, a story in which the characters and events have hidden or symbolic meanings. In a small group, decide what the main characters and actions in this story might stand for. Why might an author choose to write a story as an allegory?

Tina and the Wolf

Write a description of the Wolf King from the rabbits' point of view. Compare the description to Sally's description of Tina ("Don't Let the Bedbugs Bite"). How are Tina and the Wolf alike? What allows Tina and Sally to find common ground? Can the Wolf and the rabbits find it?

AUTHOR AT WORK

"I was writing by seven, small novels and things like that," says Ariel Dorfman. Born in South America, he moved with his family to the United States, and then later returned to South America. Through each of the moves, writing remained important to him. He says it is "something which is only yours, something almost secret." Living under the rule of dictators gave Mr. Dorfman the idea for the Wolf King.

Another Book About . . .

Political Conflict

The Middle of Somewhere: A Story of South Africa by Sheila Gordon, Orchard, 1990

Library Link This story appears in *Where Angels Glide at Dawn*, edited by Lori M. Carlson and Cynthia L. Ventura. You might enjoy reading additional selections in the book to learn the views of other Latin American authors.

WAR GAME

BY MICHAEL FOREMAN

THE KICKOFF

Goal! Will saw the ball hit the back of the net. In his imagination he had just scored for England, and he heard the roar of a huge crowd. But he knew that around the playing field there was no crowd, just a low hedge and the familiar flat expanse of the Suffolk countryside.

A group of small boys jumped around behind the goal, and a few old men sitting under the elms clapped. The church clock struck five. The game was over.

The two teams changed and joked together. "We'll come back and beat you after the war," laughed someone on the opposing team as they began their walk back to their village five miles away.

"Most of them are joining the army," said Freddie, the goal-keeper. "We should, really."

"I'd like to," said Billy, eyes shining with excitement.

"No, you're too young. If you went, I'd have to go to look after you," laughed his brother Lacey.

"It *would* be an adventure, though," said Will. "And they say it'll be over by Christmas. Be a pity to miss it."

And so they talked as they wandered back along the dusty lane into the village.

The summer of 1914 had been one of the hottest ever, and while

Will and his friends had worked long and hard in the harvest fields, far away in a place called Sarajevo an archduke had been killed. The German emperor, Kaiser[1] Bill, was using the confusion as an excuse to start a war and seize territory from his neighboring countries.

"So once again the British Army has to go overseas and sort things out," said the old men of the village over their pints of beer.

Many of the old soldiers of the village had already been recalled to the army and were on their way to the battlefields of France and Belgium. There was a lot of pressure on the young men to follow them. The British Army needed many thousands of men to stop the Germans from advancing across Europe. Recruitment posters were everywhere, and the newspapers called on every man to do his duty "for King and Country."

The day after the soccer match was a Sunday, and the vicar boomed out the same message from his pulpit. The local squire, in the front pew, wore all the medals he could get his hands on, and his son wore a brand-new, tailor-made officer's uniform. After the service, Will, Freddie, Billy,

1 **Kaiser** (*KY zuhr*) title of Germany's rulers from 1871 to 1918

and Lacey sat by the signpost under the oak and the elm at the corner of the green. Here they had sat almost every day of their lives, after church, after school, and after work.

"I think we should join," said Freddie. "None of us has ever been outside the country. It's time we saw something of the world."

"Yes! An adventure—and home by Christmas," said Billy.

Will wasn't so sure. After all, he thought, a lot of people can get killed in a war. But they agreed that the next day, after work, they would go into town and see what was happening at the Town Hall, the local army recruiting office.

THE ADVENTURE

They had never seen such a crowd. There was a great feeling of excitement and even of fun as the flags waved and the band played. Every time a lad went to join up, the crowd gave him a hearty cheer.

Before anyone could stop him, Billy was up the steps and the crowd was cheering him. Then Freddie followed. Lacey had to go to look after Billy. Will knew he couldn't let his friends go off to war without him, so to wild cheers all four joined the army. They were given railway passes and told to report to barracks in four days' time.

That evening when they got home, they had a lot of explaining to do.

Being country boys, they were all good shots, and they were assigned to the King's Royal Rifles. It sounded very grand. But so great was the rush to join that the army was overwhelmed with recruits and didn't have enough uniforms for them all. Will and the other lads were disappointed and felt foolish learning the basic training and drills wearing their ordinary clothes. They slept in bell tents in a huge field, about a dozen men to a tent. The food was poor, and the days were long and exhausting.

However, after a few weeks they were all outfitted and the adventure really started. They boarded a converted passenger ferry in Southampton and prepared to set sail at six o'clock in a great convoy.

The whole of Southampton turned out to see them off. Thousands of sailors cheered and waved their caps from destroyers in Southampton Water.

As the coast of England faded behind them, Will, like the countless young men crowded around him, felt strangely alone with his thoughts of home and of what lay over the horizon. "Come on, lads. Let's have a song," called Freddie. They sang as they sailed and felt better.

TO THE FRONT

When they reached France, they were packed into trains, which stopped and started and crawled all day along the overcrowded tracks.

The country didn't look so different. People worked the fields just as the lads had back home. Some of the workers unbent their backs and waved as the trains went by.

The soldiers finally arrived at a small station that had grown

into a vast supply depot. Trains and trucks were being shunted and unloaded. Mountains of stores, horse lines, and mule lines were everywhere, and there was a babel of shouted commands.

Then at last they were off the trains and marching. Will felt good to be out in the fresh air and swinging along with his mates. Marching through villages and towns, the troops were cheered all the way. Flowers, fruit, and bread were pressed into their arms. It seemed like a pretty good war so far, even though it had begun to rain and the long dry summer was over.

Then things began to change. The roads became crowded with

people moving back from the Front. The whole population seemed to be on the move. Families carried their children and pushed baby carriages loaded with whatever they could salvage from their lives. No more cheering crowds. These people had seen war. Their homes had been blown to bits, their farms criss-crossed by armies, trenches, and barbed wire, and pockmarked by a million artillery shells. Will could hear the almost continuous sound of shell fire in the distance.

They passed wagons full of wounded soldiers on their way back to England, and long lines of exhausted ragged troops in the mud, rain, and gathering darkness waiting to be ordered back into the action.

At last the marching came to an end, and Will, Freddie, Lacey, and Billy and the rest of the brigade were ordered onto a fleet of London buses that were to rush them up to the Front to fill a gap in the "line." They drove through the ruins of a devastated town. The lads had never been to London, yet here they were riding on a London bus in the middle of France. The

conductor's bell was still working, and one of the men kept ringing it and shouting, "Next stop, Piccadilly Circus!" The glassless windows were covered with boards, but there were plenty of holes to peep through. Will's first reaction was: "Doesn't it look pretty? Just like fireworks."

Then they were in the trenches. Not the front trench, but the reserve. In single file they moved forward along a winding communication trench to the support trench. Here they waited with the sound of battle exploding all around them.

There was a lull.

"All right, lads. It's our turn," said their sergeant, and in single file and pouring rain they slogged along another communication trench to the Front.

The trenches of the Western Front stretched across Belgium and France for a distance of 460 miles. The front trench was about three feet wide at the bottom and seven feet high. To enable the soldiers to fire over or through the parapet, a fire step was built two feet high into the forward side of the trench. It was on this that the sentries stood to keep watch.

There was still no shooting on this section of the line as Will and his mates crouched on the fire step to allow wounded and exhausted soldiers to pass by on their way to the rear.

NO-MAN'S-LAND

Will and Freddie were the first to be posted as sentries on their little section, and cautiously they stood up on the fire step. They peered over the parapet into No-Man's-Land. They could just see their own first line of barbed wire and random humps and bumps in an otherwise flat landscape that seeped rapidly into darkness. A landscape as flat as the fields of home.

Then a flare arced and spiraled slowly across the sky. Will and Freddie could see that the humps and bumps were men. Dead men. Some of them, who had cut their trousers into shorts during the hot weather, looked like fallen schoolboys.

Before the flare faded, Will and Freddie saw more lines

of wire, and beyond No-Man's-Land, the front line of German trenches.

"Less than a goal kick away," whispered Freddie.

The newcomers quickly learned the routine of trench life. An hour before dawn every morning they received the order

to "stand to." Half asleep and frozen, the men climbed onto the fire step, rifles clutched with numb fingers and bayonets fixed.

The half-light of dawn and at dusk was when attacks were most expected, and both sides had their trenches fully manned at those times. Sometimes nothing happened. Often there was a furious exchange of rifle and machine-gun fire to discourage any attack through the gloom. This was known as "morning hate."

After an hour or so the order was given to "stand down." Only the sentries remained on the fire step, and the rest of the men enjoyed what breakfast they could get among the rats, blood-red slugs, and horned beetles that infested the trenches.

As the weather grew worse, the two huge armies became bogged down in virtually fixed positions. In some places they were only thirty yards apart, so close that the heavy guns, firing from behind the reserve lines, often killed their own men when shells fell short of their target.

The mud became deeper and deeper as thousands of men, mules, horses, and heavy wagons and guns churned it up.

Now and then the soldiers were ordered to attack across No-Man's-Land, even though many lives were always lost and little or nothing was achieved. Small raiding parties ventured out at night to cause as much damage as they could and, if possible, to return with a prisoner or two who could provide some useful information. Other small teams were sent to repair or lay new barbed wire. The covering darkness could be suddenly illuminated at any time by flares. A pistol flare remained bright for about fifteen seconds. This seemed an eternity to men lying motionless in No-Man's-Land awaiting the rattle of machine-gun fire or a sniper's bullet.

The communication trenches were particularly busy at night. Dead and wounded were carried to the rear, and food and munitions were brought to the Front. When possible the dead were recovered from No-Man's-Land. Like clearing the table after dinner, ready for the generals' next game of soldiers, Will thought.

Will often thought of his family sleeping peacefully just 100 miles away, and of his own bed, dry and warm under the thatched eaves of home. Even his old dog guarding the yard and the pigs in the sty lived in more comfort than Will and the British Army.

And still it rained.

The water table of this flat land was often less than three feet below the surface. Every shell hole filled with water. The trenches were awash with mud. Here and there men hollowed out little caves or "scrapes" in the sides of the trenches to give themselves some protection from the rain, but they found little protection from the high-explosive shells that could rain down at any moment.

The enemy trenches were so close that whenever the fighting died down, each army could hear the other's voices and could sometimes even smell their breakfast. They all knew that they were sharing the same terrible conditions.

Singing in the trenches was common in 1914, and songs from one front line floated to the other on the quiet evening air. Occasionally during a quiet period a British Tommie would put a tin can on a stick and hold it above the parapet to give the Germans some shooting practice. The Germans would do likewise with tin cans or bottles, and a shooting match would develop accompanied by cheers and boos.

Sometimes the soldiers watched rival aircraft challenge each other in midair duels over the trenches.

Will, Freddie, Lacey, and Billy stayed together as much as possible and lived like soggy moles in a world of mud, attack, and counterattack.

The weather, still wet, grew steadily colder. Then, one night, as the lads returned to the Front after a few days' rest, the rain stopped and it grew bitterly cold.

That night they were relieving a Scottish regiment, and as the Scots left the Line, the Germans shouted Christmas wishes to them.

Then tiny lights appeared in the German trenches. As far as the eye could see, Christmas trees were flickering along the parapet of the German lines.

It was Christmas Eve.

A single German voice began to sing "Silent Night." It was joined by many others.

The British replied with "The First Noel," to applause from the Germans. And so it went on, back and forth across No-Man's-Land. Then both front lines sang "O Come, All Ye Faithful."

It was a beautiful moonlit night. Occasionally a star shell hung like a Star of Bethlehem.

At dawn, when the British were all "stood to" on the fire step, they saw a world white with frost. The few shattered trees that remained were white. Lines of wire glinted like tinsel. The humps of dead in No-Man's-Land were like toppled snowmen.

After the singing of the night, the Christmas dawn was strangely quiet. The clock of death had stopped ticking.

Then a German climbed from his trench and planted a Christmas tree in No-Man's-Land. Freddie, being a goalkeeper and therefore a bit daft, walked out and shook hands with him. Both sides applauded.

A small group of men from each side, unarmed, joined them. They all shook hands. One of the Germans spoke good English and said he hoped the war would end soon because he wanted to return to his job as a taxi driver in Liverpool.

It was agreed that they should take the opportunity to bury the dead. The bodies were mixed up together. They were sorted out, and a joint burial service was held on the "halfway line."

Both sides then returned to their trenches for breakfast. Will and the lads were cheered by the wonderful smell of bacon, and they had a hot breakfast for a change.

One by one, birds began to arrive from all sides. The soldiers hardly ever saw a bird normally, but Will counted at least fifty sparrows hopping around their trench.

Christmas presents for the men consisted of a packet of chocolate, bouillon cubes, a khaki handkerchief, peppermints, cocoa, writing paper, and a pencil. After breakfast a pair of horses and a wagon arrived with Princess Mary's Christmas gifts— a pipe and tobacco and a Christmas card from the King and Queen.

There were no planes overhead, no observation balloons, no bombs, no rifle fire, no snipers, just an occasional skylark. The early mist lifted to reveal a clear blue sky. The Germans were strolling about on their parapet once more, and waved to the British to join them. Soon there was quite a crowd in No-Man's-Land. Both sides exchanged small gifts. One German had been a barber in Holborn in London. A chair was placed on the "halfway line,"

and he gave haircuts to several of the British soldiers.

Then, from somewhere, a soccer ball bounced across the frozen mud. Will was on it in a flash. He trapped the ball with his left foot, flipped it up with his right, and headed it toward Freddie.

Freddie made a spectacular dive, caught the ball in both hands, and threw it to a group of Germans.

Immediately a vast, fast and furious soccer match was under-way. Goals were marked by caps. Freddie, of course, was in one goal and a huge German in the other.

Apart from that, it was wonderfully disorganized, part soccer, part ice-skating, with unknown numbers on each team. No referee, no keeping score.

It was just terrific to be no longer an army of moles, but up and running on top of the ground that had threatened to entomb them for so long. And this time Will really could hear a

big crowd—and he *was* playing for England!

He was playing in his usual center forward position, with Lacey to his left and little Billy on the wing. The game surged back and forth across No-Man's-Land. As the players warmed to the sport, greatcoats and tunics were discarded and the goalposts grew larger. Khaki and gray mixed together. Steam rose from the players' backs, and their faces were wreathed in smiles and clouds of breath in the clear frosty air.

Some of the British officers took a dim view of such sport, and when the game came to its exhausted end, the men were encouraged back to their trenches for a carol service and supper. The haunting sound of men singing drifted back and forth across No-Man's-Land in the still night air.

"Good night, Tommies. See you tomorrow."

"Good night, Fritz. We'll have another game."

But the day after Christmas passed without a game. The officers were alarmed at what had happened on Christmas Day. If such friendly relations continued, how could they get the men to fight again? How could the war continue?

The men were not allowed to leave the trenches. There were a few secret meetings here and there along the Front, and gifts and souvenirs were exchanged.

Two more days passed peacefully. Then a message was thrown over from the German side. A very important general was due to visit their section at 3:15 that afternoon, and he would want to see some action.

The Germans therefore would start firing at three p.m., and the Tommies should please keep their heads down.

At three o'clock a few warning shots were fired over the British trenches, and then heavy fire lasted for an hour. The Tommies kept their heads down.

At dawn a few days later, the Germans mounted a full-scale attack. The friendly Germans from Saxony had been withdrawn and replaced by fresh troops from Prussia. They were met by rapid and deadly fire from the British and were forced back.

The order was given to counterattack, to try to take the German trenches before they could reorganize themselves. Will and the rest of the British soldiers scrambled over the parapet. Freddie still had the soccer ball! He drop-kicked it far into the mist of No-Man's-Land. "That'll give someone a surprise," he said.

"Why are goalies always daft?" thought Will.

They were on the attack, running in a line with Will in a

center forward position, Lacey to his left, and young Billy on the wing.

From the corner of his eye Will saw Freddie dive full-length, then curl up as if clutching a ball in the best goalkeeping tradition.

"Daft as a brush," Will thought.

Suddenly they all seemed to be tackled at once. The whole line went down. Earth and sky turned over, and Will found himself in a shell hole staring at the sky. Then everything went black.

Slowly the blackness cleared, and Will could see the hazy sky once more. Bits of him felt hot and other bits felt very cold. He couldn't move his legs. He heard a slight movement. There was someone else in the shell hole.

Will dimly recognized the gleam of a fixed bayonet and the outline of a German.

"*Wasser.*[2] *Wasser,*" the German said.

It was about the only German word Will knew. He fumbled for

---

2 **Wasser** (*VAH suhr*) water

his water bottle and managed to push it toward the German with the butt of his rifle.

The German drank deeply. He didn't have the strength to return the bottle.

"Kinder?" [3] he said. Will shook his head. The German held up three fingers. Will tried to shake his head again to show that he did not understand, but the blackness returned.

Later he saw a pale ball of gold in the misty sky.

"There's a ball in Heaven," he thought. "Thank God. We'll all have a game when this nightmare's over."

At home when he had a bad dream he knew that if he opened his eyes, the bad dream would end. But here, his eyes were already open.

Perhaps if he closed them the nightmare would end.

He closed his eyes.

---

3 **Kinder** (*KIHN duhr*) children

IN RESPONSE

Group Mission

In a group, go through "War Game" and list all the ways the two armies found common ground. Review the list together. Write a generalization about finding common ground that begins like this: "War Game" tells us that people can find common ground when they . . ."

A Letter From the Front

Imagine you are Will or one of his friends at the front. Write a letter to a young man back in England. In the letter, tell him why he should or should not join the army. Use details from the story to support your argument.

Common Thread

As Christmas eve approached, the English officers and the German soldiers found that they had some things in common. With a partner, choose two other selections from this theme. For each story find at least one event that helped the characters realize they had some things in common. What were the areas of common ground in each case?

Michael Foreman grew up in a fishing village in England during World War II. He remembers that as a child he huddled in shelters during bombing raids. He also remembers watching the soldiers who came to his mother's shop for a cup of tea. He says, "The memory of those who passed through our village on the way to war will remain forever with the ghosts of us children."

Mr. Foreman often draws upon his real-life experiences when writing and illustrating books. Some people from his village can recognize their church or parts of their town in his illustrations. Sometimes he gets the idea for a story while traveling. However, Mr. Foreman explains, "My own books are never really about a place or country, but about an idea which is hopefully common to the dreams of everyone."

★ Award-winning Author

Other Books by . . .

Michael Foreman

War Boy: A Country Childhood, written and illustrated by Michael Foreman, Arcade, 1990

One World, written and illustrated by Michael Foreman, Arcade, 1990

The Boy Who Sailed With Columbus, written and illustrated by Michael Foreman, Arcade, 1992

Arn Chorn:

Born in Cambodia, Arn Chorn left his home when he was eight, fleeing the invading army called the Khmer Rouge. In the confusion, he was separated from his family. For the next four years, Arn struggled to survive, working, along with other orphans, in rice paddies in exchange for just a few grains of rice a day. When Arn was twelve, another invading army forced him to become a soldier. A year later, he escaped into the jungle and later became a refugee. Arn made his way to the United States at fourteen, and began his life anew with the Pond family in New Hampshire. Though he still has nightmares of war, Arn has used the story of his life to build hope for other children of war.

CHILDREN OF WAR

In June of 1982, when Arn was sixteen, he was invited to speak as part of a peace rally before a great crowd in the Church of Saint John the Divine in New York City. "I said what living with war had been like for me. Two or three other kids my age spoke, too. One was from Nicaragua, and one was from Japan. Her mother had been killed by the atomic bomb [in] Hiroshima. I had never heard of Hiroshima before that day."

Joining hands with the other children on the stage, Arn concluded his speech with the prayer, "Please may our suffering help other children to grow in peace."

Khmer Rouge (*kuh MEHR roozh*)

Peacemaker

from *It's Our World, Too!* by Phillip Hoose

A young woman named Judith Thompson was in the audience. As a college student, she had studied what war was doing to millions of children throughout the world. After graduation she had been working with Cambodian refugees.

A week later, she drove out to the Pond house. At first Arn didn't know what she wanted. "You know those kids who spoke with you at the cathedral?" she said. "They don't know where their parents are either. Why don't we bring together children from around the world to speak to other children about their experiences of war, about their suffering. To show them what we all have in common. Maybe then we could stop fighting. You're a good speaker, Arn. Will you help me raise money to get started?" Arn quickly agreed. Here was a way to use his own experience to bring children together. Trying to raise funds would allow him to practice speaking.

For the next month, Arn told his story to many audiences and asked them to donate money to start a group called Children of War. By the end of 1984, they had raised enough money to assemble forty-five children from sixteen war-torn nations at a house in New Jersey to prepare for the first Children of War tour.

There were children and teens from Cambodia and Vietnam, from Iraq and Iran, from Palestine and Israel, and both a Protestant and a Catholic from Northern Ireland. Their plan was to visit cities throughout the U.S., sharing their stories with American kids to show that it was possible to think beyond war. But first, as traditional enemies, they had to learn to accept each other.

For the next two weeks, the kids practiced being together in peace. First they got into a bus and sat next to those they had been trained to hate most. They made a rule: they could argue all they wanted, but they couldn't harm each other. Anyone who fought was off the bus.

Arn sat down next to a Vietnamese boy. They avoided looking at each other for a moment—and then began to scream. "You killed my family!" Arn cried. "It's not my fault!" the boy screamed back. "At first I wanted to kill him," Arn recalls, "and surely he wanted to kill me."

The whole bus rang with screams and shouts. And when they got off the bus, they talked all night. Arn's knowledge of the world grew rapidly as he listened to the others tell their stories. Only a few years before, he hadn't even known there was such a place as the United States. And he thought that Cambodians were the only people in the world who killed each other.

At the end of two weeks, each young person stood to share their feelings before the others. Most broke into tears. "We cried and cried. We tried to hug each other for the first time. Some people couldn't. We sang to each other. We had thought that we were different from each other, but we had everything in common. We had lost our families. Our governments had poisoned our minds against each other. We came to see that others had done this to us. We had not done it to each other."

By the time the bus took off to start the tour, they were a family. They spoke to children in twenty-seven cities. They found that most kids they met were caught in the middle of conflicts, too. Many said they were suffering—from shattered families, from loneliness, from being put down because their skin was dark, from feeling that there was little hope or purpose in their lives. Some talked tough and dressed tough to protect themselves. Some were in gangs. Some said they had even considered taking their own lives.

When they were able to talk—kid to kid—about the things that were bothering them, some could see themselves not as losers or victims but as courageous survivors who had done the best they could in tough situations—like the Children of War.

Using their own experiences, the kids on the tour encouraged those they met to find what they had in common—even if it was pain—and to see even those who are supposed to be their enemies as people. They hoped their experiences would inspire young people not to take sides, but to join together to end violence and build hope for the future.

Children of War from around the world overcome their differences and join hands.

Express **Yourself**

In Finding Common Ground, you explored personal conflicts among friends or family members. You also read about larger disputes between groups or countries. The selections showed you the choices that people and groups can make to resolve their differences.

Why Can't They Get Along?

Sally ("Don't Let the Bedbugs Bite"), Lonnie ("Shoot to Win"), and Bizunesh ("The Lion's Whisker") tried to get along with another person. Yet it wasn't easy. Look back at each story and find examples of what these characters did to try and make a friend. How did the other character in each story resist? What did the main characters finally do or learn to help them succeed?

Picture This!

What images come to mind when you think of social conflict? With a group, search through magazines and newspapers for pictures showing social conflict and changes. Then find quotes from the selections in this theme to support the pictures you have chosen. Cut out the pictures and create a wall-size collage called "Conflict and Common Ground."

Words From the Wise Man

In "The Lion's Whisker," the wise man tells Bizunesh: "You learned how to approach the lion— slowly." How might this statement also apply to Sally ("Don't Let the Bedbugs Bite") and Lonnie ("Shoot to Win")? Does it also apply to Willy ("War Game") or Arn ("Arn Chorn: Peacemaker")? With a partner, discuss and then write your answers.

Messages About Conflict

"War Game" and "The Rebellion of the Magical Rabbits" contain messages about conflict. What message can you find in Willy's experiences with the German soldiers? What about the Wolf's attempts to outlaw rabbits? Write the message you found in each story. Which of the two messages would be more useful to you in your life? Why?

Talk About Success

In a group, list the characters or groups in this theme who succeeded in finding common ground. Then list the characters who failed. Why did each character succeed or fail? Discuss it in your group. Then suggest what each might have done to resolve any conflicts. Take notes on your discussion and present your findings to the class.

More Books for You to Enjoy

One Sister Too Many

by C. S. Adler, Macmillan, 1991

Case, who doesn't believe in rules or regulations, keeps getting into trouble at school and at home. So no one pays much attention to her suspicions about the new baby sitter. But when her baby sister Melissa disappears, it's Case who comes to the rescue.

Just Like Martin

by Ossie Davis, Simon & Schuster, 1992

Isaac's dad, a bitter war veteran, won't let his son go to a freedom march in Washington. Then a tragedy occurs that gives Isaac the opportunity to help organize a young people's march. But can Isaac participate on his father's terms?

One-Eyed Cat
by Paula Fox, Bradbury Press, 1984

Drawn to the special birthday gift he is forbidden to use, Ned fires his new air rifle at a dark shadow. Was the target the one-eyed cat that suddenly turns up in his neighbor's backyard? Filled with guilt, Ned struggles to save the cat.

Shiloh
by Phyllis Reynolds Naylor, Atheneum, 1991

Sure that dishonest Judd Travers abuses his dogs, Marty hides Judd's runaway beagle to keep him from further harm. But how far will Marty go to save the dog he has named Shiloh—and what price will he have to pay?

Call It Courage
written and illustrated by Armstrong Sperry, Macmillan, 1990

Mafatu, the son of a Polynesian Great Chief, is afraid of the sea and is scorned by his people, who worship courage. After a dramatic journey alone to a sacred island, he confronts his fears and earns his name—Stout Heart.

Strange Encounters

"It all looked

suspicious to me."

— Jack Gantos
"Rabies"

CONTENTS

Theme Trade Books

The Boggart

by Susan Cooper
Emily Volnick and her family have
returned home after visiting their
newly inherited castle in Scotland.
However, they have not come
home alone. Emily has brought
with her the castle Boggart, an
invisible, mischievous spirit.

Jeremy Thatcher, Dragon Hatcher

by Bruce Coville
Sixth grader Jeremy Thatcher
knows every street and every
corner of Blodgett's Crossing.
He's lived there all his life. Yet
one day he stumbles on a magic
shop he has never seen before
and begins a fantastic adventure.

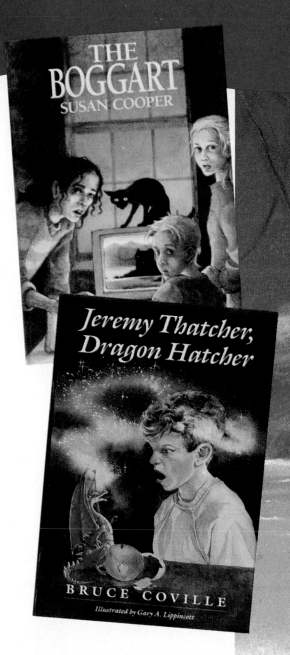

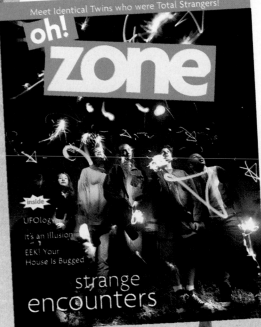

Theme Magazine

Meet identical twins who were
total strangers! Find out about the
strange creatures that live in your
house! How can a fossil fish be
alive? Read the Theme Magazine
Oh! Zone to find out.

AUNT MILLICENT

by Mary Steele

"**I**," said Angelica Tonks, grandly, "have eight uncles and eleven aunts."

Angelica Tonks had more of most things than anyone else. She held the class record for pairs of fashion sneakers and Derwent pencil sets, and her pocket-money supply was endless. Now, it seemed, she also had the largest uncle-and-aunt collection in town. Her classmates squirmed and made faces at each other. *Awful* Angelica Tonks.

Mr. Wilfred Starling dusted the chalk from his bony hands and sighed. "Well, Angelica, aren't you a lucky one to have nineteen uncles and aunts. You'll just have to choose the most interesting one to write about, won't you?"

"But they're *all* interesting," objected Angelica. "The Tonks family is a wonderfully interesting family, you know. It will be terribly hard to choose just one."

There were more squirms. The class was fed up with the wonderfully interesting Tonks family. In fact, Mr. Wilfred Starling nearly screamed. He just managed to swallow his exasperation, which sank down to form a hard

305

bubble in his stomach. Straightening his thin shoulders, he said, "Right, everyone, copy down this week's homework assignment from the board. And remember, Angelica, a pen-portrait of just *one* aunt or uncle is all I want. Just *one*." *Please not a whole gallery of tedious and terrible Tonkses,* he thought to himself.

The class began to write. Jamie Nutbeam, sitting behind Angelica, leaned forward and hissed, "If the rest of your family is so *wonderfully interesting,* they must be a big improvement on you, Honky Tonks! And, anyway, I bet the aunt I write about will beat any of yours!"

"I bet she won't," Angelica hissed back. "She'll be so *boring.* What's her name, this boring aunt?"

Jamie finished copying and put down his pen. "Aunt Millicent, and she's pretty special."

"Millicent!" scoffed Angelica. "What a name! No one's called Millicent these days!"

"QUIET, you two!" barked Mr. Starling, massaging his stomach, "and start tidying up, everyone—it's time for the bell." *Oh bliss,* he thought.

As the classroom emptied, Jamie lingered behind.

"What is it, Jamie?" asked Mr. Starling wearily, piling his books and papers together and trying not to burp.

"Well, the trouble is I haven't any aunts or uncles to do a portrait of," said Jamie, turning rather red, "so is it all right if I make one up? An aunt?"

"Oh, I see! Well, in that case . . . yes, perfectly all right," replied Mr. Starling. He gazed rather sadly out the window. "The most interesting characters in the world are usually the made-up ones, you know, Jamie. Think of Sherlock Holmes and Alice and Dr. Who and Indiana Jones . . ."

Jamie interrupted. "Does anyone need to know I've made her up? This aunt?"

"Well, *I* won't say anything," promised Mr. Starling. "It's for you to make her seem real so we all believe in her. You go home and see what you can dream up."

"She has a name already," Jamie called back as he left the room. "She's Aunt Millicent."

Aunt Millicent Nutbeam! The hard bubble in Mr. Starling's stomach began to melt away.

That evening, Jamie Nutbeam said to his family at large, "Did you know that awful Angelica Tonks has eight uncles and eleven aunts?"

"Well, everybody knows that they're a big family," replied his mother.

"Prolific, I'd call it," grunted Jamie's father from behind his newspaper.

"Yes, dear—prolific. Now, Mrs. Tonks was a Miss Blizzard," continued Mrs. Nutbeam, "and there are lots of Blizzards around here as well as Tonkses, all related, no doubt. But fancy nineteen! Who told you there were nineteen, Jamie?"

"She did—old Honky Tonks herself. She told the whole class *and* Mr. Starling—boasting away as usual. She's a *pill.*" Jamie was jotting things on paper as he talked. "We have to write a pen-portrait of an aunt or uncle for homework, and Honky can't decide which one to do because they're all so *wonderfully interesting,* she says. Urk!" He paused and then added, "I'm doing Aunt Millicent."

Jamie's father peered over the top of his newspaper. "Aunt who?"

"Who's Aunt Millicent?" demanded Jamie's sister, Nerissa.

"You haven't got an Aunt Millicent," said his mother. "You haven't any aunts at all, *or* uncles, for that matter."

"*I know* I haven't," Jamie snapped. "It's *hopeless* belonging to a nuclear family! It's unfair—I mean, awful Honky has nineteen aunts and uncles and Nerissa and I haven't got any, not one." Jamie ground the pencil between his teeth.

"You won't have any teeth either, if you munch pencils like that," remarked his father, who was a dentist.

Jamie glowered, spitting out wet splinters.

"Anyway, he's right," announced Nerissa. "It would be great to have even one aunt or uncle. Then we might have some cousins, too. Everyone else has cousins. Angelica Tonks probably has about a hundred-and-twenty-seven."

"Well, I'm sorry," sighed Mrs. Nutbeam, "but your father and I are both 'onlys' and there's nothing we can do about that, is there? Not a thing! Now, what's all this about an Aunt Millicent?"

"Oh, it's okay," grumbled her son. "Mr. Starling said to write about *an* aunt or uncle, not exactly *my* aunt or uncle. He says I can invent one."

"Will you explain that she's not real?" asked Nerissa, doubtfully.

"Mr. Starling says I don't have to, and he's not going to tell. He says I have to make people believe that she *is* real. Anyway, I don't want Honky Tonks to know that she's made up, because Aunt Millicent is going to be amazing— much better than any of those boring Tonkses. It's time Honky was taken down a peg or two."

Dr. Nutbeam quite understood how Jamie felt. From time to time Angelica Tonks visited his dentist's chair. She would brag about her "perfect" teeth if there was nothing to be fixed, but if she needed a filling her shrieks of "agony" would upset everyone in the waiting room and Mrs. Tonks would call Dr. Nutbeam a *brute*. He was often tempted to give Angelica a general anaesthetic and post her home in a large jiffy bag.

Now he folded his newspaper; Jamie's project sounded rather fun. "Right, Jamie," he said, "tell us about Aunt Millicent and let us get some facts straight. Is she my sister, or Mum's? We must get that settled to start with."

"I can't decide," frowned Jamie. "What do you think?"

"She'd better be your sister, dear," said Mrs. Nutbeam calmly to her husband. "I grew up here and everyone knows I was an only child, but you came from another town. You're more mysterious."

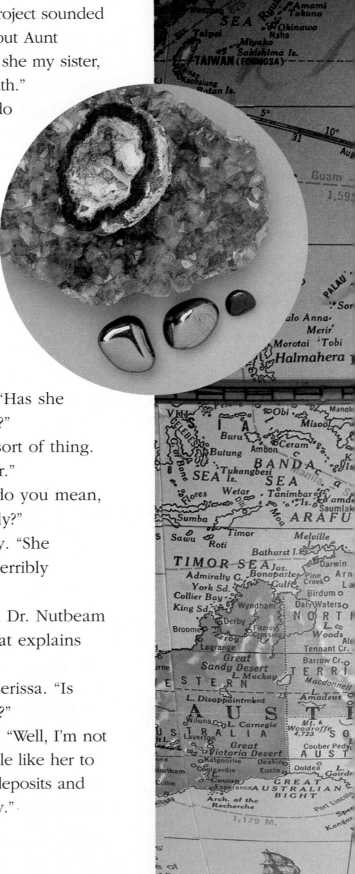

Dr. Nutbeam looked pleased. "Mm . . . mm. That's nice . . . having a sister, I mean. Is she younger than me?"

"No, older," said Jamie.

"Where does she live?" asked Nerissa. "Has she a family of her own? Lots of cousins for us?"

"No way—she hasn't time for all that sort of thing. And she doesn't live anywhere in particular."

Mrs. Nutbeam looked puzzled. "What do you mean, dear? What does Auntie Millicent do, exactly?"

"She's an explorer," said Jamie, proudly. "She works for foreign governments, and she's terribly busy—flat out."

There was something of a pause. Then Dr. Nutbeam said, "Ah," and stroked his bald patch. "That explains why we haven't seen her for so long."

"What does she explore?" demanded Nerissa. "Is there anything left in the world to look for?"

Jamie was beginning to feel a bit rushed. "Well, I'm not sure yet, but foreign governments need people like her to search for water in deserts and rich mineral deposits and endangered species and things . . . you know."

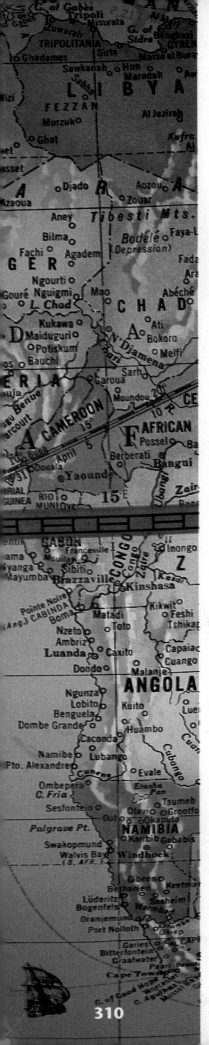

Nerissa lay on the floor with her eyes closed and began to imagine her new aunt slashing a path through tangled jungle vines, searching for a rare species of dark blue frog. The mosquitoes were savage. The leeches were huge and bloated. Aunt Millicent's machete was razor sharp . . .

"This is all very unexpected," murmured Mrs. Nutbeam, "to have a sister-in-law who is an explorer, I mean. I wonder how you get started in that sort of career?" Her own job as an assistant in an antique and curio shop suddenly seemed rather drab.

Dr. Nutbeam was staring at the wall. In his mind's eye he clearly saw his sister on a swaying rope suspension bridge above a terrifying ravine. She was leading a band of native bearers to the other side. How much more adventurous, he thought, than drilling little holes in people's teeth. He wrenched his gaze back to Jamie and asked, "Do we know what Millie is actually exploring at present?"

Jamie munched his pencil for a moment and then said, "She's in Africa, somewhere near the middle, but I'm not sure where, exactly."

"In the middle of Africa, is she?" echoed Dr. Nutbeam. "Mm . . . then it wouldn't surprise me if she were in the Cameroons.[1] There's a lot of dense forest in the Cameroons, you know."

"I thought Cameroons were things to eat," frowned Nerissa. "Sort of coconut biscuits."

"No, no, dear, those are macaroons," said her mother.

"*They're* bad for your teeth, too," remarked her father, absently, "like eating pencils."

Jamie fetched the atlas and found a map of Africa. His father stood behind him, peering at it. "There it is, in the middle on the left-hand side, just under the bump."

"It's called Cameroon here," Jamie said. "Just one of them."

---

1 Cameroons (*kăm uh ROONS*) formerly two political regions, now Cameroon, a country in West Central Africa

"Well, there's East Cameroon and West Cameroon, see," pointed his father, "and sometimes you lump them together and call them Cameroons. Look—here's the equator just to the south, so it must be pretty hot and steamy at sea-level."

"Poor Millicent," sighed Mrs. Nutbeam. "I do hope her feet don't swell in the heat, with all that walking."

Jamie examined the map closely. "That's peculiar— the north border of the Cameroons seems to be floating in a big lake . . . um, Lake Chad . . . it looks all swampy, with funny dotted lines and things. I bet that bit needs exploring. They've probably lost their border in the mud and Aunt Millicent could be on an expedition to find it."

"Is she all by herself?" asked Nerissa. "I'd be scared in a place like that."

"Of course she's not by herself," snorted Jamie. "She works for a foreign government, don't forget, and she'd have a whole support team of porters and cooks and scientists and things."

"She must be an expert at something herself, don't you think?" suggested Mrs. Nutbeam. "I would imagine that she's a surveyor."

"Yes, she'd use one of those instruments you look through, on legs," added Nerissa.

"You mean a theodolite,[2] dim-wit," answered her brother.

"She'd certainly need one of those, if she's measuring angles and distances and drawing maps," agreed Dr. Nutbeam. "My word, what a clever old sister I have!"

"I wonder if she was good at Geography at school?" said Nerissa.

---

2 theodolite (*thee AHD oh lyt*) a surveying instrument used to measure vertical and horizontal angles

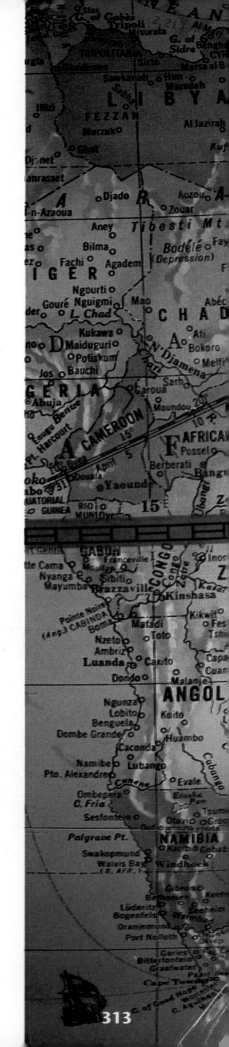

"Well, you'll be able to ask Grandma tomorrow. She's coming for her winter visit, remember?"

"Oh help! What'll Grandma *say*?" gasped Jamie. "Do you think she'll mind? I mean—we've invented a daughter for her without asking!"

"I shouldn't think she'd mind," said his mother. "We'll break the news to her carefully and see how she takes it."

Grandma Nutbeam, as it turned out, was delighted. "How exciting!" she exclaimed. "I always wanted a daughter, and it's been very lonely since Grandpa died. Now I'll have a new interest! Just show me on the map where Millicent is at the moment, please dear."

Jamie pointed to the dotted lines in swampy Lake Chad near the top end of the Cameroons, and Grandma stared in astonishment.

"Gracious heaven! What an extraordinary place to go to, the silly girl! I hope she's remembered her quinine tablets. Millicent was never very good at looking after herself, you know. Let me see—I think I'll get some wool tomorrow and knit her some good stout hiking socks."

Jamie blinked. "There's no need to do that, Grandma. She's not really real, you know."

"Well, she'll be more real to me if I make her some socks," Grandma declared.

"Wouldn't they be rather hot in the Cameroons?" objected Nerissa. "It's awfully near the equator, don't forget."

"Woolen socks are best in any climate," said Grandma firmly. "They breathe."

"Now, Mother," interrupted Dr. Nutbeam, "you can tell us what Millicent was like as a girl. I can't remember her very well, as she was so much older than me, but I have a feeling that she ran away from home a lot."

Grandma pondered a moment. "Now that you mention it, she did. She did indeed. I thought we'd have to chain her up sometimes! We lived near the edge of town, you'll remember, and Millie would look out towards the paddocks and hills and say that she wanted to know what was over the horizon, or where the birds were flying to, or where the clouds came from behind the hills. We never knew where she'd be off to next— but she certainly ended up in the right job! I'm so glad she became an explorer. If I were a bit younger and had better feet, I might even go and join her. It would be most interesting to see the Cameroons. It's full of monkeys, I believe."

"Was Aunt Millicent good at Geography at school?" Nerissa remembered to ask.

"Let me think—yes, she must have been because one year she won a prize for it, and the prize was a book called *Lives of the Great Explorers.*"

"Well, there you are," remarked Mrs. Nutbeam. "That's probably how it all started."

Next day, Grandma Nutbeam began to knit a pair of explorer's socks. She decided on khaki with dark blue stripes round the top.

Angelica Tonks had found it so difficult to select one of the nineteen aunts and uncles, that her pen-portrait was left until the very last minute and then scrawled out in a great hurry. She had finally chosen Aunt Daisy Blizzard, Mrs. Tonks's eldest sister.

Mr. Wilfred Starling asked Angelica to read her portrait to the class first, to get it over with. As he had

expected and as Jamie Nutbeam had hoped, Angelica's aunt sounded anything but wonderfully interesting. She had always lived in the same street, her favorite color was deep purple and she grew African violets on the bathroom shelf, but that was about all.

Many of the other portraits weren't much better, although there was one uncle who had fallen into Lake Burley Griffin and been rescued by a passing Member of Parliament. Someone else's aunt had competed in a penny-farthing bicycle race in Northern Tasmania,[3] only to capsize and sprain both her knees; and there was a great-uncle who had been present at the opening of the Sydney Harbour Bridge in 1932, but couldn't remember it at all as he'd been asleep in his pram at the time.

Mr. Starling saved Jamie's portrait until last, hoping for the best. Jamie cleared his throat nervously and began:

"I have never met Aunt Millicent and no one in my family knows her very well, as she hasn't been in Australia for a long time. This is because Aunt Millicent is an explorer . . ."

Mr. Wilfred Starling had been hoping for a bright spot in his day, and Aunt Millicent Nutbeam was it. He smiled happily when Jamie explained how Millicent had gained her early training as an explorer by regularly running away from home. He sighed with pleasure as Jamie described the swampy region of Lake Chad, where Millicent was searching through the mud and papyrus[4] for the northern border of the Cameroons. He positively beamed when he heard that Grandma Nutbeam was knitting explorer's socks for her daughter.

The rest of the class sat spellbound as Jamie read on, except for Angelica Tonks, whose scowl grew darker by the minute. Jamie had barely finished his portrait when her hand was waving furiously.

---

3 **Tasmania** (*taz MAY nee uh*) island state of Australia

4 **papyrus** (*puh PY ruhs*) a tall water plant common in the Nile region of Africa

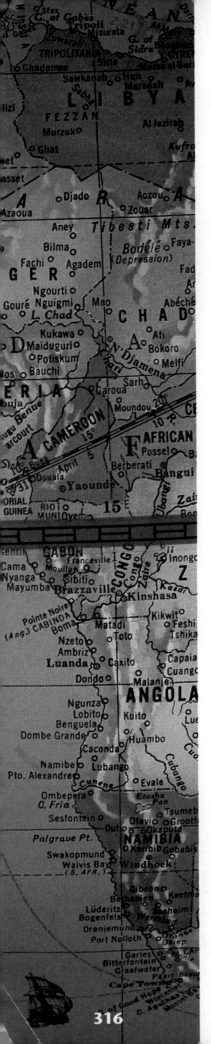

Mr. Starling's beam faded. "What *is* it, Angelica?"

"I don't believe it. Women don't go exploring! I think Jamie's made it all up! He's a cheat!"

Mr. Starling's stomach lurched, but before he had time to say anything the other girls in the class rose up in a passion and rounded on Angelica.

"Who *says* women don't go exploring?"

"Women can do anything they want to these days, Angelica Tonks! Don't you know that?"

"*I'd* really like to be an explorer or something— maybe a test-pilot."

"Well, *I'd* like to be a diver and explore the ocean floor and have a good look at the *Titanic*."

"What does your aunt wear when she's at work?"

"What color are her new socks?"

The boys began to join in.

"Can your aunt really use a machete?"

"How many languages can she speak?"

"Does she always carry a gun? I bet she's a crack shot!"

"How does a theodolite work?"

The clamor was so great that hardly anyone heard the bell. Angelica Tonks heard it and vanished in a sulk. Mr. Starling heard it and happily gathered up his books. He gave Jamie a secret wink as he left the room.

The end of the assignment was not the end of Aunt Millicent. At school, the careers teacher ran some special sessions on "Challenging Occupations for Women" after he had been stormed by the girls from Jamie's class for information about becoming test-pilots, mobile-crane drivers, buffalo hunters and ocean-floor mappers. The Science teacher was asked to explain the workings of a theodolite to the class.

At home, Aunt Millicent settled happily into the Nutbeam family, who all followed her adventures with great interest. Dr. Nutbeam brought home library books about the Cameroons and Central Africa. Jamie roared his way through one called *The Bafut Beagles*. Mrs. Nutbeam rummaged through an old storeroom at the curio shop and began to collect exotic objects. She brought home a brace of hunting spears from Kenya, which she hung on the family-room wall.

"Just the sort of souvenir Millicent could have sent us," she explained. "See—those marks on the blades are very probably dried bloodstains."

Another time she unwrapped a stuffed mongoose, announcing that Auntie had sent this from India on one of her earlier trips.

Jamie and Nerissa stroked it. "What a funny animal," said Nerissa. "Like a weasel."

Grandma was knitting her way down the second sock leg. "That funny animal is a very brave creature," she admonished, tapping the mongoose with her knitting needle. "I'll always remember Kipling's story of Rikki-Tikki-Tavi and how he fought that dreadful king cobra. Brrr!"

"Who won?" asked Jamie.

"You could read it yourself and find out, young man," said Grandma, starting to knit a new row. "I expect Millicent has met a few cobras in her time."

Nerissa had splendid dreams nearly every night. Aunt Millicent strode through most of them, wielding her machete

or shouldering her theodolite. Sometimes Nerissa found herself wading through swirling rivers or swinging on jungle vines like a gibbon. Jamie was often there, too, or some of her school friends, or Grandma followed by a mongoose on a lead. Once, Mrs. Nutbeam speared a giant toad, which exploded and woke Nerissa up. In another dream, Nerissa's father was polishing the fangs of a grinning crocodile, which lay back in the dentist's chair with its long tail tucked neatly under the sterilizer. It looked slightly like Mrs. Tonks.

Mrs. Nutbeam brought home still more curios: a bamboo flute and a small tom-tom which Jamie and Nerissa soon learned to play. Mysterious drumbeats and thin flutey tunes drifted along the street from the Nutbeams' house. School friends came to beat the tom-tom and to stroke the mongoose and to see how the explorer's socks were growing.

"Will you be sending them off soon, to the Cameroons?" they asked Grandma, who was turning the heel of the second sock.

"I think I'll make another pair, perhaps even three pairs," replied Grandma. "I might just as well send a large parcel as a small one."

"Yes, and then Aunt Millie will have spare pairs of socks she can wash," said Nerissa. "Socks must get very smelly near the equator."

Word of Millicent Nutbeam, intrepid explorer, began to spread through the town. Children told their families about the spears, the tom-tom, the mongoose and the khaki socks. Not every small town could claim to be connected to a famous international explorer—it was exciting news.

Angelica Tonks, however, told her mother that she didn't believe Jamie's aunt was an explorer at all. "I bet he just invented that to make his aunt seem more interesting than all the rest," she scoffed.

Mrs. Tonks sniffed a good deal and then decided it was time to have a dental check-up. "I'll get to the bottom of that Millicent Nutbeam, you mark my words," she told Angelica, as she telephoned Dr. Nutbeam's surgery for an appointment.

"Well, well—good morning Mrs. Tonks," said Dr. Nutbeam, a few days later. "We haven't seen you for a while! Just lie right back in the chair please, and relax!"

Mrs. Tonks lay back, but she didn't relax one bit. Her eyes were sharp and suspicious. "Good morning, Dr. Nutbeam. How is the family?" she enquired. "And how is your sister?"

Dr. Nutbeam pulled on his rubber gloves. "My sister? Which one? . . . Er, probe, please nurse."

Before he could say "Open wide," Mrs. Tonks snapped, "Your sister the so-called explorer. Huh! The one in the Cameroons."

"Ah, *that* sister. You mean Millicent . . . now, just open wider and turn this way a little. Yes, our Millie, she does work so hard . . . oops, there's a beaut cavity! A real crater!" He crammed six plugs of cotton wool around Mrs. Tonks's gums. "My word, what a lot of saliva! We'll have some suction please nurse, and just wipe that dribble from the patient's chin." He continued to poke and scrape Mrs. Tonks's molars, none too gently. "Ah, here's another trouble spot. Mm . . . have you ever been to the Cameroons, Mrs. Tonks?"

Mrs. Tonks's eyes glared. She tried to shake her head, but could only gurgle, "Arggg . . ."

"No, I didn't think you had. Such a fascinating place!" Dr. Nutbeam turned on the squealing high-speed drill and bored into her decaying tooth, spraying water all over her chin.

When he had told his family about this encounter with Mrs. Tonks, his wife complained, "It's all very well for you. *You* can just cram people's mouths full of wadding and metal contraptions and suction tubes if they start asking awkward questions, but what am I supposed to do?"

The truth was that increasing numbers of townsfolk were calling at the antique shop where Mrs. Nutbeam worked. They were eager to know more about Millicent Nutbeam and her adventurous life. They felt proud of her.

"It's getting quite tricky," Mrs. Nutbeam explained. "People are asking to see photos of Millicent and wanting us to talk at the elderly citizens' club about her. This aunt is becoming an embarrassment. I wish people weren't so curious. Sometimes I don't know what to say!"

Grandma found herself on slippery ground, too, when she met the postman at the gate.

"Morning," he said, sorting through his mailbag. "You must be Jamie's grandmother, then."

"Yes, I am," Grandma replied, rather surprised.

"Mother of the explorer, eh?"

"Gracious!" exclaimed Grandma. "Fancy you knowing about that!"

"Oh, my girl Julie has told us all about it. She's in Jamie's class at school. Funny thing—Julie's gone round the twist since she heard about all that exploring business. Says she wants to buy a camel and ride it round Australia, and one of her friends is going to apply for a job on an oil rig. I ask you!"

"Well, that's nice," said Grandma, soothingly. "Girls are so enterprising these days."

"Huh! Mad, I call it." The postman held out a bundle of letters. "Here you are. Now, that's *another* funny thing—

the Nutbeams don't get much foreign mail, come to think of it. You'd think the explorer would write to them more often, her being in the travelling line."

Grandma breathed deeply. "Oh, it's not easy, you know, writing letters when you're exploring. For one thing, there's never a decent light in the tent at night— and besides, there's hardly ever a post office to hand when you need it." She glanced through the letters. "Goodness! There's one from South America . . . Peru."

"That's what made me wonder. Is it from her?" asked the postman, eagerly.

"Her? Ah . . . Millicent. I don't know. It's for Dr. Nutbeam, my son, and it's typed. Anyway, as far as we know, Millicent is still in the Cameroons, although we've not had word for some time."

"She could have moved on, couldn't she?" suggested the postman, "Peru, eh? Oh well, I'd better move on, too. G'day to you!"

At school, Julie the postman's daughter said to Jamie, "Why has your auntie gone to South America? What's she exploring now?"

"Who said she's gone to South America?" demanded Jamie. He felt he was losing control of Aunt Millicent.

"My dad said there was a letter from her in Peru," replied Julie.

"Well, no one told *me*," growled Jamie.

At home he announced, "Julie is telling everybody that our Aunt Millicent is in Peru! What's she talking about? What's happening?"

Grandma stopped knitting. "Julie. Is that the name of the postman's girl?"

"Yes—her dad said there was a letter for us from Auntie in Peru, or somewhere mad."

"Oh, I remember—he asked me about it," said Grandma.

"Well . . . what did you *say*?" wailed Jamie.

"I just said I didn't know who the letter was from and that I thought Millicent was still in the Cameroons, but that we hadn't heard for a while where she was. That's all."

"The letter from Peru," chuckled Dr. Nutbeam, "is about the World Dental Conference on plaque, which is being held next year in Lima. It has nothing to do with Millicent."

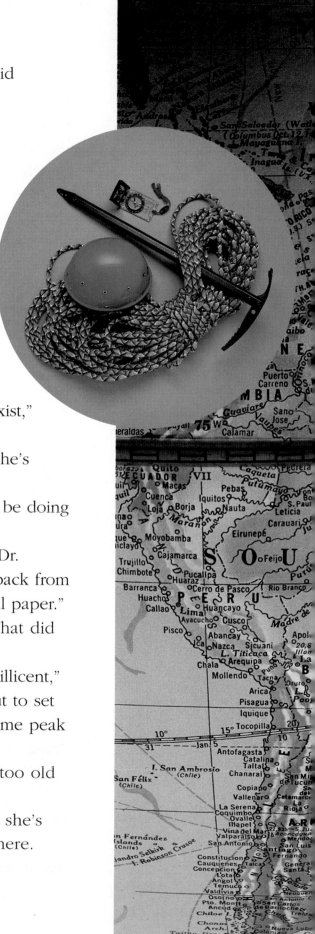

"Well of *course* it hasn't," spluttered Jamie. "She doesn't exist!"

"But Jamie, in a funny sort of way she *does* exist," said Mrs. Nutbeam.

His father grinned. "My sister is quite a girl! She's begun to live a life of her own!"

"That's the trouble," said Jamie. "She seems to be doing things we don't know about."

While they were talking, the telephone rang. Dr. Nutbeam was no longer grinning when he came back from answering it. "That was Frank Figgis from the local paper."

"Frank, the editor?" asked Mrs. Nutbeam. "What did he want?"

"He wants to do a full-page feature on our Millicent," groaned her husband. "He's heard that she's about to set out on a climbing expedition in the Andes! Up some peak that has never yet been conquered!"

"What nonsense!" snapped Grandma. "She's too old for that sort of thing."

"It's just a rumor!" shouted Jamie. "Who said she's going to the Andes? *I* didn't say she was going there. She's still in the Cameroons!"

"Calm down, dear," said his mother, "and let's hear what Dad said to Frank Figgis."

Dr. Nutbeam was rubbing his head. "I stalled for time—I said we'd not heard she was in the Andes, but that we'd make enquiries and let him know. Whatever happens, Millicent mustn't get into print. We'll all be up on a charge of false pretences or something!"

Jamie snorted. "Well, if she's climbing an Ande, it might be best if she fell off and was never seen again."

Nerissa shrieked, *"No!* She mustn't—she's our only aunt and we've only just got her!"

Mrs. Nutbeam sighed. "Listen, Jamie, perhaps the time has come to own up that Aunt Millicent is not real."

"We can't do that!" wailed Jamie. "Everyone would think we're loony . . . and that Grandma's absolutely bonkers, knitting socks for an aunt who isn't there. And what about the mongoose? Anyway, I *can't* let Honky Tonks find out now—she'd never stop crowing and she'd be more awful than ever."

Jamie decided to lay the whole problem of Aunt Millicent Nutbeam before Mr. Starling, right up to her unexpected expedition to the Andes and Mr. Figgis's plan to write a full page feature about her for the local paper. He finished by saying, "I think I might have to kill her off."

"That'd be a shame," sighed Mr. Starling. "She's quite a lady, your aunt!"

"It would be pretty easy to get rid of her," Jamie went on. "In her sort of job she could sink into a quick-sand, or be trampled by a herd of elephants, or something."

Mr. Starling shook his head violently. "No, no—it would only make things worse if she died a bloodcurdling death like that. No one would be likely to forget her if she was squashed flat by a stampeding elephant. She'd become more interesting than ever!"

"Well, she could die of something boring, like pneumonia," said Jamie. "Or . . . will I have to own up that she isn't real?"

"Do you want to own up?"

"Not really. I'd feel stupid, and I specially don't want Angelica Tonks to know I invented an aunt."

Mr. Starling quite understood. "I see! Anyway, a lot of people would be sad to discover that Millicent Nutbeam was a hoax. The girls in your class, for example—she means a lot to them."

"What'll I do then?"

"If you want people to lose interest in her, you'll just have to make her less interesting. I think she should retire from exploring, for a start."

"Aw, gee!" Jamie felt very disappointed. "I suppose so. I'll see what they think at home."

"What he means," said Dr. Nutbeam, when Jamie had repeated Mr. Starling's advice, "is that it's time my dear sister Millicent settled down."

"I quite agree with that," remarked Grandma, who was up to the sixth sock foot. "She's not as young as she was, and it's high time she had some normal home life. I think she should get married, even though she's getting on a bit. Perhaps to a widower."

"That sounds terribly boring," yawned Nerissa.

"Well, that's what we need," said Jamie, "something terribly boring to make people lose interest."

Grandma sniffed. "In my day it would have been called a happy ending."

"Well, I suppose it's a happier ending than being squashed by an elephant," conceded Jamie.

"How about marrying her to a retired accountant who used to work for a cardboard box company?" suggested his father. "That sounds pretty dull."

"Good heavens, it's all rather sudden!" said Mrs. Nutbeam. "Last time we heard of her she was climbing the Andes!"

"No, she *wasn't.*" At last Jamie felt he had hold of Aunt Millicent again. "That South American stuff was just a rumor. The postman started it because of the letter from Peru, and then the story just grew!"

Dr. Nutbeam nodded. "Stories seem to have a habit of doing that, and so do rumors! But we can easily squash this one about the Andes. I'll just explain about the World Dental Conference on plaque. I even have the letter to prove it."

Dr. Nutbeam called Frank Figgis on the phone. He explained about the letter from Peru and about the ridiculous rumor which the postman had started. "In your profession, Frank," he added sternly, "you should be much more careful than to listen to baseless rumor. It could get you into all sorts of trouble! In any case, Millicent is giving up exploring to marry a retired accountant. She's had enough."

Frank Figgis was fast losing interest. "I see—well, sometime when she's in Australia, we could do an interview about her former life . . . maybe."

"Maybe, although she has no immediate plans to return here. I believe she and her husband are going to settle down in England—somewhere on the seafront, like Bognor."

Jamie passed on the same information to his classmates. The girls were shocked.

"She's what?"

"Getting married to an *accountant?*"

"She can't be!"

"How boring for her!"

"Where in the world is Bognor? Is there really such a place?"

Angelica Tonks smiled like a smug pussycat. "See! Your Aunt Millicent is just like any other old aunt, after all!"

Jamie caught Mr. Starling's eye. It winked.

Aunt Millicent Nutbeam retired, not to Bognor but to live quietly with her family. Nerissa still had wonderful dreams. Dr. Nutbeam still brought home books about far-off places. The blood-stained spears remained on the wall and the mongoose on the shelf. Jamie and Nerissa still played the tom-tom and the bamboo flute.

Grandma Nutbeam's holiday came to an end and she packed up to return home. She left a parcel for Jamie. When he opened it, he found three pairs of khaki socks with dark blue stripes, and a card which said:

Dear Jamie,

Aunt Millicent won't have any use for these now that she has settled down, so you might as well have them for school camps. Isn't it lucky that they are just your size!

With love from Grandma.

IN RESPONSE

Special Delivery

Suppose Jamie finds out there really is an explorer named Millicent Nutbeam. She's heard about Jamie's joke, and she's hopping mad! Write a letter Jamie might send her, explaining what happened and why.

Aunt Millicent's Portrait

When Jamie presented his portrait of Aunt Millicent Nutbeam, he convinced almost everyone that she was real. Re-create one paragraph of what Jamie might have written about his imaginary aunt. Use details from the story and your own imagination.

AUTHOR AT WORK

Mary Steele has lived in Australia all her life. She grew up surrounded by pets—a flock of ducks, canaries, finches, a peacock, a cockatoo, and a parakeet.

While her children were growing up, Ms. Steele reviewed books for young readers; she also worked as a children's librarian. From these experiences, Ms. Steele learned about the kinds of books young readers enjoy most. Young people are the focus of her writing "because they are curious and full of fun, and their imaginations still work." She rewrites stories several times before she is satisfied. "By the time I've finished adding, the characters seem like old friends or part of the family."

Another Book by . . .

Mary Steele

Arkwright, written and illustrated by Mary Steele, Hyland House, 1985

Library Link "Aunt Millicent" is from a book of Australian short stories called *Dream Time,* edited by Toss Gascoigne, Jo Goodman, and Margot Tyrell.

★ Award-winning Author

THE DISOBEDIENT CHILD

by Victor Montejo

I n old times in *Xaqla'*Jacaltenango,[1] there was a very disobedient child who often disappointed his parents. No matter how hard they tried to teach him, he never changed.

One afternoon the boy ran away from home, looking for someone who would tolerate his mischief. Walking through the woods, he discovered a lonely little house and ran up to it. On the porch of the straw-covered house sat an old man, smoking peacefully. The boy stood before him without saying hello or any other word of greeting.

When the old man noticed the boy's presence, he stopped smoking and asked him, "Where do you want to go, boy?"

"I am looking for someone who can give me something to eat," the boy answered.

The wise old man, who already knew the boy's story, said, "No one will love you if you continue being so bad."

The boy did not respond except to laugh.

Then the old man smiled and said, "You can stay with me. We will eat together."

---

1 *Xaqla'*Jacaltenango (*CHAHK lah bahk ahl tay NAHNG gob*) a town in the mountains of Guatemala

The boy accepted his offer and stayed in the old man's house. On the following day, before going to work, the old man told the boy: "You should stay in the house, and the only duty you will have is to put the beans to cook during the afternoon. But listen well. You should only throw thirteen beans in the pot and no more. Do you understand?"

The boy nodded that he understood the directions very well. Later, when the time arrived to cook the beans, the boy put the clay pot on the fire and threw in thirteen beans as he had been directed. But once he had done that, he began to think that thirteen beans weren't very many for such a big pot. So, disobeying his orders, he threw in several more little fistfuls.

When the beans began to boil over the fire, the pot started to fill up, and it filled up until it overflowed. Very surprised, the boy quickly took an empty pot and divided the beans between the two pots. But the beans overflowed the new pot, too. Beans were pouring out of both pots.

When the old man returned home, he found piles of beans, and the two clay pots lay broken on the floor.

"Why did you disobey my orders and cook more than I told you to?" the old man asked angrily.

The boy hung his head and said nothing. The old man then gave him instructions for the next day. "Tomorrow you will again cook the beans as I have told you. What's more, I forbid you to open that little door over there. Do you understand?"

The boy indicated that he understood very well.

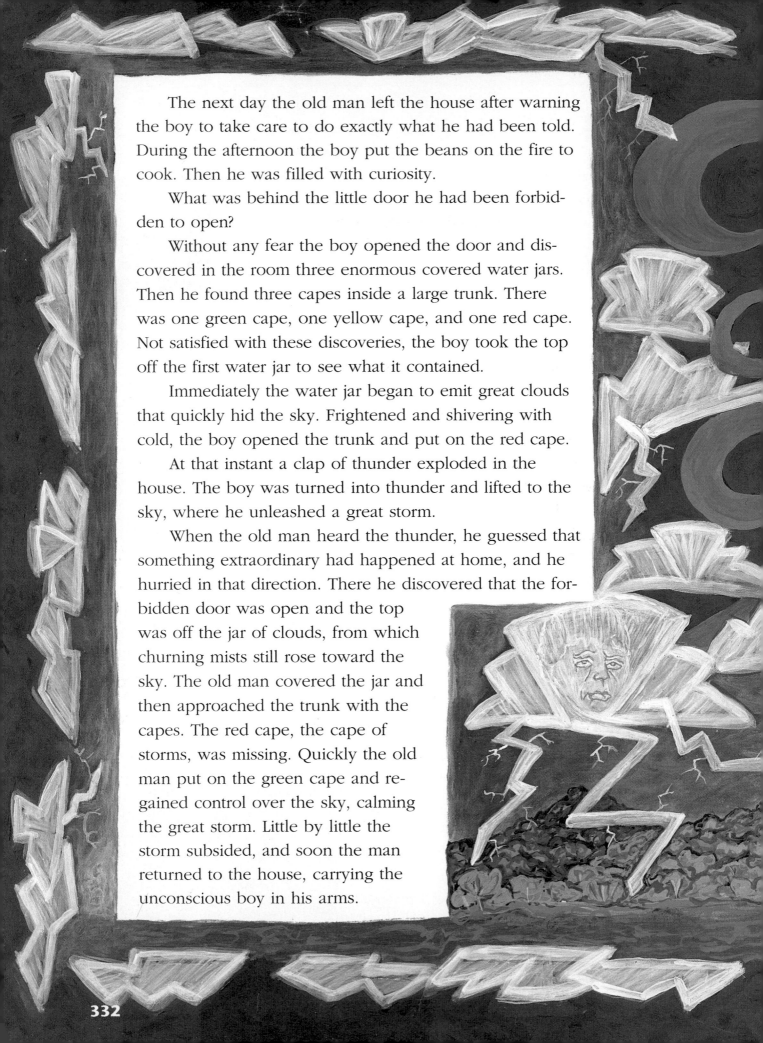

The next day the old man left the house after warning the boy to take care to do exactly what he had been told. During the afternoon the boy put the beans on the fire to cook. Then he was filled with curiosity.

What was behind the little door he had been forbidden to open?

Without any fear the boy opened the door and discovered in the room three enormous covered water jars. Then he found three capes inside a large trunk. There was one green cape, one yellow cape, and one red cape. Not satisfied with these discoveries, the boy took the top off the first water jar to see what it contained.

Immediately the water jar began to emit great clouds that quickly hid the sky. Frightened and shivering with cold, the boy opened the trunk and put on the red cape.

At that instant a clap of thunder exploded in the house. The boy was turned into thunder and lifted to the sky, where he unleashed a great storm.

When the old man heard the thunder, he guessed that something extraordinary had happened at home, and he hurried in that direction. There he discovered that the forbidden door was open and the top was off the jar of clouds, from which churning mists still rose toward the sky. The old man covered the jar and then approached the trunk with the capes. The red cape, the cape of storms, was missing. Quickly the old man put on the green cape and regained control over the sky, calming the great storm. Little by little the storm subsided, and soon the man returned to the house, carrying the unconscious boy in his arms.

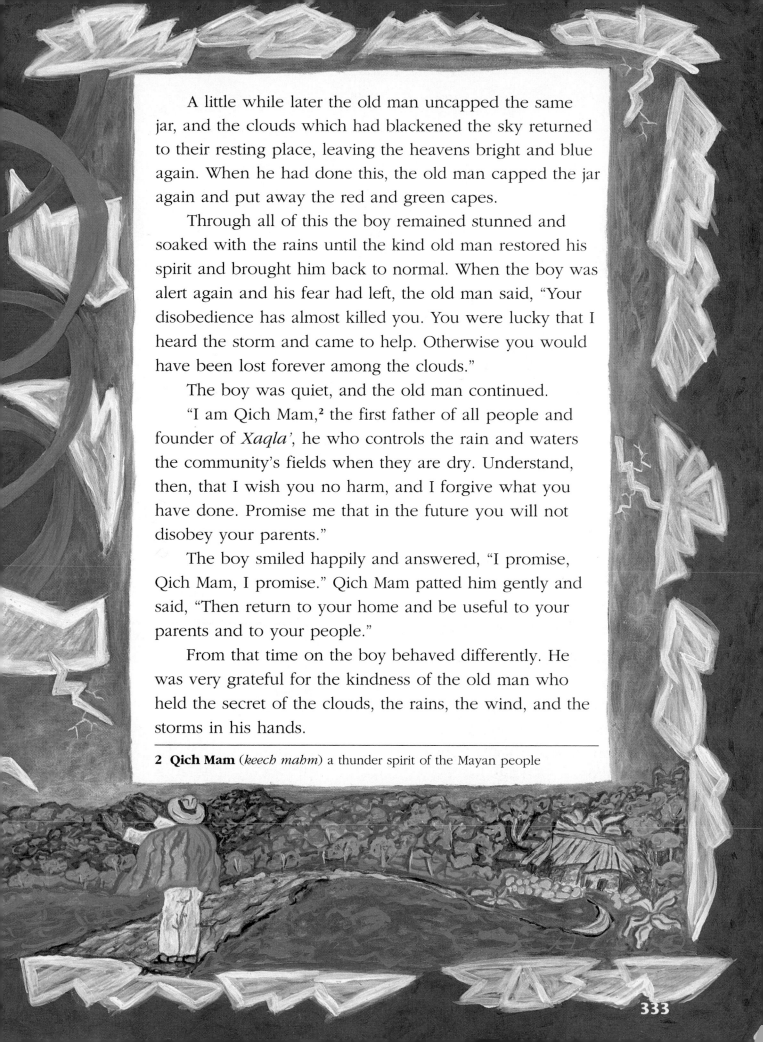

A little while later the old man uncapped the same jar, and the clouds which had blackened the sky returned to their resting place, leaving the heavens bright and blue again. When he had done this, the old man capped the jar again and put away the red and green capes.

Through all of this the boy remained stunned and soaked with the rains until the kind old man restored his spirit and brought him back to normal. When the boy was alert again and his fear had left, the old man said, "Your disobedience has almost killed you. You were lucky that I heard the storm and came to help. Otherwise you would have been lost forever among the clouds."

The boy was quiet, and the old man continued.

"I am Qich Mam,[2] the first father of all people and founder of *Xaqla'*, he who controls the rain and waters the community's fields when they are dry. Understand, then, that I wish you no harm, and I forgive what you have done. Promise me that in the future you will not disobey your parents."

The boy smiled happily and answered, "I promise, Qich Mam, I promise." Qich Mam patted him gently and said, "Then return to your home and be useful to your parents and to your people."

From that time on the boy behaved differently. He was very grateful for the kindness of the old man who held the secret of the clouds, the rains, the wind, and the storms in his hands.

---

2 **Qich Mam** (*keech mahm*) a thunder spirit of the Mayan people

TALES FROM THE
MAYAS

Victor Montejo listened to many stories like "The Disobedient Child" as a boy growing up in Guatemala. His mountain village had few books or newspapers, but it did have storytellers.

The villagers of Jacaltenango often came together to work or celebrate. Before long, listeners would gather around the village elders. The elders entertained with stories about animals, spirits, ancient gods, and times long ago. These stories taught the villagers to take pride in their Mayan heritage.

The Mayas are an ancient people. Between A.D. 250 and A.D. 900, the Mayas built more than forty cities in Central and North America. Archaeologists have uncovered their pyramids and palaces, temples and ball courts. The ancient Mayas were an advanced civilization.

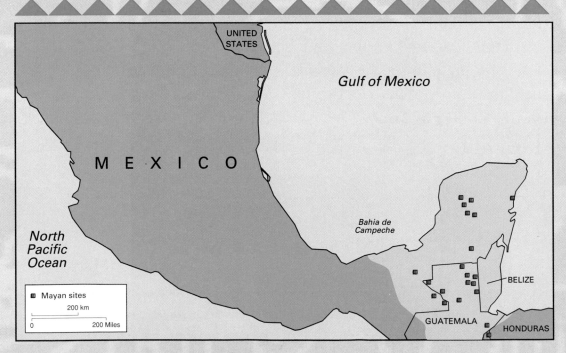

The lighter area shows the extent of the Mayan civilization in Central America.

334

Located in Teotihuacan, northeast of Mexico City, this partially excavated Temple of the Moon survives as a reminder of the complex Mayan society.

They wrote books on fig tree bark. They studied the movements of stars and planets.

Around 900 the Mayas began to abandon their great cities. As years passed, the jungle grew over their stone city buildings. Palaces and pyramids crumbled. By the time Spanish explorers arrived, in the 1500's, most Mayas lived in small villages.

The Spanish forced the Mayas to convert to Christianity. Spaniards smashed temples that honored Mayan gods. They burned the precious fig bark books. Though most Mayas did become Christians, they held onto many old beliefs and traditions.

While growing up, Victor Montejo followed some of the ancient traditions. Each spring his village held a ceremony to welcome the Mayan New Year. Villagers believed that Qich Mam had taught the New Year ceremony to their ancestors. Qich Mam, they said, was the thunder spirit who could make rain fall. He found land for his people to live on and gave them corn to grow.

Today many Mayas find it difficult to follow the old ways. Mayas living in the United States and in Guatemalan cities have often adopted the clothing and behavior of non-Mayan people. Some young Mayas would rather read comic books than listen to their grandparents tell ancient tales.

The ways of the Mayas are rapidly disappearing. Mr. Montejo recorded Jacaltenango's stories to help keep his Mayan heritage alive.

335

"I had been reading so many detective books
I began to think I was a detective myself."

Rabies

from *Heads or Tails*
by Jack Gantos

I had been reading a lot of detective novels. Dad likes to read books about World War II. Betsy reads a lot of "English literature," as she calls it. Mom reads short stories, and Pete reads picture books. I had been reading so many detective books I began to think I was a detective myself.

"Hey, Dad, can I find anything for you?"

"A new job," he said, turning a page. I wasn't that good. He had gone through five jobs in five years.

"What about you, Mom?"

"I lost an earring," she said, without looking up.

I went right to work. First, I searched where she said she'd last seen it. Nothing. So then I followed a hunch. Mom has glasses, but she doesn't wear them. She doesn't like the heavy way they feel on her nose. So when she vacuums around the house she picks up things she can't see. Once she vacuumed part of my stamp collection off my desk. So I checked the vacuum-cleaner bag and, sure enough, found the earring, twenty-eight cents, and the tiny silver key to Betsy's diary.

When I asked Betsy if I could find something for her, she said, "You should go find something worth doing."

"I need money," I whispered in her ear. "How much would you pay for the key to your diary?"

"I'll murder you in your sleep," she said. But I didn't care if she wanted to kill me. My days as a detective were numbered. I had rabies.

Four days earlier, I had been bitten by a dog. I'd left my Raleigh bike outside the library, and when I came out, a boy about my age and a big black dog were standing next to it. Dad had bought me the Raleigh three years ago for Christmas. It was red with chrome fenders, a chrome headlight and bell, and a basket on either side of the rear wheel. It was an expensive English bike and Dad had bought it back when we had money. But now there wasn't any extra money to afford "special things," as Mom put it. I had never seen another bike like it, and a lot of people stopped to admire it.

As I lifted the kickstand with my foot the dog began to growl. I swung my leg over the seat and the dog jumped at me and bit me on the ankle. I jerked my leg back and lost my balance. I fell over sideways, with the bike crashing down on top of me. I had a stack of books in my backpack and they dug into my ribs when I hit the sidewalk. The dog lunged at my face.

"Hold him back," I shouted, but the boy didn't move to call off the dog. He looked directly into my eyes and did nothing.

"Get it away from me," I yelled. He turned and walked away. "Hey! Come back here," I hollered. Maybe it's not his dog, I thought. The dog went back down to my ankle. I tried to crawl farther under the bike to protect myself. But it clamped its teeth on my leg and tried to drag me away. It wanted to bury me like a bone in its back yard. I yanked my leg back and kicked it in the face. Suddenly, it lost interest in me and ran after the boy as if nothing had ever happened. I saw the boy pet the dog on the head and then reach into his pocket and toss him a biscuit.

I stood up and walked my bike around the building. I wasn't hurt and my bike was okay, but I was mad. I rolled down my sock and looked at the two bites. They weren't bleeding, but the skin was broken in three places. I knew a kid who'd been bitten by a raccoon and had to have forty rabies shots in his stomach. Every afternoon for a month the school nurse came into the classroom and escorted him down the hall to the clinic. A half hour later he staggered back to his seat as if he'd been punched in the belly. The teacher let him rest his head on her stuffed Piglet.

One day, she asked us a math question and he raised his hand. "You must be feeling better," she remarked. He threw up on her shoes.

I didn't want forty shots in the stomach with a needle as thick and long as a pencil. But in case I got rabies, I needed to know where the dog lived. If I started foaming at the mouth and biting everyone I could tell Dad who to sue.

So I'd followed the boy up the street. I didn't want to get close because I was afraid the dog might bite me again. After five blocks, he turned onto Cactus Street and went into a small wooden house at number 1227.

"Five dollars for the diary key," I said to Betsy.

"Two," she replied. I followed her to her room. She closed the door and grabbed me around the neck. "Give it to me, you jerk."

"I'll bite you," I managed to say. "I have rabies."

She let me go. "You're gross! Now, give it to me."

"A dollar," I said. She gave me a quarter. I gave her the key. She kicked me in the leg and I dropped to the floor.

"They shoot people with rabies," she growled. "I hope I get to pull the trigger."

I thought I'd go to the library and check out more detective novels. Our school was too cheap to have its own library. A Broward County Book Mobile arrived every Friday and class by class we took turns checking out books.

But they didn't have many detective novels. Mostly they had smelly old books that had other people's names or library seals stamped on the title page. There were a lot of books on subjects like canning vegetables and how to get soup stains out of silk ties. I hate having to read books that other people think are junk. "Something is better than nothing," said Mrs. Marshall when I complained. But reading junk books is the same as having to eat someone else's leftovers.

Instead of going straight to the library, I rode my bike over to a field of thick bushes across the road from Gus's Gas Station. I was always curious about Gus's Gas Station because there were no other stations in Fort Lauderdale named after a person. We had fancy Exxon and Chevron and Texaco stations, but there was only one greasy station named after Gus. In the detective books, the most clever criminals always had their hideouts in fake businesses. I had been spying on Gus from across the road, trying to catch him and his gang doing criminal things like stuffing bodies into oil drums so they could dump them out in the ocean. Maybe they were secret agents and the giant gas tank under the station was a spy headquarters and the light pole was a radio antenna.

Whenever I was riding with Dad, I asked him to stop and buy gas at Gus's. But he wouldn't.

"He sells cheap gas," Dad said. "People say he puts water in it."

"Is that all?"

"That's bad enough," Dad replied.

As I crouched behind a bush and watched, nothing unusual happened at Gus's except for the normal stuff that would happen at any gas station. People pulled up in their cars and Gus hobbled out of his office and put gas in their tanks and washed their windshields. I didn't see anything like secret signals, or secret doors, or wanted criminals hiding behind all the used tires in his garage. He didn't even go near a water hose, or drink a glass of water. Between customers he just sat in his office and peeled an apple with a knife big enough to amputate my leg.

I got back on my bike and rode down Federal Highway. I passed by the parking lot at King's Department Store. A carnival had set up in the parking lot. "Live a little," I said to myself. "You'll soon be a goner." I parked the bike and ran to buy a ticket to the WILD ROCKET. A sign said it was the most powerful ride in the world. It was built like a cigar, with a seat in a little cage on each end. An axle ran through the middle of the cigar, and when the ROCKET spun around, it went about a hundred miles an hour. There was another sign that read: "Warning! This ride is not safe for people with heart problems." It didn't say anything about rabies.

I climbed into my cockpit and put on my seat belt. I made sure my shoelaces were tied so my shoes wouldn't come off during the ride and hit me in the head. Suddenly, the engine started and I grabbed the handlebar. In a minute I couldn't even keep my eyes open and I screamed bloody murder. Then I felt like I passed out.

When the ride stopped, a carnival worker opened my cage and unlocked my seat belt. He gave me a hand and helped me down. The world was still spinning at a hundred miles per hour. When my feet hit the ground, I stumbled forward and fell. My blood felt like Coca-Cola when you shake it up. I crawled and staggered around the parking lot until I found a light pole to lean against. I wiped my mouth on my sleeve. It was all foamy. The first sign of rabies. It was starting. My leg began to throb.

Forget the library, I thought. I've got to save myself. I turned onto Cactus Street and pedaled as hard as I could. I needed to see the dog. Because if it was still alive and not foaming at the mouth, I'd live. But as I sped by I didn't see the dog. Instead, I saw that the front door was wide open and an old beat-up couch was out on the sidewalk, along with a few cardboard boxes of junk. It all looked suspicious to me.

There were no curtains on the windows and suddenly it struck me that they had moved. "Oh, great," I said. They probably knew their dog had rabies and that I was infected and so they had to get out of town before I died and they were arrested for murder. I slowed down and circled back to the house. Even though I was afraid of the dog I stopped in their front yard and got off my bike. I walked up to the open door and knocked on it. "Hello?" I shouted. "Anybody home?" If anyone answered, I planned to ask if my friend Frankie Pagoda lived there. But there was no answer.

"Anybody home?" I yelled again. There was no answer. My ankle began to throb. Soon I'd be foaming at the mouth, running on my hands and feet, and biting the neighbors. Finally I'd be tracked down and captured by police dogs, but it would be too late to save me. I'd be shot and buried in a pet cemetery.

I limped over to the boxes of junk on the front lawn and began to search through them. I needed their names, and if I was lucky, I'd get their new address so I could find out if their dog was infected. The boxes were mostly filled with broken stuff: a chipped plate, a used toothbrush, old shoes, ripped shirts, an old Halloween mask of Spider-Man, and a broken thermos bottle. But there were a few old letters. I shoved them into my backpack. I felt really guilty going through someone's garbage, especially in the middle of the day. Real detectives always did this stuff at night when no one was looking. Plus, I knew I'd have to hide all the stuff from my mom because she really disliked "snoops

"Real detectives always did this stuff at night when no one was looking."

and sneaks," and if she caught me, she'd probably turn me in to the police.

"Hey, kid," a man hollered from next door.

I jumped up and spun around. "What?"

"Why are you going through their trash?" he asked. He was big. Maybe an off-duty cop.

"I'm looking for used books," I replied. "For our school library."

"Don't you know there's a hurricane heading our way?" He took a couple steps toward me.

"No," I said and trotted over to my bike.

"Well, you better get a move-on. That hurricane should hit the shore in a few hours."

"Thanks," I said.

The wind had already picked up. I hopped on my bike and flew down the street. During hurricane season it was pretty normal to have a lot of warnings. Just about everyone kept a hurricane-tracking map in their house and charted the movement of the latest hurricane, so they'd know if it was heading our way. But the hurricanes were unpredictable and would veer off in all directions. Nobody knew if it was really going to hit until it was actually on top of us. The best part about hurricanes was that we were always being let out of school early to go help our parents, who had gotten out of work early, to tape up the windows and tie down everything around the house that could easily be blown away.

By the time I rode up our driveway, Dad was nailing sheets of plywood over the floor-to-ceiling windows in the Florida room.

"Where've you been?" he yelled. The words seemed to blow up over his head and away. I parked my bike in the carport and went to help him. I couldn't tell him I was spying on a dog who gave me rabies. And I didn't want to tell him I was at the carnival having fun while he was working his butt off. "I was spying on Gus," I yelled back and held up one end of the plywood.

"What were you bothering him for?"

"You said he puts water in his gas tanks, and I wanted to catch him."

"You knucklehead," he said. "He wouldn't do it in broad daylight. He'd wait until it was dark."

"Well, I thought with the hurricane coming on, he might try something."

"Well, think about doing the right thing and sticking around the house when you're needed," he said. He pounded another nail through the plywood and stopped yelling.

While Dad and I finished the windows, Mom and Betsy took care of the other hurricane emergency procedures we were taught on television. They filled plastic jugs with drinking water, turned up the refrigerator to get it real cold because the electricity always goes off, put candles and matches in all the rooms, and checked the batteries in the flashlights and radios. Dad had Pete put the rake and hose and lawn tools in the utility room. I got the aluminum ladder for Dad and held it as he climbed up to the roof to remove the television antenna. When he came down, he said to me, "Make sure you put your bike in the utility room so it doesn't blow around."

"In a minute," I said. I put the ladder away, then set up some weather experiments. In science class we saw a movie on the weird power of hurricanes and tornadoes. It showed how high winds had driven plastic drinking straws through trees. I thought that was pretty cool so I went into the kitchen and got some straws. I stripped the paper off and set them out on a tree stump. I aimed them for our plywood shutters, thinking that if I was lucky they would stick in the wood like darts. Next, I had an army man with a plastic parachute. I took a marker and wrote my name and telephone number and "Reward offered for return" on the parachute, then threw it on top of the carport so it might get a flying start when the winds picked up. My last experiment was sort of dangerous but I did it anyway. Dad had some steel rods in the utility room. I took one out and sunk it into the ground by the edge of the canal. It stuck out about two feet above the ground. I was hoping it would conduct lightning and melt. When I passed through the front yard, Dad was snipping the coconuts out of the palm trees with a long tree clipper.

"I've seen these things fly through the air like cannonballs," he yelled.

All the excitement was great. Ever since I had read about the adventures of the Swiss Family Robinson, I wanted our family to be like them. My greatest wish come true would have our family carried away by a huge tidal wave and washed up on a deserted island where we had to build our own house in the trees and grow our own food and ride wild horses and educate one another.

"Did you put your bike away?" Dad asked.

"I forgot," I said.

"Well, go toss these coconuts in the canal, and then put it away like I told you."

"Okay," I said and loaded up my arms.

After I had thrown the coconuts into the water, Mom called to me. "Hurry up and get inside," she yelled. "I want you to take a shower before I fill the tub with water."

When I was undressing I reexamined my dog bite. The teeth marks were still red and swollen, and when I touched them, they throbbed. Rabies, I thought. I should tell Mom and Dad right now so they still have time to take me to the hospital. But what if it's not rabies? What if we dash to the hospital and the doctor says it's just a simple dog bite and then the hurricane gets worse and we are stuck at the hospital? Everyone will hate me for being a big baby. Dad will roll his eyes. Mom will try to be nice. Betsy will treat me like a moron, and Pete will laugh until he falls over. I decided not to tell them. It was a chance I'd have to take.

I went into my bedroom and locked the door. I turned my crummy radio on to the hurricane-watch station and began to go through the letters I had found at Cactus Street. I was in luck. Their names were Mrs. Cleo Stone and Jimmy Stone. There didn't seem to be a Mr. Stone. I had an old electric bill, a postcard sent to Jimmy from someone named Harry, a bill-collection notice for late rent, a contest application, a church-picnic notice, and a telephone bill.

I wrote their old phone number on a scrap of paper and went into Mom and Dad's bedroom. They were in the living room watching the hurricane report on the one television station we could still get. I dialed the number and got what I'd hoped for. A tape-recorded message from the phone company announced: "The number you have reached has been changed to 723-4423."

I quickly rehearsed my thoughts and dialed the new number.

"Hello," answered a boy.

"Is this Jimmy Stone?" I asked in an adult voice.

"Yes."

"This is the dog pound," I said. "We're calling to make sure your dog is properly locked up during the hurricane."

"Have you seen my dog?" he asked excitedly. "He ran away and we've been searching for him everywhere." Then he yelled away from the phone, "Hey, Mom. It's the dog pound looking for Peanut."

"Give me the phone," a woman said.

I hung up. Then I ran back to my room and peeled off

my sock. My ankle was pounding. The bruises looked dark and infected. I squeezed around a puncture and some watery pus dribbled out. I'm a dead man, I thought. Jimmy Stone's dog had gone mad and run away.

I removed my diary from under my mattress. I unlocked it and wrote: "My Last Will and Testament. Everything I own goes to Pete." I signed my name to make it official. Then I spit on the page. Under it I wrote, "This is what killed me!"

All evening long we sat in the living room and watched disaster movies on television. First we watched *Key Largo*, where a hurricane wipes out a hotel in the Florida Keys. That was followed by *The Poseidon Adventure*, which showed an ocean liner flipped over by a tidal wave. Then *Earthquake* came on and we watched a city crumble and burn. All the disaster scenes seemed real because of the hurricane winds howling around our house and the rain beating against the plywood shutters. I thought up a movie where a boy gets rabies and bites everyone in the whole town and infects them and then they begin to

"I wrote, 'This is what killed me!'"

spread out across the entire country and the President has to call out the army to shoot all the rabid fiends. But the rabid people chew up the army and the President has to decide to drop the atomic bomb on the dog people. It could be the end of civilization.

"You look like you've seen a ghost," Mom said, running her hand over my head. "Don't worry, the house won't blow away."

"I'm fine," I replied. I had only two choices now. I could just go find a safe place to die, or I could get forty shots in my stomach and throw up every day. I'd rather die.

We were watching *King Kong* when the electricity went off.

"Okay, the party's over," said Dad. "Time for bed."

Pete had already fallen asleep, and Mom carried him up the hallway to his room. I was tired and fell asleep right away. I slept through the rest of the hurricane and didn't wake up until Dad pushed open my bedroom door and yelled at me. "Jack! Get up this instant!" Even before I opened my eyes I knew he was furious. What did I do? Did I bite everyone in my sleep? My heart was pounding.

"Get out here!" he hollered. What kind of trouble was I in? I ran down the hall and out the front door. Dad was lying on his back, half under his truck, trying to pull something out from around the back axle. I stood by his feet as he wrestled with a bunch of tangled pipes. Then suddenly he got it free and pushed it toward me. It was my Raleigh bike, all twisted up like a pretzel.

"Didn't I tell you to put your bike away!" he shouted.

I started to cry.

"Well?" he asked. "I'm waiting."

"You did."

"Now look at it," he said. "It's ruined. You just don't

listen to me. How do you expect to learn anything if you don't listen?"

I looked down at the bike. Every inch of it was bent. It must have blown under the truck, and when he pulled out of the carport, it got curled up under the wheels.

"How do you expect to get good things if you can't take care of them?" Dad continued. "You know we don't have money to burn." I knew this speech and it made me sad for everyone in our family. We just didn't have the money we once had. When Dad's good watch stopped running, he'd bought a cheap Timex. We'd bought a used black-and-white television when our color set gave out. We didn't even have a car of our own. Dad had the company truck, which I'd just about ruined.

"I'm sorry," I said to him.

"I'm sorry, too," he said, but he was still mad. He got in the truck and drove off.

I guess I don't need a bike anyway, I thought. I'll be dead soon.

I got dressed and started to work around the house

"Every inch of it was bent."

like the madman I was. I picked up all the fallen tree limbs, cut them up with a hatchet, and piled them by the side of the road for the garbage truck. I raked the lawn and swept the sidewalk and driveway. I wanted to take down the plywood shutters and have the house in perfect shape for Dad's return, but Mom said they were too heavy. "What else can I do, then?" I asked her.

"If you're all caught up," she said, "you're free until your dad gets home."

"Okay." I ran around to the back of the house and checked on my experiments. I couldn't find the plastic drinking straws anywhere. I found my parachute soldier tangled up in a bush by the side of the house, and lightning had not struck the steel rod by the canal. I pulled it out and put it back in the utility room. That's when I saw Pete's new bike and got an idea.

I went into the house and knocked on his bedroom door. "Pete," I whispered.

"Yes," he said.

"Can you keep a secret?"

"Yeah, what?" he asked.

"I have something important to tell you." I slipped into his room and locked the door behind me. "Cross your heart you won't tell."

"Cross my heart," he repeated.

"Then look at this." I kicked off my tennis shoe and rolled down my sock. The bite marks were still red and puffy. "I got bit by a dog last week and now I have rabies," I said. "And I think I'm going to die."

Immediately, he started to cry.

"Don't cry," I whispered. "I think you can save me."

"How?" he asked, sniffing and wiping his nose.

"Loan me your bike. I think I know where the dog lives who bit me. If I can find it, then I'll know for sure if I have rabies." It was a new birthday bike and I knew he didn't want to loan it to me. Especially after he saw what happened to my bike. But I was desperate. "Am I foaming at the mouth yet?" I asked him. I smacked my lips together and let some drool run out of the corner of my mouth and onto my chin.

He looked at me with fear. "I don't think so," he said shakily. "You're only drooling."

"That's the first sign," I moaned. "Just make sure I don't bite you." I rolled my sock back up and put on my shoe. "Will you loan it to me? As you can see, it's a matter of life or death."

"Okay," he said. "But don't tell Dad."

"I'll be back before he comes home from work," I said.

I had a theory. I had read a book called *The Incredible Journey,* which was about a family who had moved across the country without their pets and the story was about how the pets had to track them three thousand miles to find them. I figured that the dog may have gotten confused by the move and returned to the old house.

I took Jimmy Stone's telephone number and a couple of dollars in change I had taped into my diary. My first stop was the grocery store. I went to the pet-food section and picked out a box of dog bones to keep Peanut from chewing on me if I found him. Then I rode to 1227 Cactus Street. Their old house had been kicked around by the hurricane. The windows on the east side were blown in. The door was open, and even from the sidewalk I could see water and glass on the living-room floor. The boxes of trash I had found yesterday were no longer on the front lawn. Everything had blown away. Up and down the street people were clearing debris from their lawns and raking up all the branches and leaves. I looked around to see if there were any interesting disasters. Once, after Hurricane Cleo, I had seen a canoe balanced on the roof of a house, and a tree that had crushed a station wagon. But everything on Cactus Street looked pretty normal, so I had nothing to do but enter the house and look for Peanut. I opened the box of dog bones and walked up the sidewalk. "Here, Peanut," I called out and tossed a dog bone into the empty living room. It landed with a splash. "Here, Peanut," I called from the front door and threw another bone. "Come and get it."

I took a step into the house. Now I am trespassing, I thought, and if I'm bit by a mad dog everyone will say it's my own fault, especially my dad, who will probably say something like, "Didn't I tell you never to enter a stranger's house where a mad dog is hiding?"

The water was an inch deep in the living room. I could feel the same fear run through me that I had felt when the dog bit me. "Here, Peanut," I said and threw a dog bone down the dark hallway. "Good Peanut," I called. The first door I reached was on my right. I opened it just a crack and peeked in. It was the bathroom. "Peanut," I whispered. I slipped a dog bone through the crack. As my eyes grew accustomed to the dark, I saw three more doors. The first one was open. I tiptoed to the edge of the opening and peeked in. "Here, Peanut," I said. But there was no Peanut. I took a deep breath and tried to walk quietly to the next closed door. My tennis shoes squeaked on the wet floor. I knocked. "Are you in there, Peanut?" I opened the door and threw in a dog bone. He wasn't there. There was only one more door and it was open. I peeked into the room. "Peanut? Are you in here?" I threw a dog bone in the dark corner of the room. Then something in the room's closet stirred. My heart jumped. I knew the sound of a dog's nails clacking on the concrete floor. I wanted to run, but I had to see if it was Peanut and if he was foaming at the mouth. I threw a handful of dog bones at the closet door. He barked. "Peanut, come out," I shouted. I threw another bone toward the closet. Then I grabbed the door handle and began to back out of the room. "Peanut, come out," I called. He barked once more, then lunged out of the closet. The floor was wet and he slid in a panic across the room. I screamed and pulled the door shut.

But I had to open it again. I peeked in. "Come here, Peanut," I said. "It's okay." He turned and looked at me. I threw him a dog bone. Even if he jumped at me I had time to yank the door shut before he reached me. He looked at me and barked a few times and I threw him some more dog bones. If he eats, I thought, he isn't rabid. I knew that sick animals never ate. He barked again, then sniffed at a dog bone and started to chew it. I didn't see any foam around his mouth. I threw him another bone and he pawed at it while he chewed another. He seemed really hungry. I opened the door and slowly walked toward him. "Good Peanut," I said. "Good dog." I held a bone out to him and he took it in his mouth as I pet him on his head and scratched his ears. "You dumb dog," I said. "You went home to the wrong house."

I dumped the box of bones on the floor then walked out of the room, closing the door behind me. I didn't have rabies! I didn't have to die or go mad or bite my family to death. I ran down the sidewalk and hopped on Pete's bike. There was a pay telephone at Gus's Gas Station and I rode over there as fast as I could. The gas station was closed for business. A big sign was propped against the gas pump: CLOSED—WATER IN GAS TANK DUE TO HURRICANE. Darn, I thought. Now I'll never know if he put the water in himself. I could just hear Dad saying that Gus was using the hurricane as a cover-up now that everyone was wise to him selling watered-down gas.

"I screamed and pulled the door shut."

The pay phone was on the outside of the building. I put in the dime and dialed Jimmy Stone's number.

"Hello," he answered.

"Is this Jimmy Stone?" I asked in my adult voice.

"Yes," he said.

"This is the city dog pound, and we've found your dog in the back bedroom at 1227 Cactus Street."

"Oh, that's great," he cried. "Hey, Mom," he yelled. "They found Peanut at our old house."

"Let me have the phone," she said.

Oh no! I slammed down the phone. I stood still for a minute. Then suddenly I shouted, *"Case closed!"*

IN RESPONSE
Jumping to Conclusions

Jack has an active imagination. For example, he jumps to conclusions when his mouth foams after the carnival ride, when he finds out the dog's family has moved, and when his father wakes him. List three of Jack's conclusions. Use the examples above or look for others. For each one, write how Jack came to that conlusion. Then suggest a more reasonable conclusion.

Collecting Information

Detective Jack gathers information to find out if a dog has rabies. The Nutbeam family ("Aunt Millicent") gathers items such as a pair of explorer socks and a tom-tom to make their fabricated aunt seem more real. In a group, compare the methods that Jack and the Nutbeams used to gain more information about the dog and Aunt Millicent. Tell why they felt this information was important.

AUTHOR AT WORK

The story "Rabies" is from a book of fictional diary entries describing the adventures of a sixth-grade boy who changes schools often. Although imaginative, many of the book's entries reflect the experiences of Jack Gantos, the book's author. Mr. Gantos attended different schools when he was growing up. He also kept a diary—with a bug collection squished between the pages.

Mr. Gantos's books often show an admiration for the humor, playfulness, and enthusiasm of young people. Mr. Gantos lives in Boston and teaches at Emerson College.

★ Award-winning Author

Other Books About . . .

Strange Encounters

From the Mixed-Up Files of Mrs. Basil E. Frankweiler, written and illustrated by E. L. Konigsburg, Aladdin, 1987

My Side of the Mountain by Jean Craighead George, Puffin Books, 1991

Library Link This story was taken from *Heads or Tails: Stories from the Sixth Grade* by Jack Gantos. You might enjoy reading the entire book to find out about Jack's up-and-down year.

THINGS THAT GO

GLEEP

IN THE NIGHT

by Walter Dean Myers

Kevin Battle poured a glass of orange juice with one hand while he pushed the buttons on the television remote with the other. The picture on the screen broke into a thousand diagonal pieces and the sound crackled noisily. The next channel was no better. He started to put the juice back into the refrigerator, noticed that there were Fig Newtons on the shelf, and grabbed a handful. He flicked the power switch on the remote to "off" and watched as the brightly colored patterns first faded and then shrank. He would watch television in his room, he thought.

He checked the time—three-fifteen. He'd start his math homework at five-fifteen so he'd be halfway through it by the time his mother got home at six.

He hadn't remembered leaving the light on in his room, but he saw the glow coming from the door as he reached the second floor of the Battle household. Maybe his mother had been in his room after he had left for school, he thought. He pushed the door open with his foot as he tried to remember how he had left the room. Messy enough, he knew, to get a lecture about neatness.

Inside the room he froze. The overhead light wasn't on and yet the room was bathed in an eerie green light. In the mirror over his dresser he could see his closet. The door was partially open and he saw that the glow came from within. He eased the orange juice and Fig Newtons down on his dresser, took a deep breath, and held it for a long moment before speaking.

"Hello?"

"Hello?" a voice answered. The green glow began to fade.

"Hey, Jimmy, is that you fooling around?" Kevin remembered that he hadn't seen his best friend on the school bus.

"Kevin Battle?" The voice from the closet spoke softly as the door opened. "Are you really Kevin Battle?"

Kevin jumped back, one hand flat against the wall of his room, as a pale, thin figure emerged from the closet. Kevin would have run if there hadn't been something vaguely familiar about what clearly looked to be a youngish, if odd-looking, man. He was dressed strangely. The white tunic he wore came down nearly to his knees, and his sandals were strapped over his

ankles so that they looked almost like boots.

"I'm Kevin Battle." Kevin felt a cold trickle of sweat down the back of his neck. "Who are you?"

"I'm Orion[1] Battle." The quick answer was accompanied by a smile. "And I'm thrilled and honored to meet you."

"Orion Battle?" Kevin didn't move from the door. "You stay right there. And how did you get in here in the first place?"

"It's kind of a long story," he said. "I'd love to tell you if you'll just give me a chance. And don't worry, I won't say gleep or anything."

"Gleep?"

"That's what some people think ghosts do"—Orion Battle sat on the edge of Kevin's bed—"go around sneaking up on people and saying gleep!"

"Ghosts?"

"I'm from a long time from now," Orion said. "The year 3003, to be exact. And technically I'm not alive, so I imagine you'd call me a ghost."

"And ghosts go gleep?" Kevin looked at him. "Whatever happened to boo!"

"Boo?"

"Forget it," Kevin said. "I don't believe a word of what you're saying."

"I was sure you'd have trouble understanding," Orion said. "But I was also pretty sure a man as wise as you would listen to me."

"Yeah, maybe." Kevin relaxed slightly. "Go ahead."

"Well, a while back, I think it was 2500, something like that—"

"A while back?"

"From my point of view," Orion added quickly. "Anyway, around that time we finally conquered death. Found out that it was a virus. But people still had to be—you know—moved out of the way so new people could be born. So we started doing it by lottery."

"You mean, so you picked a number and you were killed?" Kevin asked.

"Not exactly," Orion said. "I've just been deenergized. I'll become part of some other form, perhaps even another person. So nobody ever 'dies' the way they used to in your time. But a really neat thing that we have, is that after we get deenergized we can travel in time for a short while before we

---

1 **Orion** (*oh RY uhn*)

lose consciousness and start the transference part."

"Yeah?"

"And since I had the chance," Orion said, "here I am."

"So let's get this straight," Kevin said. "You're a ghost from the future, and you decided to come here to see me before you just kind of float away into random energy?"

"Yeah, I knew you'd get it," Orion said. "I mean, with your wisdom and all. Can you imagine how proud I am of having you for an ancestor?"

"I'm your ancestor?" Kevin asked.

"According to the records we could find," Orion said. "You're my great-great-great-great-great-great-great-great-great-grandfather. You're also one of the most famous men in this century. Well, I guess you're going to be. We're still quoting your wisdom in the year 3003."

"Like what wise sayings?" Kevin took a sip from his orange juice.

"My personal favorite was when you said that Truth is circular and that life goes in a straight line, which was the basic cause of human confusion."

"Yeah, that's uh . . . what I've been thinking about a lot," Kevin said.

"It took me a while to understand it," Orion said. "But when I did, it was just wonderful."

"Glad you liked it, Orion," Kevin said. "It is Orion?"

"Yes, that's right. Anyway, when my number came up I thought I'd take the chance to meet you." Orion stood and started stretching his hands over his head and touching his toes. "And find out about one of the minor religions in your time that nobody in our time could really figure out."

"What minor religion?" Kevin wondered if this guy was some kind of nut. "And what are you doing?"

"Oh, circulation exercises," Orion said. "In our time we don't do much in the way of physical activities. Got to save the old oxygen, you know."

"You people have problems with the atmosphere?"

"Not since the domes were built," Orion said. "We manufacture as much oxygen as we need, but we can't use it too quickly. It gets too expensive."

"And what religion do you want to know about?" Kevin asked.

"There's some controversy about what you people call it." Orion stopped exercising and cupped his chin in his hand. "Some of our archaeologists think you called it B-Ball and some think you called it Hoops—"

"B-Ball? Hoops?" Kevin scratched his head. "We've got a lot to talk about, friend."

"Uh—what shall I call you? Grandpa?"

"Sure, why not," Kevin said.

"Look, Grandpa, I don't have a lot of time here. I'll be deenergizing in an hour or so. So if you explain it to me in a quick way, I would appreciate it."

"Okay, let me get this straight. You guys in the future don't do many physical things, right?"

"We don't do anything physical, really," Orion said.

"And you don't know anything about our 'religion' of Hoops?"

"Well, we know some things," Orion said. "We know there were two goals. One that is Good and the other Evil. You had people who were magicians and others who could fly through the air."

"And you still quote my wisdom?"

"Yes, I'm proud to say." Orion beamed. "How old are you now?"

"Fourteen," Kevin said.

"Then you have just started saying your wise things," Orion said.

"Okay, look, I'm going to show you some of our 'hoops,'" Kevin said.

"I'd be honored," Orion replied.

Kevin took the phone. He punched the number he wanted with one hand and flicked on the television with the other. "You people still use televisions?"

Orion looked at the television and nodded. "We call it 'Vision.'"

"Vision?" Kevin was amazed. "After a thousand years you just call it vision? That's it? Do you have holographic vision?"

"What's that?" Orion asked.

"Hello, Jimmy?" Kevin spoke into the phone. "Look, I want to get up a three-man run. You up to it?"

"Yeah, I guess so." Jimmy's voice seemed far away on the phone. "Who we going to play against?"

"Call up Eddie Farrell, and Billy Garcia, see if he can get his brother and Sean Harmon."

"You got to be kidding. Sean Harmon can dunk backwards!" Jimmy said.

"Don't sweat it, Jimmy," Kevin said. "I know what I'm doing. I mean, I am a little wiser than you. I'll meet you in the gym in twenty minutes."

"Yeah, right," Jimmy said. "We're going to get killed and you're talking about how wise you are."

It was a short walk to the gym, but Kevin had to walk slowly. In the first place Orion was out of breath after the first half block, and then he had to stop to see everything.

"It's really wild that you guys have oxygen that's just floating

around and doesn't even need a dome to keep it in," Orion said.

"Well, we're trying our best to keep it," Kevin said. "At least some of us are."

"I think that's a wise thing too," Orion said. "You really are wise."

"What's the wisest thing you know I've said?" Kevin asked.

"Oh, that thing about the end of Truth being the beginning of oppression," Orion said. "That's my personal favorite."

"I can understand that," Kevin said.

"And tell me, were you the one who discovered that by adding microbes to the garbage dumps you would have a source of perpetual energy?"

"I've been thinking about it," said Kevin.

"Fantastic!"

They reached the basketball court just as Jimmy arrived with Eddie.

"Sean and the Garcia brothers were already here," Jimmy said. "Who's this guy?"

"Hello, my name is Orion. I'm Kevin's—"

"Friend," Kevin added quickly.

"That's a truly funky outfit, man," Jimmy said. "You get it at the mall?"

"No," Kevin said quickly. "It's kind of homemade."

Kevin found a seat for Orion. "You're in for a treat," he said. "Harmon is like the best ever."

"I'll be respectful," Orion said.

"And we're only going to use one goal," Kevin said. "It's three on three."

"Is it the goal of Good or the goal of Evil?" Orion asked.

"Who knows?" Kevin shrugged as he tightened the laces on his sneakers.

"It's the search for truth?" Orion asked.

"Yeah, something like that," Kevin said.

The game started just about as Jimmy thought it would.

Juan Garcia, the shorter of the Garcia brothers, dribbled around Jimmy and passed the ball to Sean Harmon, who dunked it.

"Turkey!" Sean looked down from his six-three frame and scoffed at Kevin.

Kevin looked over at Orion. His great-great-great-great-great-great-great-great-great-grandson's mouth was wide open. He was impressed.

"Anybody can do a simple dunk," Kevin said.

Kevin took the ball out and passed it in to Jimmy, who missed the shot but got his own rebound. He passed the ball out to Kevin. Kevin shot, watched the ball roll off the ring and fall into the waiting hands of Sean Harmon.

"I got him! I got him!" Kevin yelled.

Sean dribbled toward the basket, took a huge step as he reached the lane, and went up, up, up. He twisted his body in the air and brought the ball down hard over his head in a vicious behind-the-back slam dunk!

"Lucky!" Kevin whispered. "You don't have any moves, man."

Sean took over the game. He dribbled around and over Kevin's team with a vengeance. He dunked with one hand, with two hands, on an alley-oop, and finally ended the game with a spinning three-sixty whammer-jammer dunk.

"See you guys later," Kevin said.

"Yeah, when you learn to play some ball," Eddie Farrell said.

"So, what do you think?" Kevin asked Orion as they reached his house.

"It was truly a wonderful experience," Orion said. "But did you decide if the goal was the goal of Good or Evil?"

"It was the goal of Good," Kevin said.

"And the flying magician reached it more than you," Orion said. "And still you are pleased."

"The goodness of the Goal is more important than those who seek it," Kevin said.

"How wise! How perfectly wise!" Orion said.

"Yeah, I guess so." Kevin nodded.

"I am . . . I am . . ." Orion was taking deep breaths.

"What's wrong?" Kevin asked.

"I am disintegrating again," Orion said. "Let me get back into this small room. It's easier on my eyes in the darkness."

Kevin opened the door, and pushed aside some of his old sneakers so that Orion could sit inside the closet. When he closed the door he saw a faint glow around the edges.

"It has been a . . . wonderful . . . wonder . . . wonderful experience," came from the closet.

"Hey, I'm glad you came," Kevin said.

"It has been a . . . wonderful . . . experience," came yet another muffled call from the closet.

"Don't mention it," Kevin said.

The light from the closet grew brighter, and then suddenly disappeared. Kevin waited a long time. Finally, he went to the closet and opened it. The floor where Orion had been sitting was bare except for the sneakers and an old baseball with a torn cover.

The next day in school he ran into Jimmy on the way to the cafeteria.

"I don't know why you wanted to get us creamed like that," Jimmy said. "What did your friend have to think about it?"

"He thought it was a great game," Kevin said.

"What is he," Jimmy asked, "some kind of a wise guy?"

"No," Kevin answered with a broad smile. "I'm the wise guy."

IN RESPONSE

A Distant Relative

Suppose that Kevin were asked to write an imaginary portrait of a relative living in 3003. He might start with his memories of Orion. To invent extra details, he could ask himself questions about Orion like the ones the Nutbeams ("Aunt Millicent") asked each other about their imaginary relative. How might Kevin describe Orion?

Game Wrap-up

Imagine that instead of deenergizing, Orion returns to the future. His friends are eager to find out what he learned about "Hoops." Write a game wrap-up Orion might give to describe the game he observed and explain its rules and deeper meaning.

AUTHOR AT WORK

Writing came naturally to Walter Dean Myers. Even as a teenager, he won awards for some of his poems and stories. Mr. Myers kept writing through high school and in the army. However, he didn't intend to make writing a career because he "never knew writing was a job. People didn't think of being a writer as a legitimate kind of work." Only later, after working in jobs from mail clerk to messenger, did he decide that writing would become his life's work.

Mr. Myers has published fairy tales, ghost stories, mystery stories, science fiction, and historical fiction and nonfiction.

★ Award-winning Author

Other Books About . . .

Warps in Time

Keeping Time by Colby Rodowsky, Farrar, Straus and Giroux, 1983

The Root Cellar by Janet Lunn, Puffin Books, 1985

Library Link "Things That Go Gleep in the Night" was taken from *Don't Give Up the Ghost,* edited by David Gale. You might enjoy reading other ghost stories included in *Don't Give Up the Ghost.*

Art Encounters

Artists can record meetings that take place as well as meetings that might never take place. Artists can even offer a person a chance to meet a character the artist has created.

In the scene below, who's meeting whom? Compare the scene below with the monument at the right. Which character would you like to meet? Explain your choice.

Lithograph by Mabel Dwight (United States), *Queer Fish,* **1936**

Colossal stone monuments of Olmec rulers are often unearthed by farmers digging in their fields in Mexico. How would you feel if *you* encountered an eleven-foot-high, twenty-ton Olmec head?

Carved head of an Olmec leader, about 1200 – 900 B.C.

Southbound
ON
THE Freeway

by May Swenson

A tourist came in from Orbitville,
parked in the air, and said:

The creatures of this star
are made of metal and glass.

Through the transparent parts
you can see their guts.

Their feet are round and roll
on diagrams or long

measuring tapes, dark
with white lines.

They have four eyes.
The two in back are red.

Sometimes you can see a five-eyed
one, with a red eye turning

on the top of his head.
He must be special—

the others respect him
and go slow

when he passes, winding
among them from behind.

They all hiss as they glide,
like inches, down the marked

tapes. Those soft shapes,
shadowy inside

the hard bodies—are they
their guts or their brains?

Miss Fabergé's Last Daze

by Jenny Wagner

The girls in Miss Fabergé's class cried when she left. Even the boys seemed quieter than usual; their clamor as they crowded round to say goodbye was muted and melancholy, and they signed her going-away card with gruff, tough messages to remember them—or else.

Tracey's friend Marianne cried louder than anyone; and Tracey, who was only a little tougher, drew a pink heart in her autograph book and blew her nose as she got Miss Fabergé to sign it.

She knew she was losing the best teacher in the world. Miss Fabergé was young, sweet-faced and elegant, had Italian shoes with matching handbags, and never worried about homework, or why you were late, or whether you talked in class.

Her replacement, Miss Blackstone, arrived three days later on a wet Monday morning.

Tracey and Marianne, watching from the library window, saw a light-brown station-wagon with rust stains round the doors drive in through the gate marked BUSES ONLY, bump across the lawn, and park crookedly in the space reserved for the deputy headmaster.

"That's her," said Tracey, watching her get out of the car.

It had to be. Only someone called Miss Blackstone could be so gross, so ugly, so badly dressed, so utterly opposite from everything Miss Fabergé had stood for.

She was tall and heavily built. She wore flat, thick shoes like a man's, with ankle socks instead of stockings, and a checked skirt that looked like a horse blanket. She wore no make-up, and her hair, flattened to her head by the rain, was so thin that her white scalp shone through.

"She needs a hat with horns," said Marianne. She giggled as the woman, covering her head with a newspaper, lumbered towards the verandah. "And saucepan lids for her chest."

"I think she needs a broomstick," muttered Tracey.

They met officially a few minutes later when the bell went for assembly. The whole school, smelling of wet wool, squeezed into the hall to mumble its way through the oath of allegiance and the national anthem, and to salute the flag, which was hanging in a corner of the hall like damp washing.

Miss Blackstone stood on the stage with the rest of the staff, and stared down at them.

If Tracey had needed another reason to dislike Miss Blackstone, that stare was enough. There was something unnerving about it; even at this distance her eyes looked odd: they were pale and round, as if she had found them in a river-bed.

Tracey suppressed a giggle; she had a sudden image of Miss Blackstone fossicking[1] among the pebbles in a dry river, trying them in her eye-sockets until she found a pair she liked.

She nudged Marianne, wanting to share the joke with her, and in that moment found herself looking straight into those terrible eyes. A fear as cold as stone struck through her; in panic she fixed her eyes on a portrait of the Queen that hung at the back of the stage, and pretended she had been looking at that all along.

Marianne nudged her in return. "What?"

Tracey, still staring at the Queen in case she met Miss Blackstone's eye, struggled to remember. But the joke had withered and died.

"Go on," said Marianne, nudging her again. "What was it?" But try as she might, Tracey could not remember what she had wanted to say; her mind had gone quite blank.

And that was when she realized she had been mind-razed.

She had all the symptoms: a vague tingling in her hands and feet, a sudden absence of memory, and a lingering dislike of the pebbly-eyed person who had caused it.

---

1 fossicking (*FAHS ihk ing*) searching for any object that will bring gain

Tracey had no doubt it was Miss Blackstone. She remembered those pale eyes; they were just the sort of eyes you would expect to find on someone who could raze minds.

It followed that Miss Blackstone was an alien. That also explained the terrible dress sense.

Up on the stage the headmaster announced a new bus timetable and cancelled the swimming, and then he introduced Miss Blackstone to the school and told everyone to "welcome her by acclamation."

He didn't tell them that she had the power to raze minds, thought Tracey; but that might be because he hadn't found out yet.

Tracey clapped along with everyone else, so as not to draw attention to herself. She clapped the way Miss Fabergé used to, elegantly patting her palm with her finger-tips, and she was pleased to find how little noise it made.

She was also pleased to find that the mind-razing had not been entirely successful: she still remembered who Miss Fabergé was.

Tracey intended to keep her discovery to herself for a while; she had found that people did not always believe her when she told them extraordinary things. This time, she told herself, she would watch and wait and gather evidence, and not tell anyone until she had absolute proof.

But because Marianne was her friend, she let her into the secret while they walked along the verandah to their classroom.

"I don't believe you!" said Marianne. It was what she always said.

"Didn't you see her eyes?" said Tracey, "They were like . . . like . . . I forget what they were like," she said, puzzled.

"Last year," said Marianne, "you thought your neigh-bors were aliens. You said that two aliens disguised as an elderly couple had rented the house next door and were using it as a communications base."

"You thought so too!" said Tracey.

"Only because you talked me into it."

When they got to the classroom Miss Blackstone was already waiting for them. "See what I mean?" whispered Tracey. "How could she have got here so fast?"

Some crawler[2] had written WELCOME MISS BLACKSTONE across the blackboard in red chalk. It would be a week before anyone could get it off, but nevertheless Miss Blackstone, after a jovial thank you, was making everybody try.

While they took it in turns to rub away at the board Miss Blackstone moved her table from the corner of the room to the middle, and sat on it.

"I'm your new class teacher," she said. Since this was something they all knew, everyone started shuffling their feet and rattling pencil cases and looking for rubber bands to flick.

Miss Blackstone took no notice. "I'm going to teach the same subjects that Miss Fabergé did,"—a sigh of regret went up from the class at the mention of Miss Fabergé's name—"and I expect you all to work. There'll be homework. And there'll be tests."

"Now do you believe me?" whispered Tracey.

And as Miss Blackstone settled herself more comfortably on the table, Tracey, with the miserable

---

2 **crawler** (*KRAWL ur*) Australian slang, someone wishing to be the teacher's favorite

person's determination to find even more cause for misery, noticed something else: under her ankle socks she was wearing stockings.

She did not tell Marianne at once for fear of being mind-razed again, but at lunchtime when the rain had stopped and they were sitting under the pine trees, she made Marianne watch as Miss Blackstone marched across the yard.

"See that?" said Tracey, pointing at the stockings. "What did I tell you?"

"That doesn't mean she's an alien," said Marianne. "She might just have cold legs."

"Miss Fabergé used to wear boots," said Tracey. "Creamy-colored suede ones, with little gold buckles."

Just then Miss Blackstone saw them and waved. Tracey, mindful of the eyes, looked away and studied a line of black ants that was escaping to higher ground. But she knew without looking that Miss Blackstone was coming over to them. With a slow, deadly compulsion, as if she were locked on a tractor beam, Tracey found herself turning away from the black ants and looking up. Miss Blackstone had just joined them.

"I wonder if you would help me," said Miss Blackstone, beaming at them. "I have some things to put in the car."

Tracey stared at the tip of Miss Blackstone's nose. Not only was it safer than looking at her eyes, it was more interesting: the cold had reddened it, giving her an unexpectedly jolly look, like Father Christmas.

"I'd be awfully grateful," said Miss Blackstone.

Marianne, who was like putty in anyone's hands, fell for it. "I'll help you," she said, jumping up.

And Tracey, who could not let her best friend walk into danger alone, had to go with her. She cheered herself up by deciding it was a chance to gather clues.

But she was disappointed. There were no clues. Besides putting equipment in her car for sport that afternoon, Miss Blackstone was just removing some of the bits and pieces Miss Fabergé had left behind.

Although Miss Fabergé's outward appearance had always been perfect (even the wayward little curls that fluttered round her face had not really escaped, but had been put there by a hairdresser), her desk was a strange contradiction. Once when Miss Fabergé was rummaging through it looking for the class roll, Tracey looked over her shoulder and saw a surprising jumble of books, tissues, jars of cream, lipsticks, felt-pens, nail files and empty perfume bottles.

It had given Tracey a feeling of tenderness to know that Miss Fabergé wasn't perfect.

But now Miss Blackstone took from Miss Fabergé's desk the few things that were left—a half-used lipstick, an emery board, a knitting needle, a used-up note pad—and dropped them in a plastic bag. She sealed the top with sticky tape and tossed it on the back seat of the car.

Tracey felt a dark, mutinous rage bubble up within her.

"They do that in gaol," said Marianne later on, as they were walking down to the sports oval. "And with dead people."

"Do what?" said Tracey.

"Put their things in a plastic bag," said Marianne. "That's what my uncle reckons." Marianne's uncle was a policeman.

Tracey was struck by an idea that was perfect and breathtaking in its simplicity. Suddenly everything was clear, suddenly everything fitted: the mind-razing, the collecting of Miss Fabergé's things, everything.

"Miss Fabergé's been kidnapped," she said.

Marianne stood still. "Don't be stupid."

"Miss Blackstone did it. First she mind-razed her, then she kidnapped her."

"Whatever for?"

"How would I know? So that she could take her place, I suppose. That's what aliens do, isn't it? I expect Miss Fabergé's being held prisoner in Miss Blackstone's house in a huge, dark mansion covered in creeper, with bars over the windows."

"Miss Blackstone lives in the block of flats just down from the laundromat," said Marianne. "Eleven A. My uncle helped her move in." Marianne's other uncle was a removalist.[3]

The mention of Marianne's uncle—even the wrong one—made Tracey think of getting her to tell the right uncle—the policeman—about Miss Fabergé's predicament.

But then she realized it could be embarrassing. She had met him once before, when she had to explain to him why she was trespassing on next door's property with a yellow bucket on her head. The bucket had been to ward off death rays, and was very successful—she was still alive to be embarrassed—but Marianne's uncle, who must have been slightly affected by the rays, did not believe her.

"And that's the silliest thing I ever heard of," said Marianne, after a pause in which she had apparently considered all the other silly things she had heard of.

"Are you going to help me?" asked Tracey.

---

3 removalist (*ree MOOV uh list*) a mover; a person who moves furniture

"No."

Tracey was silent. Clearly she would have to rescue Miss Fabergé herself.

She thought for a while about asking one of the boys to help her. It was always more interesting to do these things in company, and there were one or two boys whose company she quite liked. But there was the problem of getting them to believe her; if she hadn't been able to convince Marianne, she didn't think she could convince anyone else.

She thought about it all through sport, and got her shins bruised as a result. But by half-past three she could see there was no alternative.

"I'll go by myself," she told Marianne. "Even though I'm not sure which flat it is, and even though I might get into trouble."

"I'll show you which flat it is," said Marianne. "But from across the street. I'm not coming any closer, okay?"

The block of flats was disappointingly ordinary. None of the flats had bars over the windows; none of them had strange antennae on the roof; there was no hum of alien machinery coming from deep inside.

The building was ordinary pale-colored brick, with ordinary prickly plants in a garden of pale, round river stones. The stones reminded Tracey of something; she stared at them for several seconds, trying to think what it was, but her mind was a blank.

The door of Number Eleven A was painted a sunny yellow that was beginning to peel, and the number was askew.

Before Tracey had time to knock, Miss Blackstone opened the door and beamed at her. "Tracey!" she said. "I was wondering when you'd get here. Come on in."

Tracey clutched her school bag more tightly—her palms were beginning to sweat—fixed her eyes on the third button from the top of Miss Blackstone's shirt, and edged inside.

The inside of the flat was just as disappointingly ordinary as the outside. There was a beige self-patterned carpet, striped curtains, a table, some chairs, a sofa, and bookcases with books in them. Nothing else.

"I'm just having a cup of tea or coffee," said Miss Blackstone. "Would you like one?"

Tracey hesitated. There could be worse things than mind-razing; a cup of alien tea or coffee might be one of them.

Miss Blackstone went into the kitchen. "I'll make you one anyway," she called back.

While Miss Blackstone was out of the way Tracey examined what she could see of the flat. It was significant, she thought, that the flat was so tidy. There were no newspapers on the sofa, no Lotto forms on the table, no scissors or old light bills on the mantelpiece like there were at home. In particular there were no signs of Miss Fabergé such as lipsticks or empty perfume bottles; obviously Miss Blackstone had tidied them away.

That was where aliens slipped up, thought Tracey. They never could understand how sloppy human beings were.

But although the room showed no sign of human occupancy, it showed no sign of alien occupancy either. There were no tall cylinders made of perspex,[4] and no strange-looking radios; there were no star maps on the wall, and no control consoles with flashing lights.

"I know what you're thinking," said Miss Blackstone, coming back with two mugs and a packet of biscuits.

Tracey jumped.

"You're wondering whether it's tea or coffee," said Miss Blackstone, putting the mugs on the table. "I'm afraid I can't tell you. It tastes like a mixture of both; I got it from the school canteen."

---

4 **perspex** (*PER spehks*) clear, strong, inflexible acrylic

For the first time that day Tracey felt reassured. She had once tasted school tea or coffee at a film night, and knew that no alien would ever touch it. Aliens had their own food, which came in jewel colors of blue, green and purple, and they got it from dispensers built into the wall. There were no such dispensers here.

She helped herself to a mug of whatever it was, and was pleased to find it tasted exactly like the tea or coffee at school film nights.

"I got it because I knew you were coming," said Miss Blackstone. "Normally I wouldn't touch the stuff."

Tracey choked into her mug, realizing her mistake.

Just then a door to another room swung open and a blonde disheveled figure wearing cream boots and a matching suede suit tottered out. "Oh, goodness gracious," it murmured. "Just look at this skirt. I'll never get the creases out."

"Miss Fabergé!" yelled Tracey.

Miss Fabergé turned to look at her. "Tracey, isn't it? How sweet of you to come." Miss Fabergé's eyes as she looked at Tracey seemed vague, almost dazed, and there was a smudge on her cheek that looked like grease. Tracey felt a pang of fear.

"Are you all right?" she whispered.

"Oh, I'm fine, fine, don't you worry about that," said Miss Fabergé. "Why don't you take a half day off?"

Tracey told her school was over for the day.

"Tomorrow, then," said Miss Fabergé with her sweet smile, and started filing her nails. Miss Blackstone watched her.

Tracey watched both of them. She was thinking of all the films she had seen in which the hero said "If I'm not back in ten minutes, call the cops," and she wished she had said something of the sort to Marianne, with instructions of course to make sure it wasn't her uncle.

She glanced at the window to see if Marianne was still outside, but a lace curtain spoiled her view. And then she caught sight of something else: on the floor under the table there was an old-fashioned black telephone.

A telephone!

She edged towards it.

"Leave that alone." Miss Blackstone's voice was jovial as ever, but her foot pushed the phone out of reach. Tracey moved back again. She was not particularly disappointed; she had not been looking forward to telling the operator that she was imprisoned in a flat by an alien.

She looked round, at the ordinary flat with its ordinary decoration, at Miss Blackstone quietly sipping her coffee or tea, and Miss Fabergé noisily filing her nails. Miss Fabergé didn't seem to be in any danger; surely all Tracey had to do was simply stand up, announce she was going home, and go.

She half-closed her eyes and rehearsed it in her mind: she would get up and say "Thank you for the tea or coffee," and make straight for the door.

She opened her eyes and studied the door to see where the handle and catches were.

"Have I got the right earrings on?" asked Miss Fabergé, peering up at Miss Blackstone.

"They look fine to me," said Miss Blackstone.

That decided it. The thought of leaving the elegant Miss Fabergé to the mercy of Miss Blackstone's fashion sense was more than Tracey could bear. She would take Miss Fabergé with her, no matter what the cost. She stood up. "Come on, Miss Fabergé," she said. "We're leaving."

"Oh, no," said Miss Fabergé. "I couldn't. I definitely have to stay here."

"No, you don't," said Tracey. "You just think you have to because you've been mind-razed. But if you come with me we'll find a doctor or something. You'll be all right, honest."

Miss Blackstone moved in front of the door. "That's very kind of you, Tracey,"—she gave Tracey one of her beaming smiles—"but Miss Fabergé hasn't been very well, and she really does have to stay here till she's better."

The rage that had bubbled in Tracey earlier now overflowed. "I know what you're up to!" she yelled. "Don't think I don't know because I do! I know exactly what you're doing!"

Miss Blackstone looked surprised, then pleased. "Really?"

Tracey nodded. "Yes," she said, but with a little less certainty this time.

"In that case," said Miss Blackstone, looking rather relieved, "you must know that this teaching android has been malfunctioning for some time. It's been giving us no end of trouble."

"I'm fine, just a little malfunction, don't you worry about that," said Miss Fabergé, dabbing lipstick on her fingernails.

"We've had several tries at getting it to self-repair," said Miss Blackstone, "but without any luck; and that's why I've been called in. Well," she corrected herself, "down, really."

In answer to Tracey's look she explained, "I'm an android mechanic."

Slowly Tracey got up. She went over to the door that Miss Fabergé had tottered through, and pushed it open.

In the room were two large perspex cylinders, some strange-looking radios, a control console with flashing lights, and an illuminated star map. Set into one wall was a slot with a glass door in front, and beside it were pictures of jelly in jewel colors of blue, green and purple.

"There'll be homework when I'm better, you'll see, my word there will be," said Miss Fabergé, dabbing lipstick on her ears.

Miss Blackstone kicked the black telephone further under the table. "Don't use that telephone, it's a direct line to Vega—for ordering parts and so on. If you want an ordinary phone there's one in the kitchen."

"You mean I'm allowed to ring up?" asked Tracey.

"Why not?" asked Miss Blackstone.

Tracey thought about that for a while. But since she could not think of anyone she fancied telling her story to, it did not help her very much.

"Am I allowed to go home?"

"If you like," said Miss Blackstone.

"Well," said Tracey, "thank you for the tea or coffee, then." She started towards the door.

"It was a pleasure," said Miss Blackstone, opening it for her. "You must come again some time."

Tracey took one last look at Miss Fabergé, who was dabbing lipstick on her nose. "Goodbye, Miss Fabergé."

"Oh, not goodbye, *au revoir*,[5] said Miss Fabergé. "A number, *n*, increases as the square of its homework and earrings, and certain logical outputs vary indiscriminately."

---

5 au revoir (*oh ruh VWAHR*) until we meet again; good-bye

"Thank you," whispered Tracey, and slipped out.

Marianne, who had been waiting in the laundromat, came to meet her. "What on earth have you been doing? I've been freezing out here. I thought you were never coming out."

Tracey was startled to find it was nearly dark; it gave her an odd, unreal feeling, as if she had just come out of a cinema. "Well?" said Marianne. "Did you rescue her?"

"No," said Tracey.

"I told you it was a dumb idea," said Marianne.

Miss Blackstone taught them for a week, and then on Monday morning, to everyone's delight, Miss Fabergé came

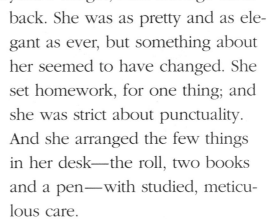

back. She was as pretty and as elegant as ever, but something about her seemed to have changed. She set homework, for one thing; and she was strict about punctuality. And she arranged the few things in her desk—the roll, two books and a pen—with studied, meticulous care.

Miss Blackstone moved out of her flat at the end of the week, according to Marianne, whose uncle helped her move. And by a coincidence, Tracey's next-door neighbors, the elderly couple, moved on the same day. They left behind a lot of rubbish—perspex cylinders, strange-looking radios, consoles with flashing lights, and the like—which the next occupants, with a good deal of grumbling, carted to the tip.[6]

---

6 **tip** (*tihp*) trash collection site

IN RESPONSE

Alien Alert

Tracey knows how to spot an alien, but no one else does! Make a poster that Tracey could use to help other people identify aliens. Be sure to include clues to aliens' behavior as well as their appearance. What other clues can you include?

A Real Surprise

"Things that Go Gleep in the Night" and "Miss Fabergé's Last Days" both begin like realistic fiction and end like science fiction. In a group, discuss how the authors make their stories seem realistic in the beginning. Give specific details about the characters or setting. Which story surprises you more later on? Why?

AUTHOR AT WORK

Jenny Wagner lives in Australia, surrounded by her pet dogs and cats. Before becoming an author of books for young adults, she was, among other things, a sculptor and a secondary school teacher. Her fanciful stories explore situations that might occur when a person encounters the unknown.

★ Award-winning Author

Another Book About . . .

Alien Adventures

The Computer Nut by Betsy Byars, Puffin Books, 1986

Library Link "Miss Fabergé's Last Daze" was taken from *Dream Time,* a collection of short stories about strange events, edited by Toss Gascoigne, Jo Goodman, and Margot Tyrrell.

Express Yourself

In the theme Strange Encounters, you read about encounters with real and imaginary beings that changed the lives of ordinary people. You saw how a strange encounter could teach a person something new about a future time, a far-off place, or about himself or herself.

Beware of First Impressions

In "Things That Go Gleep in the Night," Kevin's impression of Orion changes as they get to know each other. In "Miss Fabergé's Last Daze," the reader's first impressions of Miss Blackstone and Tracey change. How do Orion, Tracey, and Miss Blackstone appear at first? What about later on? Why do you think an author might keep a character's true nature hidden at the start?

What Do You Know?

One character in each selection of this theme knows something other characters do not. Why does each character decide not to share the information? Which characters have similar reasons? Which information would you keep hidden? Which would you share? Explain why.

An Imaginative Debate

Several stories in this theme show how people's imaginations can influence their behavior. Jack ("Rabies"), the Nutbeam family ("Aunt Millicent"), and Tracey ("Miss Fabergé's Last Daze") all have active imaginations. Do you think an active imagination is a good thing? Debate the question with a partner. Take opposite sides and support your position with evidence from the stories.

A Happy Ending?

Jack ("Rabies") and Tracey ("Miss Fabergé's Last Daze") both solve mysteries. How do they feel once their mysteries are solved? Give examples of what the characters do or say that tells you how they feel. Why do you think they feel differently? How would you feel if you were in their shoes?

Strange Encounters

Strange encounters change the lives of many characters in this theme. With a group, identify the strange encounter in each selection. How are characters' lives changed because of who or what they encounter? In the end, are they better or worse off?

More Books for You to Enjoy

Appointment

by Alan Benjamin, illustrated by Roger Essley, Green Tiger Press, 1993

Facing death in the marketplace in Baghdad, the servant Abdullah begs his master to help him escape his fate. Who can guess what will happen in this tale of suspense and surprise?

Willie Bea and the Time the Martians Landed

by Virginia Hamilton, Aladdin, 1989

On October 30, 1938, Willie Bea is looking forward to celebrating Halloween as relatives gather for Sunday dinner at the family homestead. Little does she realize what terror the night will bring when a radio broadcast announces that Martians have landed.

Switching Well

by Peni R. Griffin, Margaret K. McElderry Books, 1993

San Antonio is quite a different place in 1891. Twelve-year-old Amber learns this and more when she is transported back in time and changes places with Ada, who is amazed to learn what life is like in 1991.

Invitation to The Game

by Monica Hughes, Simon & Schuster, 1990

In the year 2154, the government controls where you live, what you wear, your work, and perhaps even your dreams. Life is bleak for Lisse and her classmates until they receive an invitation to participate in The Game.

Mrs. Frisby and the Rats of NIMH

by Robert C. O'Brien, illustrated by Zena Bernstein, Atheneum, 1971

Facing the bulldozing of her family home, Mrs. Frisby, a widowed mouse, seeks help from a colony of rats. She discovers that these rats are no ordinary rodents but a highly intelligent group who have escaped from the NIMH laboratory.

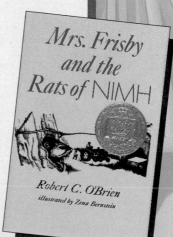

Survival

"Courage, stamina, and
a cool head help, too."

—Bill Littlefield
"Leader of the Pack"

CONTENTS

Theme Trade Books

Drylongso

by Virginia Hamilton
A great wall of dust rolls across a family's drought-stricken farm. They turn for help to a young man called Drylongso, who blew into their lives with the storm.

The Crystal Drop

by Monica Hughes
In the summer of 2011, the death of their mother sends Megan and her younger brother, Ian, on a dangerous journey across Canada. As they struggle to find their uncle, they cross a country ravaged by drought and chaos.

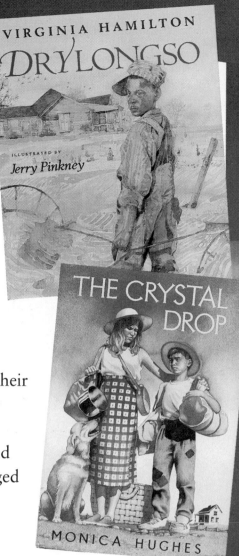

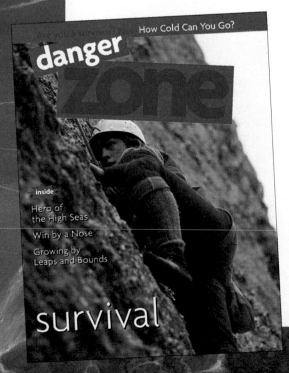

Theme Magazine

What can you do to survive the cold? Why can you die of thirst on the ocean? How can surviving the outdoors help you find your hidden strengths? Read the Theme Magazine *Danger Zone* to find out.

Kinship

from *Woodsong* by Gary Paulsen

Cold can be very strange. Not the cold felt running from the house to the bus or the car to the store; not the chill in the air on a fall morning, but deep cold.

Serious cold.

Forty, fifty, even sixty below zero—actual temperature, not windchill—seems to change everything. Steel becomes brittle and breaks, shatters; breath taken straight into the throat will freeze the lining and burst blood vessels; eyes exposed too long will freeze; fingers and toes freeze, turn black, and break off. These are all known, normal parts of intense cold.

But it changes beauty as well. Things are steeped in a new clarity, a clear focus. Sound seems to ring and the very air seems to be filled with diamonds when ice crystals form.

On a river in Alaska while training I once saw a place where a whirlpool had frozen into a cone, open at the bottom like a beautiful trap waiting to suck the whole team down. When I stopped to look at it, with the water roaring through at the bottom, the dogs became nervous and stared down into the center as if mystified and were very glad when we moved on.

After a time I stopped trapping. That change—as with many changes—occurred because of the dogs. As mentioned, I had hunted when I was young, trapping and killing many animals. I never thought it wrong until the dogs came. And then it was a simple thing, almost a silly thing, that caused the change.

Columbia had a sense of humor and I saw it.

In the summer the dogs live in the kennel area, each dog with his own house, on a chain that allows him to move in a circle. They can only run with the wheeled carts on cool nights, and sometimes they get bored being tied up. To alleviate the boredom we give the dogs large beef bones to chew and play with. They get a new bone every other day or so. These bones are the center of much contention—we call them Bone Wars. Sometimes dogs clear across the kennel will hold their bones up in the air, look at each other, raise their hair, and start growling at each other, posturing and bragging about their bones.

But not Columbia.

Usually Columbia just chewed on his bone until the meat was gone. Then he buried it and waited for the next bone. I never saw him fight or get involved in Bone Wars and I always thought him a simple—perhaps a better word would be primitive—dog, basic and very wolf-like, until one day when I was sitting in the kennel.

I had a notebook and I was sitting on the side of Cookie's roof, writing—the dogs are good company for working—when I happened to notice Columbia doing something strange.

He was sitting quietly on the outside edge of his circle, at the maximum length of his chain. With one paw he was pushing his bone—which still had a small bit of meat on it—out and away from him, toward the next circle.

Next to Columbia was a dog named Olaf. While Columbia was relatively passive, Olaf was very aggressive. Olaf always wanted to fight and he spent much time arguing over bones, females, the weather—anything and everything that caught his fancy. He was much scarred from fighting, with notched ears and lines on his muzzle, but he was a very good dog—strong and honest—and we liked him.

Being next to Columbia, Olaf had tried many times to get him to argue or bluster but Columbia always ignored him.

Until this morning.

Carefully, slowly, Columbia pushed the bone toward Olaf's circle.

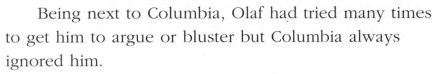

And of all the things that Olaf was—tough, strong, honest—he wasn't smart. As they say, some are smarter than others, and some are still not so smart, and then there was Olaf. It wouldn't be fair to call Olaf dumb— dogs don't measure those things like people—but even in the dog world he would not be known as a whip. Kind of a big bully who was also a bit of a doofus.

When he saw Columbia pushing the bone toward him, he began to reach for it. Straining against his chain, turning and trying to get farther and farther, he reached as far as he could with the middle toe on his right front foot, the claw going out as far as possible.

But not quite far enough. Columbia had measured it to the millimeter. He slowly pushed the bone until it was so close that Olaf's claw—with Olaf straining so hard his eyes bulged—just barely touched it.

Columbia sat back and watched Olaf straining and pushing and fighting and when this had gone on for a long time—many minutes—and Olaf was still straining for all he was worth, Columbia leaned back and laughed.

"Heh, heh, heh . . ."

Then Columbia walked away.

And I could not kill or trap any longer.

It happened almost that fast. I had seen dogs with compassion for each other and their young, and with anger and joy and hate and love but this humor went into me more than the other things.

It was so complicated.

To make the joke up in his mind, the joke with the bone and the bully, and then set out to do it, carefully and quietly, to do it, then laugh and walk away—all of it was so complicated, so complex, that it triggered a chain reaction in my mind.

If Columbia could do that, I thought, if a dog could do that, then a wolf could do that. If a wolf could do that, then a deer could do that. If a deer could do that, then a beaver, and a squirrel, and a bird, and, and, and . . .

And I quit trapping then.

It was wrong for me to kill.

But I had this problem. I had gone over some kind of line with the dogs, gone back into some primitive state of exaltation that I wanted to study. I wanted to run them and learn from them. But it seemed to be wasteful (the word *immature* also comes to mind) to just run them.

I thought I had to have a trapline to justify running the dogs, so I kept the line.

But I did not trap. I ran the country, and camped and learned from the dogs and studied where I would have trapped if I were going to trap. I took many imaginary beaver and muskrat but I did no more sets and killed no more animals. I will not kill anymore.

Yet the line existed. Somehow in my mind—and until writing this I have never told another person about this—the line still existed and when I had "trapped" in one area I would extend the line to "trap" in another, as is proper when you actually trap. Somehow the phony trapping gave me a purpose for running the dogs, and would until I began to train them for the Iditarod,[1] a dogsled race across Alaska, which I had read about in *Alaska* magazine.

But it was on one of these "trapping" runs that I got my third lesson, or awakening.

There was a point where an old logging trail went through a small, sharp-sided gully—a tiny canyon. The trail came down one wall of the gully—a drop of fifty or so feet—then scooted across a frozen stream and up the other side. It might have been a game trail that was slightly widened, or an old foot trail that had not caved in. Whatever it was, I came onto it in the middle of January. The dogs were very excited. New trails always

---

1 **Iditarod** (*eye DIHT uh rahd*)

get them tuned up and they were fairly smoking as we came to the edge of the gully.

I did not know it was there and had been letting them run, not riding the sled brake to slow them, and we virtually shot off the edge.

The dogs stayed on the trail but I immediately lost all control and went flying out into space with the sled. As I did, I kicked sideways and caught my knee on a sharp snag, felt the wood enter under the kneecap and tear it loose.

I may have screamed then.

The dogs ran out on the ice of the stream but I fell onto it. As these things often seem to happen, the disaster snowballed.

The trail crossed the stream directly at the top of a small, frozen waterfall with about a twenty-foot drop. Later I saw the beauty of it, the falling lobes of blue ice that had grown as the water froze and refroze, layering on itself. . . .

But at the time I saw nothing. I hit the ice of the stream bed like dropped meat, bounced once, then slithered over the edge of the waterfall and dropped another twenty feet onto the frozen pond below, landing on the torn and separated kneecap.

I have been injured several times running dogs—cracked ribs, a broken left leg, a broken left wrist, various parts frozen or cut or bitten while trying to stop fights—but nothing ever felt like landing on that knee.

I don't think I passed out so much as my brain simply exploded.

Again, I'm relatively certain I must have screamed or grunted, and then I wasn't aware of much for two, perhaps three minutes as I squirmed around trying to regain some part of my mind.

When things settled down to something I could control, I opened my eyes and saw that my snow pants and the jeans beneath were ripped in a jagged line for about a foot. Blood was welling out of the tear, soaking the cloth and the ice underneath the wound.

Shock and pain came in waves and I had to close my eyes several times. All of this was in minutes that seemed like hours and I realized that I was in serious trouble. Contrary to popular belief, dog teams generally do not stop and wait for a musher who falls off. They keep going, often for many miles.

Lying there on the ice I knew I could not walk. I didn't think I could stand without some kind of crutch, but I knew I couldn't walk. I was a good twenty miles from home, at least eight or nine miles from any kind of farm or dwelling.

It may as well have been ten thousand miles.

There was some self-pity creeping in, and not a little chagrin at being stupid enough to just let them run when I didn't know the country. I was trying to skootch myself up to the bank of the gully to get into a more comfortable position when I heard a sound over my head.

I looked up and there was Obeah looking over the top of the waterfall, down at me.

I couldn't at first believe it.

He whined a couple of times, moved back and forth as if he might be going to drag the team over the edge, then disappeared from view. I heard some more whining and growling, then a scrabbling sound, and was amazed to see that he had taken the team back up the side of the gully and dragged them past the waterfall to get on the gully wall just over me.

They were in a horrible tangle but he dragged them along the top until he was well below the

waterfall, where he scrambled down the bank with the team almost literally falling on him. They dragged the sled up the frozen stream bed to where I was lying.

On the scramble down the bank Obeah had taken them through a thick stand of cockleburs. Great clumps of burrs wadded between their ears and down their backs.

He pulled them up to me, concern in his eyes and making a soft whine, and I reached into his ruff and pulled his head down and hugged him and was never so happy to see anybody probably in my life. Then I felt something and looked down to see one of the other dogs—named Duberry—licking the wound in my leg.

She was not licking with the excitement that prey blood would cause, but with the gentle licking that she would use when cleaning a pup, a wound lick.

I brushed her head away, fearing infection, but she persisted. After a moment I lay back and let her clean it, still holding onto Obeah's ruff, holding onto a friend.

And later I dragged myself around and untangled them and unloaded part of the sled and crawled in and tied my leg down. We made it home that way, with me sitting in the sled: and later when my leg was sewed up and healing and I was sitting in my cabin with the leg propped up on pillows by the wood stove; later when all the pain was gone and I had all the time I needed to think of it . . . later I thought of the dogs.

How they came back to help me, perhaps to save me. I knew that somewhere in the dogs, in their humor and the way they thought, they had great, old knowledge; they had something we had lost.

And the dogs could teach me.

IN RESPONSE

Learning from Dogs

Gary Paulsen says, "The dogs could teach me." Write a brief newspaper article describing what Mr. Paulsen might learn from or about his dogs. Include examples from the story.

Looking for Insight

In a group, discuss what happened to Mr. Paulsen as he watched Columbia push the bone toward Olaf. What did Mr. Paulsen see in the dogs' actions? How did he react to what he saw? How do you think you would react if you had seen the dogs' actions?

AUTHOR AT WORK

Gary Paulsen recalls changing schools often and receiving average or below-average grades. Then a librarian gave him a library card. "When she handed me the card, she handed me the world. . . . It was as though I had been dying of thirst and the librarian had handed me a five-gallon bucket of water. I drank and drank."

Of writing Mr. Paulsen says, "I write because that's all I can do. Every time I've tried to do something else I cannot, and have to come back to writing,

though often I hate it—hate it and love it." He has managed to write over two hundred articles and nearly forty books.

Other Books by . . .

Gary Paulsen

Dogsong by Gary Paulsen, Bradbury, 1985

Tracker by Gary Paulsen, Bradbury, 1984

Library Link This story was taken from *Woodsong* by Gary Paulsen. You might enjoy reading the entire book to learn more about Paulsen's experiences with his dogs.

★ Award-winning Author

LEADER OF THE PACK

BY **BILL LITTLEFIELD**
from *Champions*
PAINTINGS BY **BERNIE FUCHS**

For Susan Butcher, it was a day like any other: brutally cold, windy, and snowing hard enough so that it was impossible to see more than a few feet in front of the heavy four-wheel vehicle her sled dogs were dragging for practice. In short, as far as she was concerned, everything was perfect.

Then suddenly Butcher's lead dog went "gee" (right) when Butcher shouted "Haw!" (left), and the four-wheeler, the dogs, and Butcher plunged off a twelve-foot cliff and into a clump of alder trees.

There was, of course, no path out. The trail Butcher and the dogs had fallen from was little traveled, and she figured it might be several days before somebody happened by. She had no saw and no ax. It was only supposed to be a little training run. With pliers, a wrench, and a broken screwdriver, she chopped at the alders. She got the dogs working together, and they pulled the four-wheeler up the hill.

411

Sometimes they'd make as little as twelve inches of progress before Butcher would have to begin hacking away with her pliers and wrench again, but five hours after they'd fallen, Butcher and her dogs were on the road back to her cabin. Butcher had learned not to leave home, even for practice, without all her tools. And she hoped her lead dog had learned that "Haw!" meant "Haw!"

On that day when she and her team fell off the trail, Susan Butcher was training herself and her dogs for the Iditarod, the annual sled dog race that covers the eleven hundred miles between Anchorage and Nome, Alaska. Over the years, Butcher's consistently excellent finishes in this most grueling of athletic events have become the stuff of legend, and some of the tales of her training runs are no less dramatic than the races themselves. In a funny way, Butcher's preparation for the Iditarod began before the race ever existed. When she finally entered it for the first time in 1978, Butcher must have felt like she'd finally discovered where she belonged.

As a little girl growing up in Cambridge, Massachusetts, Susan Butcher only knew where she did *not* belong. She hated the congestion of the busy streets, the constant noise of the traffic, and the pollution all around her. She begged her parents to move to the country, or at least to let her live in a tent in the backyard. Her best friends were the dogs she kept. In first grade she wrote an essay entitled "I Hate Cities." That was the first, last, and only sentence in the paper.

When she was finally old enough to leave home, she put Cambridge behind her in favor of Colorado. When the Rockies no longer seemed sufficiently remote,

she headed for Alaska. She finally settled in a town called Eureka, which you will not find on many maps. There she cobbled together four one-room cabins, a doorless outhouse, and 120 doghouses. Butcher's dogs have outnumbered the two-legged citizens of Eureka by as many as 150 to 13.

Eureka is a fine place to prepare for the Iditarod, since a chief feature of both is isolation. A pitcher who's gone to a full count on the batter with the bases loaded in the ninth inning of a tie game might feel lonely. A marathoner who has run beyond whatever certainty her training can provide and still has miles to go might feel that way, too. But the Iditarod exists primarily as a tribute to the conviction that everybody ought to be able to take care of himself or herself with the help of a dozen or so dogs, and there is perhaps no loneliness like the loneliness of someone lost and snow-blind in the middle of Alaska.

Brooks Range, Alaska, provides an excellent location for spring training runs.

A very fast and disciplined dog team with an experienced and fortunate musher can complete the race in a little over eleven days. Some competitors take as long as three weeks, and a lot of starters, as high as 30 or 40 percent some years, quit. Leaders and losers alike spend hours and hours alone and cold in a blasted white landscape. When their dog teams are traveling up a hill, the mushers run along behind

them or kick with first one numb foot, then the other. When the teams are traveling downhill, the mushers hold on for their lives and pray that the wind won't freeze their eyes shut or tear the sled from their hands, leaving them without even the company of their dogs. For as long as they can stand it, they swerve over frozen rivers, navigate through the stumps of burned-over forests by the insanely inadequate glow of a single small headlight, and hope they won't suddenly crash headlong into a bear or a moose or the dog team of some poor fool who has become completely confused and started racing backward on the trail.

All these obstacles appeal to Susan Butcher, who's felt since early childhood that taking heat, light, and shelter for granted was missing the point. Only when she has felt close to nature's essentials has she felt challenged. And only when she has felt challenged has she felt entirely alive.

Joe Redington invented the Iditarod in 1973. He'd always loved the wilderness, particularly the Alaskan wilderness, and he was worried that what he loved was falling into the hands of snowmobilers and settlers with satellite dishes. He scratched his head and wondered how to remind everybody of the toughness and independence that Alaska had always demanded of its residents, and he came up with a race that would require sled drivers and their dogs to brave screaming winds, blinding blizzards, hunger, lack of sleep, and a dozen other hardships that most athletes would just as soon consider only from a great distance. He called the race the Iditarod after an Alaskan ghost town bearing the name, which is an old Indian word meaning distant place.

As an incentive to take up this crazy challenge, Redington offered $50,000 to the winner of the first Iditarod, though when the race started he didn't have the money. Twenty days later, when that first race ended, Joe had the dough. He'd hustled it from various individual and corporate donors. But over the years the payoff for winning the Iditarod continued to be a little on the shaky side. Winners have sometimes had to settle for their prizes in installments, unlike all the professional baseball, basketball, and football players who are secure in their guaranteed contracts.

Joe Redington first met Susan Butcher a few years after he'd come up with the Iditarod, and right away he was sure she'd win it one day. Or he was almost sure. He proposed a sled dog trek to the summit of Alaska's Denali,[1] also known as Mount McKinley, per-

Bleak, wind-swept Mount McKinley provided one of Susan Butcher's first trials as a musher.

haps partly to test the mettle of this remarkable young woman who'd come to the far north in search of escape from cars, buildings, and too many people. Together with seven dogs and a sled, Butcher and Redington made the 20,320-foot climb through hundred-mile-an-hour winds and over 2,000-foot-deep crevasses.[2] It took them forty-four days. Nobody'd mushed that route before. Nobody's done it since. When they were finished, Redington was *absolutely* sure Susan Butcher would one day win the Iditarod.

---

1 Denali (*duh NAHL ee*)
2 crevasses (*kruh VAS uhs*)

But the extent to which Ms. Butcher fulfilled his prophesy must have surprised even Redington himself. Perhaps it shouldn't have. By the time she began to pile up first-place finishes in the Iditarod and other races in the late eighties, Susan Butcher had paid her dues. She'd learned from her limping pups to line up several friends year-round to help her knit booties for race days. Run out of booties on the trail, and the ice would cut the best team's paws to hamburger. She'd learned how to recognize a potential lead dog in a litter and how to raise all the dogs in her team to have confidence in her. And perhaps most important, she'd learned that her loyalty and attention to the needs of her canine partners would sometimes be rewarded by the special gifts the dogs had to give.

As dogs and musher cross a frozen river, a musher must rely on the dogs' sense of danger.

Eight years before she ever won an Iditarod, Butcher was mushing perhaps her best lead dog ever, Tekla, and fourteen other huskies across a frozen river in a practice run when suddenly Tekla began pulling hard to the right. Butcher kept tugging on the team to follow the trail, but Tekla wouldn't respond. Though she'd never balked before, the dog insisted on pulling the sled off the trail to the right. Butcher finally shrugged and decided to follow Tekla's lead. A moment after she'd made that decision and left the track, the whole trail itself sank into the river. "She [Tekla] had a sixth sense that saved our lives," Butcher told Sonja Steptoe of *Sports Illustrated* years later. "That day I

learned that the wilderness is their domain. The dogs know more about it than I do, and I'm better off trusting their instincts."

Of course instinct is only part of it. Courage, stamina, and a cool head help, too. In 1985, with a superb team and high expectations, Susan Butcher seemed to be on her way to winning the Iditarod for the first time. But she ran into a problem no measure of preparation or instinct could have forestalled. Veering around a sharp bend in the trail one night, she was startled to find in the beam of her headlight a full-grown female moose. The dog team hit the animal before Butcher knew the moose was there. By the time Butcher could figure out what had happened, the moose was hopelessly entangled in the harnesses that connected the dogs. In the carnage that followed, two of Butcher's dogs were kicked to death and several others were badly injured. While Butcher fought to free the remaining dogs from their harnesses, the moose stomped on her shoulder and might have killed her, too, if another musher hadn't arrived on the scene and shot the moose. Butcher and her team limped to the next checkpoint and resigned from that Iditarod in the low point of her racing career.

And then, beginning in 1986, the high points began coming in quick succession. Between 1986 and 1990, she won the Iditarod four times. The hottest selling T-shirt in the state bore the legend "Alaska: Where Men Are Men and Women Win the Iditarod." After Butcher's third win in a row in 1988, Joe Redington laughed and told a reporter, "It's getting pretty damn hard for a man to win anything anymore. Maybe we should start a race especially for them."

It has been suggested that the formula for winning the Iditarod involves having good dogs, a good musher, and good luck—in about equal measure. The good musher is the one who can smile into the wrath of an unexpected hundred-mile-per-hour wind, but he or she better make sure the smile is behind several layers of ski mask, because when that wind joins below-zero temperatures, a smile will freeze on the lips for hours, and maybe forever. Susan Butcher proved she could brave the most vicious weather, but by the time she started winning the Iditarod, she'd learned to prepare herself and her dogs so well that all but the most hideous storms seemed routine. She'd also

Sometimes wind speeds and subzero temperatures leave a musher's dogs covered in ice.

learned that by working closely with her dogs every day from the hour they were born, she could build a level of trust and loyalty that her competitors could only envy. Of course, this relationship demanded a good deal from Butcher, too. In 1991, she passed up the chance to win her fifth Iditarod when she decided that a blizzard raging over the last hundred miles of the course would unreasonably endanger her team. She prolonged a rest stop, waiting for the weather to improve, and finished second that year.

Even when the blizzards hold off and the moose stay out of the way, the Iditarod demands a tremendous amount from a musher. The rules require one mandatory rest period of twenty-four hours during the race, and once having met that requirement, no serious competitor stops for more than four hours at a

time. Nearly all of the four hours of each stop are taken up by feeding the dogs, melting snow so they'll have water, checking their paws for cuts or cracks, mending the harnesses, and maybe catching something to eat—hot chocolate if you're fortunate enough to be stopping at a checkpoint where somebody's cooking, melted snow if you're not.

That doesn't leave much time for sleep, so the Iditarod's exhausted competitors have been known to hallucinate on the trail. In a book entitled *Woodsong,* a musher named Gary Paulsen wrote of a fellow who appeared on his sled wearing horn-rimmed glasses, clutching a stack of important-looking papers. "He is the most boring human being I have ever met," Paulsen says in his diary-like account. "He speaks in a low voice about federal educational grants and he goes on and on until at last I yell at him to shut up. The dogs stop and look back at me and of course I am alone."

Although there is little time to rest during a race, Ms. Butcher does make time to relax with her dogs.

Though Susan Butcher also might well be susceptible to hallucinations, her dogs probably know her too well to be surprised by anything she could say or do. Certainly she knows them well enough to astonish her friends. "Folks ask how I can call one hundred and fifty of them by name," she says, "but it's natural. They're like children. If you had one hundred and fifty kids, you'd know all their names, wouldn't you?"

Becoming the world's most successful musher and one of the very few sled dog drivers capable of making a living at the sport has never turned Susan Butcher's head, though it has gone some way toward fulfilling her dream. "I never got into this to make a lot of money," she told an interviewer before winning her fourth Iditarod, in 1990. "But to live just the way you want, to do what you love to do. . . . How could you have any complaints?"

Still, success at the Iditarod *has* changed Susan Butcher, if only a little. Before she became a celebrity, at least by Alaskan standards, she used to go off and live alone for six months or so. No people, no running water, no nothing. Now, in deference to the fact that people want to contact her and because raising and training 150 dogs takes the sort of money only sponsors can provide, she has a phone in her cabin. She has a husband there, too. His name is David

Monson, and as a matter of fact the phone was probably his idea. He serves as Susan Butcher's business manager, and he probably got pretty tired of hitching up the dogs and mushing more than twenty miles every time he had to make a call.

Which is not to suggest that David Monson is exactly a softy. He got to know his future wife when they were both unknown mushers competing in the 1981 Iditarod. Monson was struggling to climb a hill and lost control of his sled, which wound up off the trail in the brush. It was the same stretch of brush Susan Butcher had already fallen into a few minutes earlier, and while they were both working to straighten out their dog teams, a third musher also skidded off the trail and landed on them. Monson remembers it as chaos: forty-five dogs and three mushers, including a very angry and competitive woman and one guy (Monson) who didn't really

have much idea what he was up to. When they all finally got back on the trail, Butcher told Monson he'd better rest his dog team, and that was the last he saw of her in the race. If it wasn't love at first sight, it was close enough for the two mushers, now partners as well as competitors.

Not all the others who tackle the Iditarod have been as comfortable with Susan Butcher's triumphs in the race as David Monson has been. Rick Swenson,

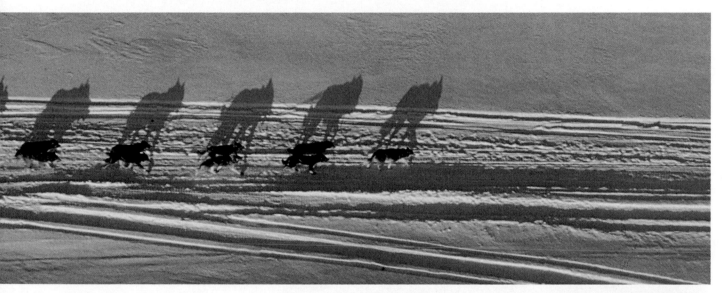

Mushers maintain that the peace and serenity of the environment makes the work and hardship of the Iditarod worthwhile.

the only person to have won the race as often as Butcher has, tried for some years to get the Iditarod's organizers to adopt a handicapping system that would, in effect, penalize Butcher and other women racers for weighing less than the men who mush against them. When that didn't work, Swenson took to intimating that Butcher won only because she had a lead dog of supernatural strength and endurance, an unintentional compliment, since Butcher had raised and trained the dog. Butcher herself tends to shrug off the bitterness of the men who resent a woman's success in a sport they'd like to claim as their own. "Yes, I am a woman," she told writer Carolyn Coman in an

interview for the book *Body and Soul.* "Yes, it is a victory for me to win the Iditarod. But it isn't amazing that I, a woman, did it. I did it because I am capable, and women are capable."

Being capable may never before have involved such an effort. Butcher has said on several occasions that training for the Iditarod—which involves raising, feeding, running, and training her dogs as well as keeping herself in shape—is an eleven-month proposition. Small wonder that sometimes she thinks about turning her attention exclusively to some of Alaska's shorter races—the three-, four-, or five-hundred-mile jaunts. She already knows these races well. She holds the records in most of them, just as she does for the Iditarod. So easing up a little is a pleasant possibility that occupies Susan Butcher sometimes when she thinks about a post-Iditarod future.

Susan Butcher delights in the isolation of her home in Eureka, Alaska.

Unhappily, there's an unpleasant possibility that concerns her, too. She has adjusted to the modern improvements David Monson has made in their cabin, but other adjustments won't come so easily to the woman who hated the noise and pollution and hustle of Cambridge when she was a little girl. The authorities have begun to improve the roads up Susan Butcher's way, and Butcher has watched "progress" suspiciously. "In ten years we may have ten or fifteen neighbors," she was overheard to say. "If that happens, we'll be gone."

IN RESPONSE

Illustrate an Article

Imagine you are the artist for a magazine article about the challenges Susan Butcher faces or has overcome in racing the Iditarod. There is space for four illustrations. Tell what you would include in each illustration and draw one as a sample.

Dog Talk

With a partner, play the roles of Susan Butcher and Gary Paulsen ("Kinship"). Both of you are guests on a radio talk show called *Dog Talk*. Tell how each of you feels about surviving in the rugged north, and how you rely on your dogs for survival. Be sure to use examples from the story to keep your audience interested.

AUTHOR AT WORK

Bill Littlefield, well-known radio sports commentator and program host, has been writing about sports for almost twenty years. He admires the sports heroes he writes about and believes that from them "we can learn something about finding a passion and working hard and believing in ourselves."

★ **Award-winning Author**

Another Book About . . .

Survival in Alaska

Race Across Alaska by Libby Riddles and Tim Jones, Stackpole Books, 1988

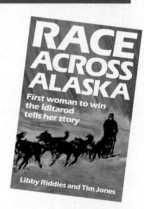

Library Link This story was taken from *Champions* by Bill Littlefield. You might enjoy reading Mr. Littlefield's other profiles of other people who excel in sports.

SGT. DOBETTER'S DEEP FREEZE

by Bill Van Horn

Characters

FAT JACQUES LASPRATT,
notorious outlaw

TWO MOUNTIES

BUCK, *a dog*

SGT. RICHARD DOBETTER

COL. HENRY WELLINGTON

DEBORAH WELLINGTON,
his wife

LOUELLA LOVEJOY,
Richard's fiancée

TIME: *Wintry day, 1900.*

SETTING: *Barren wasteland of the frozen north. Bare stage, with a few "snow patches" and scrubby pine tree.*

AT RISE: **FAT JACQUES LASPRATT** *backs on right, holding rifle on* **MOUNTIES,** *who also walk in backwards.*

JACQUES: Halt! (**MOUNTIES** *halt, face audience and shiver.*)

1ST MOUNTIE: Brrr! It's freezing!

2ND MOUNTIE: It must be 40 below.

JACQUES: Stop complaining and look at the bright side.

1ST MOUNTIE: Bright side? We're your prisoners!

2ND MOUNTIE: We're twenty miles from the North Pole!

1ST MOUNTIE: Knee deep in snow!

2ND MOUNTIE: And why must we continually walk backwards?

1ST MOUNTIE: Indeed. I've got a stiff neck.

JACQUES: Ha-ha! Walking backwards will fool Colonel Wellington when he comes looking for you.

1ST MOUNTIE: Colonel Wellington is too busy to come looking for us.

2ND MOUNTIE: Yes. He's training for the annual cross-country ski race.

1ST MOUNTIE: But Sgt. Dobetter will find us. And he will capture you, Fat Jacques LaSpratt. Dobetter always gets his man.

JACQUES: Not this time! Dobetter will be fooled, too. He will think that we have gone this way (*Points right*), but we will have gone the other way. (*Points left*) Ha ha! (**1ST MOUNTIE** *is drawing arrow in snow with foot*) Hey! What are you doing?

1ST MOUNTIE: Merely doodling in the snow. I always doodle when I'm nervous.

JACQUES: You should be nervous. If your Colonel Wellington does not pay me two million dollars, he will never see you Mounties again.

2ND MOUNTIE: Sgt. Dobetter will save us! He will, he will!

MOUNTIES (*Cheering*): Dobetter, Dobetter, he's our man! If he can't do it, nobody can!

JACQUES: Bah! Now, forward—I mean, backward, march! (*He and* **MOUNTIES** *march off left, backwards. After short pause,* **DOBETTER** *and* **BUCK** *enter right.* **BUCK** *is sniffling and sneezing.*)

DOBETTER: Poor Buck. (*Pats him on head*) It must be extremely difficult to pick up the scent when you have a stuffy nose. (**BUCK** *nods, blows nose.*) But we must find the missing Mounties and their captor, Fat Jacques. (**BUCK** *yelps, points.*) Aha! Footprints! And they go in that direction. (*Points right.* **BUCK** *yelps and points again.*)

427

What's this? An arrow in the snow. And it points that way! (*Points left*) Which way did they go? Left or right? Right or left? (*He and* **BUCK** *scratch their heads.*) Oh, I must rest. (*Sighs*) I'll just sit down on this old snow-covered railroad track for a moment. (*Sits*) Ah . . . it feels good to rest. (*After a pause; tries to wiggle*) Great Scott! I'm frozen to the rail! I can't move! Buck! (**BUCK** *prances over to him.*) Go to the outpost and bring back Louella. She's the only one there. The Mounties have been kidnapped, and the colonel is training for the ski race. Hurry, Buck! Go get Louella! (**BUCK** *yelps, turns a few circles, and dashes off right, barking.*) Oh, I'm freezing. Soon I shall be just another insignificant ice cube in the great Arctic Freezer. Help! Help! (*Stagehands throw "snowflakes" on stage.*) Oh, no. It's beginning to snow! I shall be buried alive! (*Stagehands lay white sheets on stage, drape sheet or plastic over* **DOBETTER** *as "ice," leaving his face uncovered, then exit.*) Help! I'm frozen stiff, and covered with snow. Alas, I shall never be found. (*Voices are heard off right.*) What's that? (*Turns head*) It's Colonel Wellington and his wife! Help! Help! (*Coughs*) Oh, no. I'm losing my voice. My vocal cords are freezing. I can't talk. (*Feebly*) Help! (*Voice fades.*) Help. Help . . . (*Falls silent, mouthing calls for help.* **COL. HENRY WELLINGTON** *and* **DEBORAH WELLINGTON** *enter on skis, right. She is full of energy; he is exhausted.*)

DEBORAH: Come along, Henry, come along. (*Breathes deeply*) Ah, this Arctic air is so invigorating, isn't it?

HENRY (*Panting*): Yes, dear.

DEBORAH: Why, Henry, you aren't fatigued, are you?

HENRY: Definitely not, Deborah. (*Panting*) But for your sake I do think we should take a brief rest. (*Leans on ski poles*)

DEBORAH: How thoughtful of you, dear. But for your sake I think we must push on.

HENRY (*Pained*): My sake?

DEBORAH: Have you forgotten? The purpose of today's outing is to get you into shape for next week's 40-mile cross-country ski race.

HENRY: Forty miles? (*Groans*)

DEBORAH: Yes. And I'm so proud of you for entering.

HENRY: It wasn't my idea, Deborah. Remember, you submitted my name when I wasn't looking.

DEBORAH: And you'll be such an inspiration to your men. (*He collapses on his poles, then falls asleep.*) You, Henry Wellington, are such a heroic role model. (*She goes to* **DOBETTER.** **HENRY** *snores.*) My, such a lovely snowman. Who could have created such a delightful snow sculpture out here in the frozen wilderness? (*Looks closely*) Oh, my goodness! Henry. Henry! (**HENRY** *awakens with a start.*) This snowman looks like Sgt. Dobetter. A frozen image of him.

HENRY: Impossible. Dobetter is hot on the trail of the missing Mounties.

DEBORAH: Maybe he has cold feet.

HENRY: Cold feet? Never! Dobetter won't rest until he finds his men. He's no stick in the ice. (*Moves to* **DOBETTER**) I say . . . (*Laughs*) what a funny fellow indeed. He could do with a bit of a face lift. Let me see. Larger ears, perhaps. (*Pulls at* **DOBETTER'S** *ears.* **DOBETTER** *mouths a scream.*) Jolly good fun! Would you like a turn, Deborah?

DEBORAH: Oh, why not? I think I shall tweak his nose a bit. (*Pulls at* **DOBETTER'S** *nose*) Henry! His nose is wiggling!

He's trying to communicate with us. Look, three short wiggles, three long wiggles, three short ones.

HENRY: Impossible.

DEBORAH: I've got it! Three dots, three dashes, three dots. His nose is sending out Morse code. He's spelled out S.O.S. What does that mean? It sounds somewhat familiar.

HENRY: Yes. Quite. I've got it! S.O.S. Save our snowman!

DEBORAH (*Puzzled*): Save our snowman?

HENRY: Yes. (*Pats* **DOBETTER's** *head*) Well, old fellow, we shall heed your request, and let you stand here all winter long.

DEBORAH: Henry! Now his nose is moving frantically.

HENRY: Merely a loose connection. His nose is probably connected to batteries inside his body. A cleverly contrived apparatus to enhance the lifelike qualities of the snowman.

DEBORAH: How reassuring. I thought it was almost human. Well, on we go. Only ten more miles. (*Starts off right*)

HENRY (*Painfully*): Ten more miles.

DEBORAH: Perhaps I could take your place in the race.

HENRY: Never! You're too delicate. (*She moves off.*) I say, wait for me. (*Struggles off*)

DEBORAH: Remember your favorite bedtime story, dear.

HENRY: I think I can, I think I can, I think I can. (*Exits right.* **MOUNTIES** *enter left, carrying saw and ax.* **JACQUES** *follows, carrying large bucket and rifle.*)

1ST MOUNTIE: Oh, if only Dobetter were here!

JACQUES: Stop complaining and get to work!

2ND MOUNTIE: What do you want us to do?

JACQUES: Find the nearest glacier and chip off some ice. And I want it in small pieces.

1ST MOUNTIE: Small pieces of ice? Why?

JACQUES: We're going to make ice cream.

2ND MOUNTIE: Ice cream?

1ST MOUNTIE: But it's forty below!

JACQUES: Stop complaining, or I'll feed you to the fish! Hurry up and chop!

2ND MOUNTIE: But the nearest glacier is two miles away.

JACQUES (*Roaring*): Move it! (**MOUNTIES** *cross to center.*)

2ND MOUNTIE: Look! What luck! (*Points to* **DOBETTER**) Right out here in the middle of the snow field. A giant ice cube!

1ST MOUNTIE: How did it get here?

2ND MOUNTIE: Who cares? Let's chip it up.

JACQUES: Hurry! (**MOUNTIES** *approach* **DOBETTER**.)

2ND MOUNTIE (*Touching* **DOBETTER**): Uh-oh. This ice is harder than rock. We'll have to break it up before we can chip it. (**DOBETTER** *mouths a silent "Help!"*) You saw, I'll chop. (*He raises ax.* **1ST MOUNTIE** *is about to saw.* **DOBETTER** *screws up his face.*) Hold it! This isn't an ice cube. It's a frozen snowman.

JACQUES: Hurry up, or you'll be sorry!

2ND MOUNTIE: Yes, sir. Here we go! (**MOUNTIES** *get ready to saw and chop.* **DOBETTER** *screws up face.*) Wait!

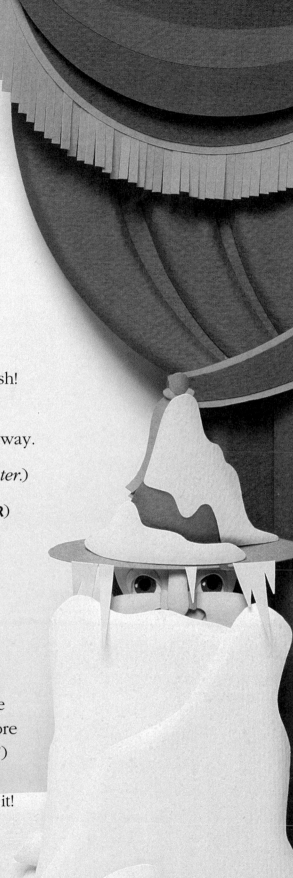

1ST MOUNTIE: Now what?

2ND MOUNTIE: I can't do it. The snowman looks too lifelike.

1ST MOUNTIE: Hm. You're right. And somewhat familiar. How strange.

2ND MOUNTIE: If Dobetter were here, he'd solve this mystery. He'd examine it closely, touch it, shake it, and find out all about it.

JACQUES: So . . . Dobetter would touch and shake this pillar of ice?

1ST MOUNTIE: Oh, yes. And he'd kick it and poke it.

2ND MOUNTIE: Dobetter is a very curious person.

JACQUES: Ha ha. And it was curiosity that killed the cat! Good. So much for your Sgt. Dobetter. (*Takes small box from pocket, fiddles with it and places it behind* **DOBETTER**)

1ST MOUNTIE: What are you doing?

JACQUES: I have booby-trapped the snowman. The slightest vibration will set off the bomb and blow up the snowman and anyone who touches it. Since Dobetter is coming after us, he will see the snowman, examine it, touch it, and poof! (*Laughs evilly*) Now, let's hurry back to my hideout where we shall await the big explosion! (*Pushes* **MOUNTIES** *off left.* **LOUELLA** *enters right, pulling* **BUCK** *on sled.* **BUCK** *holds large sack.*)

LOUELLA: Is this the place, Buck? (**BUCK** *yelps and points at* **DOBETTER.**) But there's nothing here except this huge iceberg. Oh, Richard, Richard, where are you? It is I, Louella Lovejoy, your long lost lady love. Where are you? Where? (*Sobs uncontrollably*)

DOBETTER: I'm here, Louella.

LOUELLA: Richard? Richard! Where are you? (*Looks around wildly*)

DOBETTER: Under this snowdrift, frozen solid. I cannot move, but I can talk, thanks to your warm tears that melted my voice box. Go away! Go away!

LOUELLA: Go away? Go away! After I have trudged through wind and snow these hundreds of miles to find you? How can you be so cold and so cruel? (*Weeps again*) Perhaps a good shaking will bring you back to your senses! (*Goes to shake him*)

DOBETTER: Shake me! Oh, no!
(**LOUELLA** *picks up booby trap.*)

LOUELLA: Why, what is this?

DOBETTER: A booby trap! Put it down! Put it down, carefully.

LOUELLA: No need to worry, love. My tears have frozen over the trigger mechanism and rendered it quite harmless. No need to fret.

DOBETTER: Get rid of it, Louella!

LOUELLA: Whatever you say, Richard. (*Throws box off-stage. There is a loud explosion. Lights blink.*) Oh, dear. My warm hands must have melted the ice on the trigger. But no matter. We are safe now.

DOBETTER: But not for long!

LOUELLA: What makes you say that? (*Train whistle is heard offstage.*)

DOBETTER: That! A train is coming and I'm frozen to the tracks! I shall be crushed. I shall be smashed!

LOUELLA: I'll be dashed if you'll be smashed! (*Takes paper, crayon from* **BUCK'S** *sack, scribbles quickly. Train noises become louder.*)

DOBETTER: You'd better write it in shorthand! Here comes the train! (*Cardboard cutout of train is pushed on left. As it is about to hit* **DOBETTER, LOUELLA** *hangs sign around his neck. Train halts, backs off.*) Saved! What does the sign say?

LOUELLA: "This is a National Landmark." (*Removes sign*) No one will destroy a national landmark.

DOBETTER: How clever of you. Thank you. (*Rises and sheds sheets*)

LOUELLA: How wonderful! You have softened up.

DOBETTER: Yes. Your salty tears thawed out my vocal cords, your warm words melted my prison of ice, and the hot ashes from the train heated up my thermal underwear.

LOUELLA (*Feeling his forehead*): But you're still a bit chilly, Richard.

DOBETTER: Yes, I am. (*Shivers violently and freezes*)

LOUELLA: Richard? Oh, no, he's frozen again. Evidently he warmed up too quickly and his perspiration caused him to chill down. What can I do? (*Takes thermos from sack*) This hot soup may help thaw him out. (*Feeds him soup, which is composed of small ice cubes. Ice cubes tumble from his mouth.*) Oh! His words have frozen and tumble out as frozen cubes. Luckily I fed him alphabet soup, for thus I can decipher the meaning of his frozen words. Let me see. (*Pretends to rearrange cubes*) Ah! I have it. TEALINIMENT. (*Frowns*) Tealiniment? (*Suddenly*) Oh! Tea and liniment! Of course. Tea for the inside and liniment for the outside. (*Takes items from sack*) Here's the liniment. (*Rubs liniment on* **DOBETTER**. *He begins to move slowly.*) Good. He's thawing on the outside. Now a drink of hot tea from this tin cup. (*Puts cup to his mouth. His tongue "freezes" to cup.*) Oh, dear, his tongue has frozen to the tin! (**DOBETTER** *shrieks, slowly peels cup away from tongue.*) Are you all right, Richard?

DOBETTER (*Fanning tongue*): Yes, thanks to you, Louella. (**MOUNTIES** *enter.*) Why, look! It's the Mounties! How did you ever escape?

1ST MOUNTIE: It was easy. We sang a lullabye and he fell asleep.

2ND MOUNTIE: But we must get away before he wakes up!

DOBETTER: Then, hurry! Onto the sled before he catches you! (**MOUNTIES** *pile onto sled, next to* **BUCK**.) Louella, I will meet you back at the outpost as soon as I have captured Fat Jacques. (*Takes her hands*) Until then, farewell.

LOUELLA: Farewell, Richard. Be careful. And please don't sit on any more railroad tracks. (*Waves good-bye as* **DOBETTER** *exits left*)

2ND MOUNTIE: Time to move out.

1ST MOUNTIE: Right. Let's go.

LOUELLA: But who is going to pull the sled?

2ND MOUNTIE: Guess who? (*Hands her the rope*)

LOUELLA (*Starting to pull sled off*): It is as they say. Men work from dawn to sun, but woman's work is never done. (*Sighs heavily, exits pulling sled as curtain closes*)

THE END

Nature's Power

Nature inspires artists in different ways. Some artists choose to portray the beauty of nature. Others choose to explore its power.

What do the colors in this painting tell you about the storm? How would you describe this painting?

Painting by Joseph Mallord William Turner (English),
Valley of Aosta—Snowstorm, Avalanche and Thunderstorm, 1836–1837

Painting by Richard
Bosman (United States),
The Rescue, 1983

What details of the paintings on this page give you a
clue to what is happening? Look carefully at the
people's faces. What do their expressions tell you
about their feelings?

Painting by Francisco
Goya (Spanish), *La
Nevada (The Snow
Storm),* 1786–1787

THE GRANDFATHER TREE

MORNING GIRL
MICHAEL DORRIS

from *Morning Girl*
by Michael Dorris

This story begins about five hundred years ago, as a hurricane rages through the Bahama Islands, home of the Taino people. Star Boy, swept away by the wind and water, tells of his experiences during the storm. Morning Girl, his sister, tells what happened after the storm.

STAR BOY

The first thing the wind moved was my blood. It ran faster in my arms and legs, pushing against the skin, warning me. I looked east, where the sky was barely turning pink, and instead of being pale, the clouds were the color of dark boulders scattered on a wet beach.

The rain, when it came, didn't fall in the proper way but rushed to the west, fast as a flock of sparrows chasing a hungry gull from their nests. Soon the fronds of the palms and the grasses in the marshy place behind our house were straining in that same direction.

The land tried to flatten itself, to become so smooth that the storm could slide across it quickly without hooking on to anything.

I had been outside studying the sky from our cassava patch, had watched the stars drown one by one, and had felt the pull of the storm's tow myself. Our house, just across the short grass from where I lay, leaned and groaned, begging to go. In a flash of lightning, I saw my father standing in the doorway. His hair was flying in all directions at once. Even his eyes seemed to stretch, and there was a worry on his face I had only seen there once before—the time when the bad visitors, their bodies painted white for death, were spotted in three big rafts to the south of the nearest island.

My father called to my mother, and she appeared beside him, holding to his waist with both arms. Next to her, Morning Girl was excited.

"Star Boy," my mother shouted over the wind. She turned her head from side to side, shielding her eyes from the rain with her hand, searching for where I might have gone.

"I'm here," I cried, but my words fled west, too, and never reached her, so I got up and started to cross the clearing to our house. Then I was being pushed, shoved, a giant fist at my back and beneath my knees, and all I could hear was the wail of a hill of noise, the whipping leaves. Sand stung my face, but by squinting I could see Morning Girl pointing in my direction. My father got down on his hands and knees and crawled toward where I was headed, dragging himself forward by reaching first for a stump, then for a rock. Suddenly I was back on the ground, trying to grab on to something myself, something that didn't want to go, but no sooner would my fingers close around a plant than it would break off at the stem, no sooner would my heels find a root than I would be skidded forward, skipping like a flat rock thrown on a pond. The rain was before me and behind me and all around me, a thick crashing wave, and all I knew was water and movement that slammed and hissed and screamed my name.

But no, it was my father's voice, changed by his worry, made louder than I had ever heard it. I couldn't catch all the words, just some, like "find" and "come" and "help," and then a strange calmness poured over my thoughts, and I was watching what was happening to me as if it were happening to someone else. I saw my wet arms, my twisting legs. I saw the roof of our house, the yellow fronds soaked a dark tan, become a

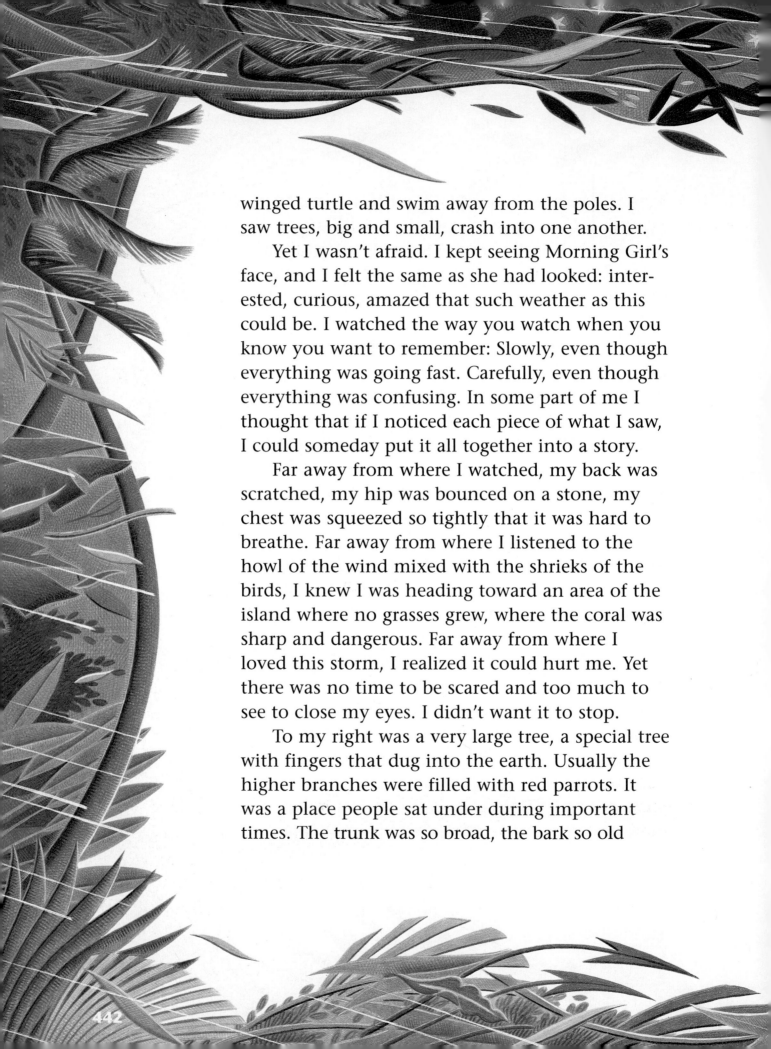

winged turtle and swim away from the poles. I
saw trees, big and small, crash into one another.

Yet I wasn't afraid. I kept seeing Morning Girl's
face, and I felt the same as she had looked: interested, curious, amazed that such weather as this
could be. I watched the way you watch when you
know you want to remember: Slowly, even though
everything was going fast. Carefully, even though
everything was confusing. In some part of me I
thought that if I noticed each piece of what I saw,
I could someday put it all together into a story.

Far away from where I watched, my back was
scratched, my hip was bounced on a stone, my
chest was squeezed so tightly that it was hard to
breathe. Far away from where I listened to the
howl of the wind mixed with the shrieks of the
birds, I knew I was heading toward an area of the
island where no grasses grew, where the coral was
sharp and dangerous. Far away from where I
loved this storm, I realized it could hurt me. Yet
there was no time to be scared and too much to
see to close my eyes. I didn't want it to stop.

To my right was a very large tree, a special tree
with fingers that dug into the earth. Usually the
higher branches were filled with red parrots. It
was a place people sat under during important
times. The trunk was so broad, the bark so old

and carved, that you could find in its designs the faces of all the people who have ever died, if you needed to talk to them once more. We went there to look for the new sister when she didn't come home, and there she was, not far from my grandfather.

Even in the dim gray light, even with the thunder in my ears, even when I lost the sense to know up from down, I could see that I was coming closer and closer to that tree. Then it rose tall before me, and—clear as I knew that Mother was still calling my name, true as I knew that Father was still making his way to the place I had been, sure as I knew that Morning Girl would want to hear all that had happened to me in the storm and be jealous that it had happened to me and not to her—I knew it was the one tree that would surely remain tomorrow in the same spot it had been today.

I couldn't exactly move my body where I wanted it to go, and I couldn't exactly stop it either, but by throwing my shoulders to one side I managed to shift my course a little bit. So I did it again. And again. And the fourth time, my hand hit against one of the large tree's fingers, I grasped it and held on. A short time later the wind retreated, as if it were sucking in a large

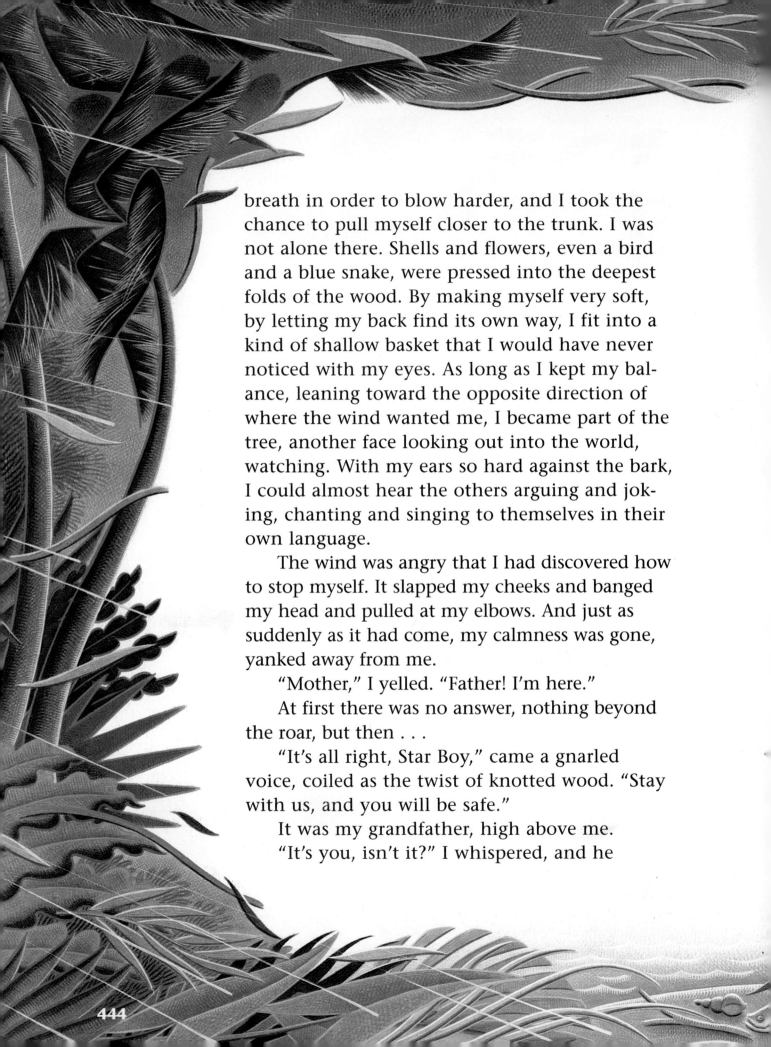

breath in order to blow harder, and I took the chance to pull myself closer to the trunk. I was not alone there. Shells and flowers, even a bird and a blue snake, were pressed into the deepest folds of the wood. By making myself very soft, by letting my back find its own way, I fit into a kind of shallow basket that I would have never noticed with my eyes. As long as I kept my balance, leaning toward the opposite direction of where the wind wanted me, I became part of the tree, another face looking out into the world, watching. With my ears so hard against the bark, I could almost hear the others arguing and joking, chanting and singing to themselves in their own language.

The wind was angry that I had discovered how to stop myself. It slapped my cheeks and banged my head and pulled at my elbows. And just as suddenly as it had come, my calmness was gone, yanked away from me.

"Mother," I yelled. "Father! I'm here."

At first there was no answer, nothing beyond the roar, but then . . .

"It's all right, Star Boy," came a gnarled voice, coiled as the twist of knotted wood. "Stay with us, and you will be safe."

It was my grandfather, high above me.

"It's you, isn't it?" I whispered, and he

laughed the way I remembered, when he used to hold me against his warm skin and tell me stories about the sort of man I would grow up to be.

"I'll visit with you as long as this storm lasts," he said. "You must sit very still, and you must never tell anyone that I was here or what I say. It will be a secret between us."

"At least one person," I begged him.

"You always argue, Star Boy," he sighed. "All right. Only Morning Girl, but she won't believe you."

Then we talked and talked and talked.

Later, when the rain once again began to seek the ground, when the palm fronds still attached to trees could once again return to their usual shapes, when I caught sight of my mother running toward me through the tangle of broken branches and heard my father promising her that they would find me soon, I thanked my grandfather and told him good-bye.

MORNING GIRL

No one had died. The storm had damaged nothing that could not be built again. Who needed a roof when the sun shone so friendly or when the stars glowed overhead, watching our sleep? The wind had cleared a new path across the island, wide and open, and all

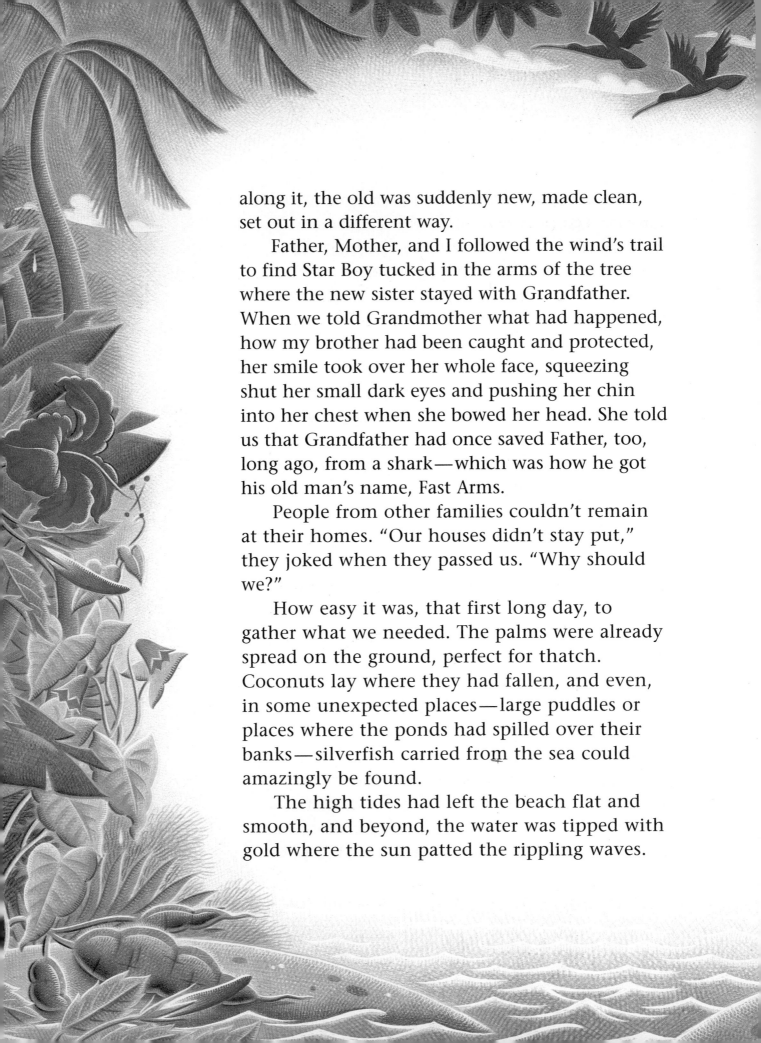

along it, the old was suddenly new, made clean, set out in a different way.

Father, Mother, and I followed the wind's trail to find Star Boy tucked in the arms of the tree where the new sister stayed with Grandfather. When we told Grandmother what had happened, how my brother had been caught and protected, her smile took over her whole face, squeezing shut her small dark eyes and pushing her chin into her chest when she bowed her head. She told us that Grandfather had once saved Father, too, long ago, from a shark—which was how he got his old man's name, Fast Arms.

People from other families couldn't remain at their homes. "Our houses didn't stay put," they joked when they passed us. "Why should we?"

How easy it was, that first long day, to gather what we needed. The palms were already spread on the ground, perfect for thatch. Coconuts lay where they had fallen, and even, in some unexpected places—large puddles or places where the ponds had spilled over their banks—silverfish carried from the sea could amazingly be found.

The high tides had left the beach flat and smooth, and beyond, the water was tipped with gold where the sun patted the rippling waves.

Of course, there was much work to be done . . . but not on the first day, Father decided, and not on the second, either. Instead, he said this was a chance to be happy together, to dance and make music on hollow logs, to watch ball games, to sing good-bye to the wind, and to share the food that had been presented to us as its apology. It was the time for each person to tell a story, to act it out while the rest of us held our heads in fear or covered our mouths when the laughter grew too strong to contain.

Mother found dry sticks and poured fire from her pot, then roasted some sweet potatoes in a pit she dug in the ground. Star Boy and I searched among the trees, looking under branches and drooping leaves to find fruit that had not burst. I tried not to count or notice that I found three more than he did. After all, my arms were longer, and, anyway, I knew his story would be better than mine.

A large crowd of grandparents, adults, children, and babies had already assembled near The Digging Stick, the place where the land rocks curve into the ocean. I was shy at first because of seeing so many people at once—that almost never happened except when there was a marriage or when someone died. Another thing was different, too, though for a while I couldn't

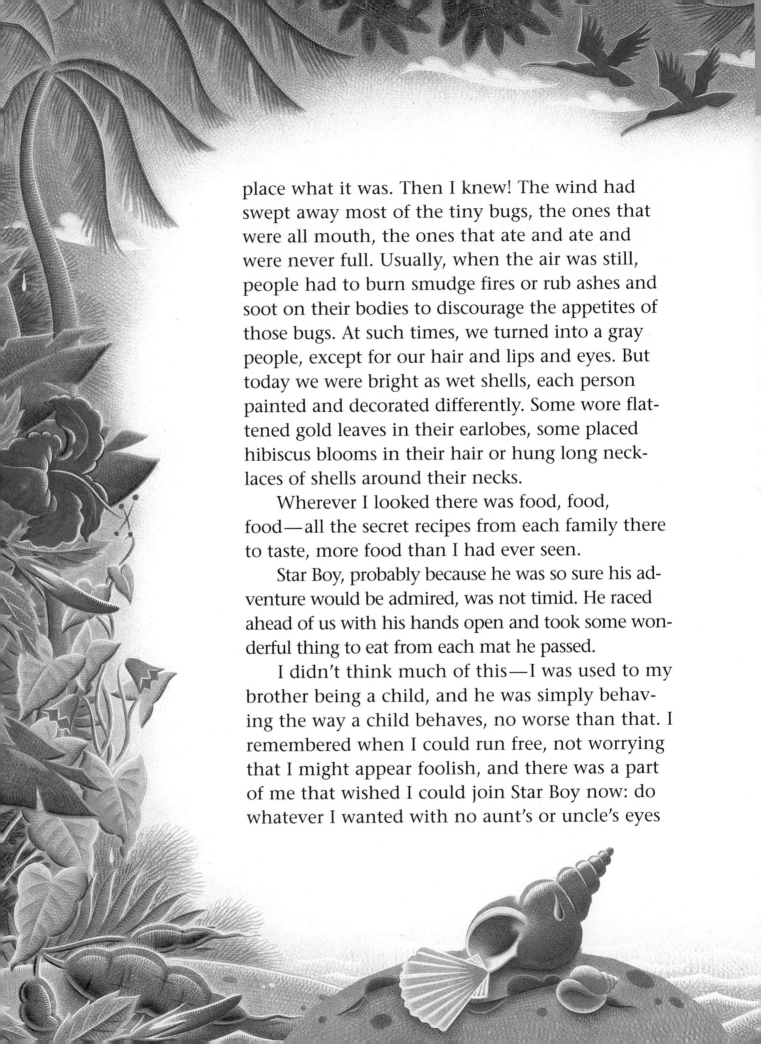

place what it was. Then I knew! The wind had swept away most of the tiny bugs, the ones that were all mouth, the ones that ate and ate and were never full. Usually, when the air was still, people had to burn smudge fires or rub ashes and soot on their bodies to discourage the appetites of those bugs. At such times, we turned into a gray people, except for our hair and lips and eyes. But today we were bright as wet shells, each person painted and decorated differently. Some wore flattened gold leaves in their earlobes, some placed hibiscus blooms in their hair or hung long necklaces of shells around their necks.

Wherever I looked there was food, food, food—all the secret recipes from each family there to taste, more food than I had ever seen.

Star Boy, probably because he was so sure his adventure would be admired, was not timid. He raced ahead of us with his hands open and took some wonderful thing to eat from each mat he passed.

I didn't think much of this—I was used to my brother being a child, and he was simply behaving the way a child behaves, no worse than that. I remembered when I could run free, not worrying that I might appear foolish, and there was a part of me that wished I could join Star Boy now: do whatever I wanted with no aunt's or uncle's eyes to correct me or to embarrass Mother by staring at me too hard. I had received those looks only once, and that had been too much, more than enough to remind me that though I had not yet become a woman, I was no longer a child.

And then, as I watched, I realized that Star Boy was not a child anymore, either, that he had become too old for such play in public, and I saw all around him those terrible looks, pointed at him.

Now he'll learn, I thought, with more rightness than kindness.

But Star Boy didn't notice. His eyes were full of the surprise of not blowing away, too proud, too excited, too—

A big boy, Never Cry, spoke the word I was thinking:

"Hungry!" Never Cry called to my brother. "You're well named."

A few people laughed, and didn't even cover their mouths. Father touched Mother's arm just above her elbow. Her lips pressed together, and I knew how she felt: how could Star Boy be wrong on so fine a day?

"I'm not Hungry any more," my brother told Never Cry, loud enough for all to hear. He was so pleased with himself, that he hadn't understood. "I'm Star Boy now, because—"

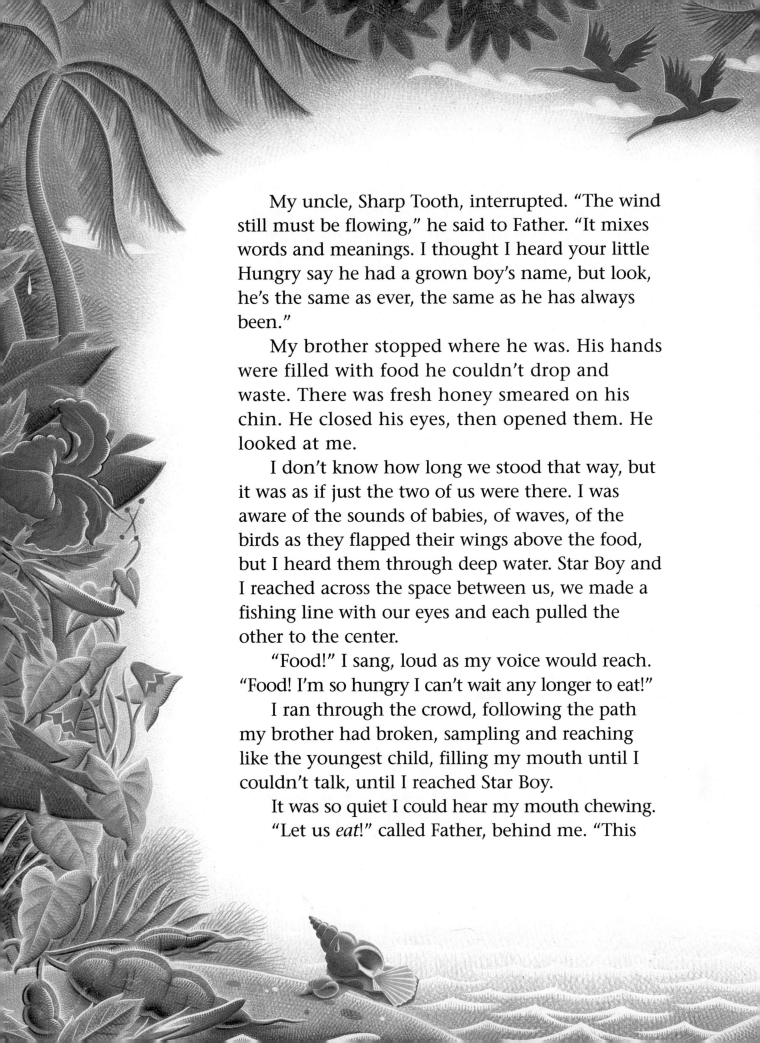

My uncle, Sharp Tooth, interrupted. "The wind still must be flowing," he said to Father. "It mixes words and meanings. I thought I heard your little Hungry say he had a grown boy's name, but look, he's the same as ever, the same as he has always been."

My brother stopped where he was. His hands were filled with food he couldn't drop and waste. There was fresh honey smeared on his chin. He closed his eyes, then opened them. He looked at me.

I don't know how long we stood that way, but it was as if just the two of us were there. I was aware of the sounds of babies, of waves, of the birds as they flapped their wings above the food, but I heard them through deep water. Star Boy and I reached across the space between us, we made a fishing line with our eyes and each pulled the other to the center.

"Food!" I sang, loud as my voice would reach. "Food! I'm so hungry I can't wait any longer to eat!"

I ran through the crowd, following the path my brother had broken, sampling and reaching like the youngest child, filling my mouth until I couldn't talk, until I reached Star Boy.

It was so quiet I could hear my mouth chewing.

"Let us *eat*!" called Father, behind me. "This

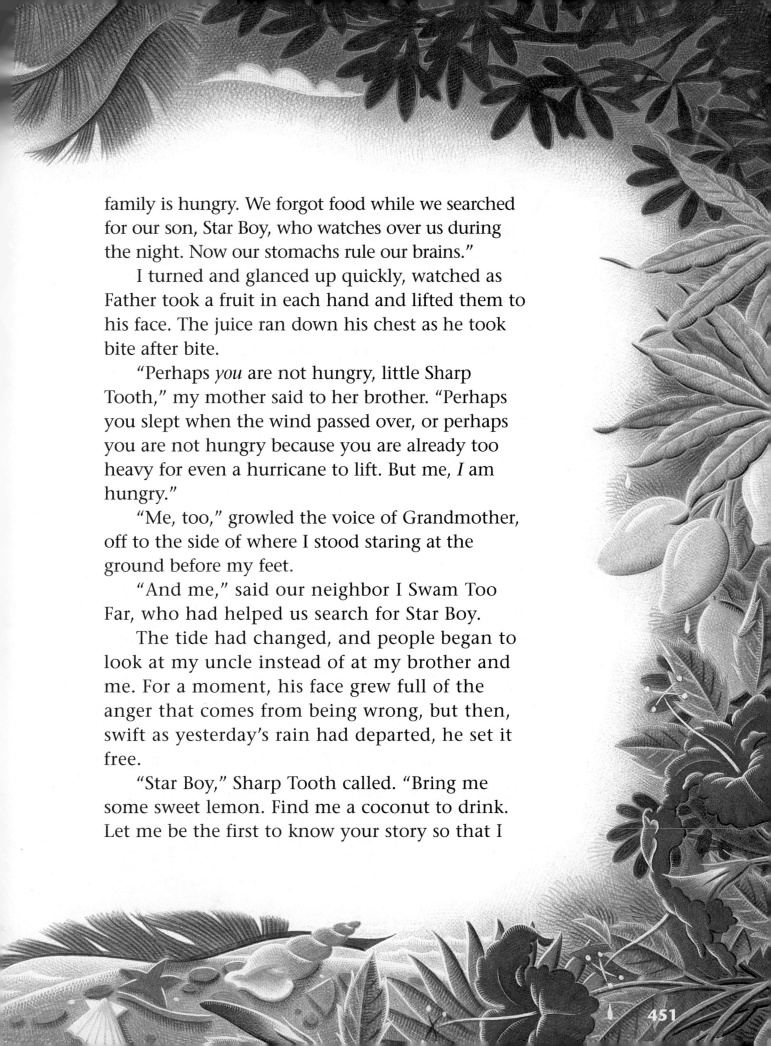

family is hungry. We forgot food while we searched for our son, Star Boy, who watches over us during the night. Now our stomachs rule our brains."

I turned and glanced up quickly, watched as Father took a fruit in each hand and lifted them to his face. The juice ran down his chest as he took bite after bite.

"Perhaps *you* are not hungry, little Sharp Tooth," my mother said to her brother. "Perhaps you slept when the wind passed over, or perhaps you are not hungry because you are already too heavy for even a hurricane to lift. But me, *I* am hungry."

"Me, too," growled the voice of Grandmother, off to the side of where I stood staring at the ground before my feet.

"And me," said our neighbor I Swam Too Far, who had helped us search for Star Boy.

The tide had changed, and people began to look at my uncle instead of at my brother and me. For a moment, his face grew full of the anger that comes from being wrong, but then, swift as yesterday's rain had departed, he set it free.

"Star Boy," Sharp Tooth called. "Bring me some sweet lemon. Find me a coconut to drink. Let me be the first to know your story so that I

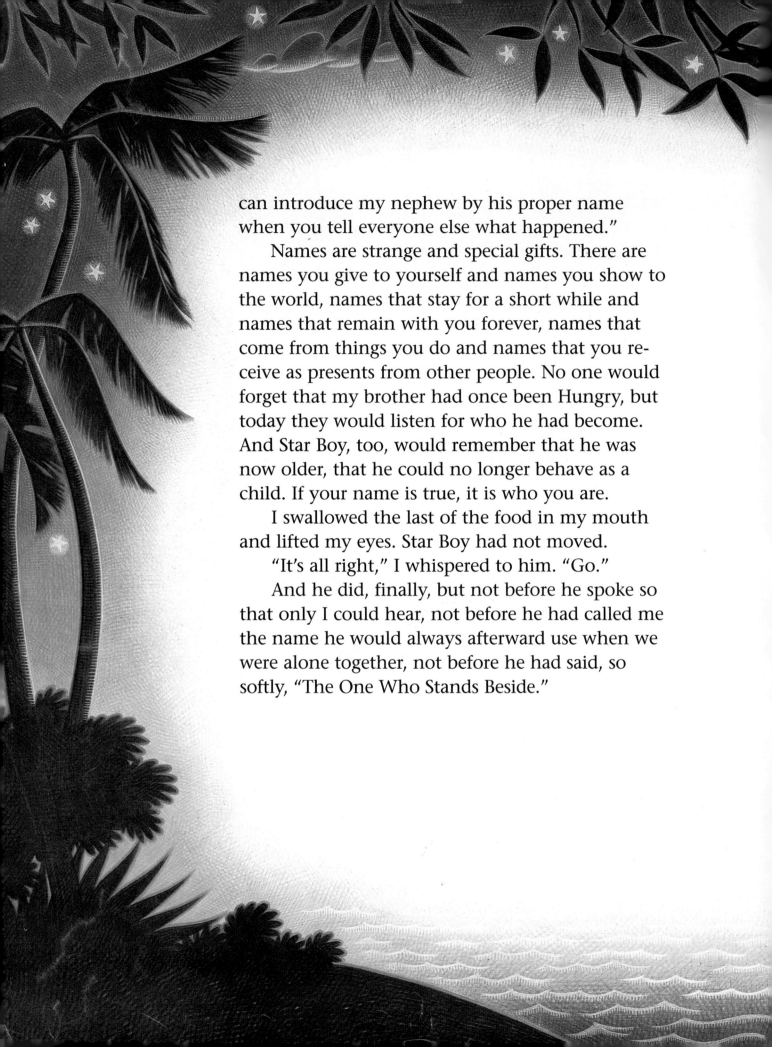

can introduce my nephew by his proper name when you tell everyone else what happened."

Names are strange and special gifts. There are names you give to yourself and names you show to the world, names that stay for a short while and names that remain with you forever, names that come from things you do and names that you receive as presents from other people. No one would forget that my brother had once been Hungry, but today they would listen for who he had become. And Star Boy, too, would remember that he was now older, that he could no longer behave as a child. If your name is true, it is who you are.

I swallowed the last of the food in my mouth and lifted my eyes. Star Boy had not moved.

"It's all right," I whispered to him. "Go."

And he did, finally, but not before he spoke so that only I could hear, not before he had called me the name he would always afterward use when we were alone together, not before he had said, so softly, "The One Who Stands Beside."

IN RESPONSE

Welcome Star Boy Home

Imagine that you are at the feast as Star Boy describes what happened to him during the storm. What questions would you ask to find out how Star Boy feels about his grandfather and about the tree?

What's in a Name?

Morning Girl explains, "Names are strange and special gifts. There are names . . . that come from things you do." Write a paragraph telling what you think Morning Girl's new name means. Use examples from the story to support your ideas. Decide which, if any, of the names in the story you would like to have.

MICHAEL DORRIS

★ **Award-winning Author**

Michael Dorris, of French, Irish, and Native American (Modoc) descent, grew up in Montana and Kentucky. An interest in his background led him to pursue studies in anthropology.

While Mr. Dorris was doing research for one of his books, he noticed the lack of information on the Taino, the people who inhabited the Bahama Islands when Columbus first arrived. From Columbus's diary he knew they were friendly and were unfamiliar with weapons, and that one of the first people to greet Columbus was a young girl. Mr. Dorris began to wonder about that girl and what her life had been like before Columbus arrived.

"History books seldom speculate about the Taino, beyond the fact that they were reportedly handsome, trusting, and gentle. We know that eventually some were shackled and sent to Spain as slaves and that most of those who remained were soon wiped out by Old World diseases. Often treated as mere footnotes in the great drama of conquest and discovery, the Taino deserve to be re-membered and appreciated for themselves. *Morning Girl* was written in their honor."

Another Book by . . .

Michael Dorris

Guests by Michael Dorris, Hyperion Books, 1994

Library Link

"The Grandfather Tree" was taken from *Morning Girl* by Michael Dorris. You might enjoy reading the entire book to learn more about Morning Girl and Star Boy.

Hurricane

by James Berry

Under low black clouds
the wind was all
speedy feet, all horns and breath,
all bangs, howls, rattles,
in every hen house,
church hall and school.

Roaring, screaming, returning,
it made forced entry, shoved walls,
made rifts, brought roofs down,
hitting rooms to sticks apart.

It wrung soft banana trees,
broke tough trunks of palms.
It pounded vines of yams,
left fields battered up.

Invisible with such ecstasy—
with no intervention of sun or man—
everywhere kept changing branches.

Zinc sheets are kites.
Leaves are panic swarms.
Fowls are fixed with feathers turned.
Goats, dogs, pigs,
all are people together.

Then growling it slunk away
from muddy, mossy trail and boats
in hedges: and cows, ratbats, trees,
fish, all dead in the road.

457

One Dark

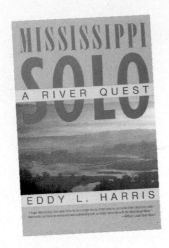

from *Mississippi Solo* by Eddy L. Harris

Eddy Harris, determined to accomplish a lifelong dream, sets out in central Minnesota to canoe the length of the Mississippi River. The first leg of the trip is fifteen miles long and ends at Coffee Pot, a campsite where his friend Robinovich has agreed to meet him.

Three miles took forever. Twelve more should take four times as long. But no! The next twelve will take much longer. But how can this be? I was rested. The sun was still high. I had just eaten. And the river straightened. On top of that I was gaining experience as a canoeist with every stroke. How could I not make the next twelve miles in a hurry?

I'm feeling really fine. The river deepens and the rice marsh lines only one bank. The other bank is woodsy for now.

Too quickly the marsh and the meanderings are back, but only for a short time. Still, the going is not swift. Soon the sun is slipping down beyond the pines. When the sun goes, the cold comes. And now I'm deeper in the woods where the air is naturally fresher and cooler. I put on my gloves and don a sweatshirt with a hood. Robinovich has my warm jacket. I was thinking she would need it more than I. After all, all this paddling so far has kept me warm. In the sun.

I come to a low wooden dam that threatens to force me out of the canoe. But I'm feeling expert. I can ride this. I do, but the riding is tricky and I get

Night

wet. The wet makes me colder. The beaver dams take time. Time takes away my light. There is another obstruction and I'm forced out of my canoe to portage around it. More time. More effort. More cold coming fast into the valley. Whose idea *was* this?

Rapids. They are loud and swift and the rocks are boulders and I'm scared. I may be expert, but I'm not *that* expert. But what choice have I? I've got to shoot them, and shoot them I do. A long series of rapids after rapids—probably because of the shallow water in autumn—and with each one I gain more and more confidence. After each one I shout with triumph and glee. But with each one I get wetter. And as the darkness descends, each one gets more difficult to see and thus trickier to negotiate.

One time the river spins me into a rock and I nearly fly from my seat. The rock spins me around sideways and soon I'm going swiftly downstream backwards. I can't turn around. The river narrows and the canoe won't fit. I'm stuck.

Another time I'm thrown into the side of the river. Low branches force me into the bank and I can't turn around. The water from the side is too fast and strong for me. I have to get out and push the boat around. My shoes get soaked and my feet get cold and my gloves get wet.

To dry the gloves I lay them on the struts. The next set of rapids tosses up the front end of the canoe. Only a keen sense of balance—no canoeing skill—keeps me from falling into the icy water.

I look. My gloves are gone.

The river has become an adversary. I see deer munching leaves on the shore. They know better than to do what I'm doing and they feel safe from me. How can I get at them even if I want to? They watch me and I feel stupid.

Finally it's dark. Then it's night. I'm freezing right through to the bone and my hands and feet are numb. I'm worried about frostbite. I'm worried about being lost. I'm worried about how to find Robinovich out there in the night. I don't know how far I've come or how far I've got to go. I'm scared. So I sing. I worry about running across more rapids, falling in, freezing to death.

That rushing sound, the sound of rapids, terrifies me each time I hear it. The river has begun to meander again and the bank has hidden deep behind the marsh that has popped up again. I can't get out of the river because I can't get out of the canoe. I don't know if I'll find solid ground or if I'll sink to my waist. I'm forced on.

The sound of rapids is the same sound of water falling over those huge beaver dams that threaten my progress. I hate the dams but I fear the rapids even more. The dams I can go around—when I can see them. The ones that completely cross the river I can plow over. The ones that are too thick I can approach and step out on and slide the canoe over. I'm hoping beavers don't bite.

Finally the moon rises and throws down its light. I breathe easier. I can see a bit. But it's still very dark and mostly what I must do is listen. Hearing, smelling: other senses take over when you can't see and right now (despite the moonlight) my eyesight is fairly useless. I rely on a sense I didn't even know I had and it somehow keeps me in the water, upright, away from the marsh and out of too much trouble. I carry on and I sing.

I'm wondering how long before the search party comes looking for me. Off in the distant night sky a signal flare shoots a bright arc and falls. Someone, I'm sure, is looking for me. Pretty soon a helicopter will thump through the air overhead and shine down an intense spotlight on the river. A voice in a loud speaker will ask me if I'm all right and will light my path on the water. I'm sure of it.

But no. I'm still all alone and still miserable. My toes are dead numb and my fingers are swollen. They're locked around the paddle and cannot unbend. Frostbite.

Off in the distance, high on a hill, a light. I aim straight for it and tell myself when I get close, I'll get out and hike. It's a good mile straight up a hill, but at least I know there's a house. I can phone from there or get a ride to Coffee Pot. But dogs are howling up there on the hillside. I keep going.

Beaver dams. Each time I step from the canoe to go over them my feet get wetter. I'm just freezing. In my pocket I do have a box of waterproof matches. If I could find a place to pull out I could at least build a fire and dry off and warm up a little.

Up on a rise, not far from the river, a shed. Old and rickety, but made of wood. I can burn that thing if I need to, burn it to the ground for warmth, and yes I need to. My life or the life of this old shack.

But then I smell smoke. Someone else has built a fire. Hunters maybe, or Robinovich. I keep going.

A big mistake. I find no fire, no hunters, no Robinovich. My spirit is sinking fast. I sing to keep from losing it completely. Between songs I call out to Robinovich. No reply. Just my own voice echoing hollowly back to me from the walls of the night.

I can give up, get out right now and just die. It'll be easier.

I find every scrap of energy that's in me and push on. I can't see any better now and I don't need too much speed to make me crash into something or send me into the weeds. I pick my way carefully.

And then I see the light from a fire. I smell smoke. I see the lights from a car. I'm yelling my head off but no sound comes back to me. How far away am I?

Finally I arrive. Coffee Pot. The fire, a big smoky blaze, is ours. Robinovich has built it. She's gone, though, when I pull out from the river, gone to search for me. Not knowing where or how to search she quickly returns. The car lights I saw were hers.

One
Great
Thing

by Kitlinguharmiut Eskimos

I think over again
my small adventures,
when I drifted out with a shore wind
in my kayak
and thought I was in danger.
My fears,
those small ones,
that I thought so big,
were for all the vital things
I had to get and to reach.

And yet, there is only
one great thing—
to live to see, at home or on journeys,
the great day that dawns,
and the light that fills the world.

Four Against the Sea

from *A Boat to Nowhere*
by Maureen Crane Wartski

Young Mai,[1] her brother Loc,[2] and their grandfather Thay Van Chi[3] have decided to leave their war-torn homeland of Vietnam in hopes of finding a better life. Along with the orphan boy Kien,[4] they set out in a small boat for Malaysia, hundreds of miles across the open sea.

After several days at sea, Thay Van Chi falls gravely ill, and only a little food remains. If the four are to reach Malaysia, Mai must trust Kien with her family's survival.

---

1 Mai (*my*)
2 Loc (*lahk*)
3 Thay Van Chi (*ty vahn chee*)
4 Kien (*KEE ehn*)

It was as if they had always lived on the sea. Their feet had been chilled forever by the cold water that washed into the boat. Their faces, shoulders, and arms had always been scorched by the sun— the sun that also cracked their lips and made drinking painful.

They had always been hungry, it seemed. The food given to them by the Thai women lasted six long days. They ate the chicken first, because it would spoil, and then the mangoes, one by one. The green bananas had turned brown before they were devoured, but soon they, too, were gone.

They kept the coconuts for last, sharing first the milk of a coconut, and then the sweet white meat. Nibbling at the fruit bit by bit, they made each coconut feed all four of them for a day. It would have been easier if they could have caught some fish, but the fish were wary of the hook they let down into the sea and none were caught. By the time they were down to their last coconut, all of them had lost a great deal of weight, and the old man was very sick.

Thay Van Chi tried to hide this from the others. He made a joke of his cough, saying that it was his old lungs' way of reacting to clean sea air. But Kien and Mai could see how the fever burned in him, so that his eyes were almost glazed with it.

On the sixth day after leaving Thailand, Kien heard the old man whisper, "*Toi chong mat* . . . I am dizzy."

Kien's heart squeezed with fear. The fever was getting worse, and there was no medicine, no food, and no port in sight. Supposing the old man died . . .

Kien quickly tried to push the thought away, but it kept coming back. Suppose the old man died? He was the only one who knew these waters, and it was he who was piloting the *Sea Breeze* toward Malaysia. He had all the maps locked inside that wise old brain . . . the brain that was burning with fever!

What happens, Kien asked himself, when the Old One can't think straight anymore?

He looked over to where Mai was trying to coax the last bit of coconut into the old man. "Please, Grandfather, you need to eat," Mai was saying.

"I'm not hungry." The old man shook his head stubbornly.

"But you have to eat!" Mai was near tears.

"You eat it, Mai. You need it more than I do. Why, you're skin and bones."

This was true, Kien thought. Well, all of them were like that now. Mai's cheekbones stuck out like ridges under her skin, and the hand that held the piece of coconut trembled from weakness. Looking at the food, Kien couldn't keep his empty and aching stomach from growling loudly.

"Give it to Loc," the old man said. "Or Kien."

Kien shook his head, but Loc started to put out his hand eagerly. After a moment, however, he drew it back. "No, Grandfather," he said with a great effort, "you haven't eaten your share. I have."

"And I never liked coconuts." Kien forced himself to joke. "You eat, Uncle. Anyway, we need to have you strong and healthy. How could we reach Malaysia without you?"

The old man seemed to realize that Kien spoke sense. He took the piece of coconut and began to chew the white meat. After a while he began to cough again, and when he spat over the side of the boat, Kien was sure he saw blood. If Thay Van Chi's sickness had reached the lungs, it was really bad. Now Kien was very frightened.

To make things worse, it stormed that day. It had rained off and on since they had left the Thai village, and they were grateful for the rainwater, which they could drink. But this was a storm like nothing they had yet experienced. It began as a darkness gathering swiftly on the horizon and then spreading across the sky. Although it was only just after sunset, the world seemed completely wrapped in darkness. The wind began, and the *Sea Breeze* commenced to lurch and pitch.

"This one will be bad," Thay Van Chi warned. "We had better lower the sail immediately."

"Will it be as bad as that first storm?" Mai worried, but her grandfather didn't say anything. "Worse?" Mai faltered.

"Let's hope not." The old man was making an effort to help Kien and Mai with the sail. "We have gone through a great deal, my grandchildren. Heaven will help us through this storm."

No one said anything. They waited for the storm, listening to the fierce sound of the wind blowing across the sea. Soon the black and sullen sea was heaving, and it began to rain. Tons of water, suddenly released, came foaming down on them. Wind shrieked across the bare mast, making the boat heel first to one side and then to the other, turning and twisting it without mercy. The force of the wind was so tremendous that Kien, clinging to the mast, was nearly torn loose and thrown into the sea.

Thay Van Chi leaned close to Kien and bawled something in his ear. Kien couldn't hear. The old man shouted, "Tie Loc and Mai and yourself to the mast! Use the rope from the sail!"

Kien knew that if they were blown overboard, they would drown. There was no way they could hope for rescue. But to get the rope from the sail he needed to let go of the mast himself. Kien was afraid to let go. Suppose, he thought, I am blown into the sea?

"It's all right . . . it's all right . . ." the old man shouted. "I'll hold on to you. I won't let you go!"

The old man wrapped one arm around the mast and hooked his free hand into Kien's shorts. Kien looked at the frail old arm and thought, If he coughs and weakens, he might let me go. But at the same moment a wicked wind rocked the boat, and Loc was torn loose from the mast. Mai screamed, but her voice was carried away by the wind. Kien, without thinking, let go of the mast to catch Loc and haul him away from the heaving water. Only when Loc was safe did he realize that the old man's grasp on him was sure and strong.

"The rope!" Thay Van Chi shouted over the storm, and Kien began to tug the rope free from the sail. "Don't lose the sail!" the old

man ordered, so Kien ended up by wrapping the sail around the mast first. Then he began to tie Mai, Loc, and himself to the mast.

"Tie Grandfather too!" Mai screamed, but the rope was too short. Kien had an idea.

"Hold hands . . . all of us hold hands!" he bellowed, as the wind snarled and shrieked around them. He grabbed Loc's hand with his right hand and the old man's with his left. Mai held Loc's free hand and her grandfather's. Then Mai began to scream.

"Look!" she wailed. "Look . . ."

The *Sea Breeze* was poised at the top of a monstrous swell that was as high as a mountain. Down below was a valley of water. As they slid down into that valley, Kien closed his eyes. He popped them open a second later and screamed, too, as he saw black, hungry, foamy water waiting for him an inch away. It rushed into the boat

with such force that they could not breathe.

We're drowning . . . we're going, Kien thought, and then the boat shot up another swell. Up, down, up . . . there seemed to be more water inside the *Sea Breeze* now than outside! Down, up, down . . .

"We're going to die . . . We're going to die!" Mai began to scream. Loc was howling, but his open mouth made no sound above the roar of the rain and the wind and the sea. "We're all going to die!" Mai shrieked.

Over the noise, Kien heard a new and strange sound. The old man was leaning next to him and he was speaking. No, he was singing! Kien stared at the old man, thinking he had gone crazy, that the storm had driven him insane. But the gentle old eyes were clear, and it seemed to Kien that Thay Van Chi was smiling.

Kien could hardly hear the words of the old man's song, but he soon recognized snatches of the melody. It was the Vietnamese song that they had all sung six days ago when they sailed into the Thai port. The half-recognized melody made Kien's eyes sting with tears as he remembered good rice, and laughter, and forests, and everything else he had taken for granted. He began to sing too.

Now Mai stopped screaming to listen. And she, too, began to sing. Loc, exhausted and limp against the mast, grew quiet as the others sang the familiar words. Some of the horrible fear lessened. It was as if Thay Van Chi was saying, The storm will soon be over, and the good things we've had before are waiting for us.

Their voices never rose above the storm, but they could hear each other sometimes, and it made them feel better. They clung to each other's hands and sang and sang. After a while even Loc began to sing.

It was dawn before the storm finally subsided. It had stormed for hours. Long ago they had stopped singing and now they slumped, exhausted, against the mast. They hardly knew the storm was over as they half rested, half dozed. The *Sea Breeze* sloshed with water taken on during the storm, and the hair that fell across Mai's face, hiding it as she slept, was wet too. Neither she nor anyone else saw something huge and dark pass them in the dawn light.

Aboard the tanker *Casa Verde*,[5] Ramirez was just coming off duty. It had been a bad night and he was tired. He was also very hungry, though just a few hours before, his stomach had been lurched around by the stormy sea.

Now that sea seemed so calm. Looking around at the water, Ramirez suddenly stopped, stared.

"Eh, Felipe!" he shouted to another crewman who had come off duty with him.

"Now what's wrong?" the other man asked anxiously.

"Do you see what I see? To starboard . . . over there!" Ramirez pointed, and his friend frowned into the gray dawn.

"I see a boat with people," Ramirez said.

"Um," Felipe nodded. "Vietnamese boat people, I'd say. No one else would be crazy enough to be out in the middle of the ocean in a little fishing boat.

---

5 **Casa Verde** (*KAHS ah BEHR day*)

I'm surprised the storm last night didn't finish them off."

"I'd better get the skipper," Ramirez said, but as he was hurrying off the deck the other man stopped him.

"Don't do that, Ramirez. You know the skipper didn't get much sleep last night. He wouldn't want you waking him on account of some boat people."

"But we can't just leave them out there," Ramirez said, shocked.

"Who asked them to leave Vietnam in their miserable little boats?" Felipe retorted. "Listen, you know what the policy of our company is. We take no boat people aboard. It prevents a lot of embarrassment and trouble. No country wants those refugees anyway, and we can't support them all, can we?"

Ramirez looked over his shoulder, for the dark shape of the fishing boat was now behind him. It bobbed up and down in a forlorn way. Ramirez cleared his throat. "We could let the skipper decide," he began uncertainly.

"*You* call him up here. I don't want *my* head chewed off! I'm going to get some hot coffee!"

Ramirez remembered how hungry he was. The thought of hot coffee made his mouth water. But before he followed Felipe down into the galley, he looked once more at the fishing boat, now far behind the *Casa Verde.*

It's not my fault they're out there, Ramirez said to himself. Shrugging, he went down to breakfast.

When they awoke, arms and legs stiff and sore from clinging to the mast all night, it was well into day.

The sun was blazing down on them and had already baked them dry. The sea had calmed, and gentle swells lifted the *Sea Breeze,* moving it back and forth. Kien came awake first, and then Mai.

Loc snored loudly, but the old man leaned forward against the mast, his face hidden by his thin arms.

He was so still that Mai was afraid.

"Is he . . ." she began, and Kien reached over and shook Thay Van Chi, who muttered but did not awaken.

"He's all right," Kien said. He felt sick with relief. "We got through the storm all right!"

Will we get through another one? Mai wondered.

"Kien, Grandfather's very sick!"

"I know that! What can I do?" Kien's voice was high with frustration. "What can any of us do? We have to get to Malaysia, that's all!"

"The storm must have blown us off course," Mai sighed.

Kien knew this more than anyone, but Mai's words made him angry. "What good is it to talk to you? According to you, we should jump overboard and end it all . . ."

He stopped, staring into the water. "Oh . . . no!"

"What now?" Mai demanded.

"Look!" Roughly, Kien grabbed Mai's arm and shook her. "Look!" he repeated.

Near them, floating lazily, were two dark triangles that rose above the water's surface.

"Sharks!" Mai screamed.

Her scream woke Loc.

"Sharks?" he asked confusedly. "Has Big Tam brought home a shark?"

The old man awoke, too. "Sharks?" he muttered dazedly. "Where are the sharks?"

Kien pointed out the triangular dorsal fins. "They know where to find their dinner," he said shortly.

"But how did they get here?" Mai pushed her clenched fist against her mouth and her eyes were enormous with fear.

"Who knows? They don't wait to be invited. These are shark

waters and the sharks are the tigers," Kien replied.

Thay Van Chi started to speak but could not, for coughing. Finally he managed to gasp, "Don't bother them . . . and they won't bother us. Don't throw anything overboard . . . and *don't* fall into the water!"

"Will they eat me if I fall into the sea?" Loc demanded, with his eyes bigger even than Mai's.

"In two gulps! Mai, help me hoist the sail," Kien said. "Thay Van Chi, how far off course are we?"

By some miracle the old man knew. By calculating when the sun was at its highest point, he figured out their latitude and told Kien that he felt they were not too far off course. "In three days, if we're lucky, we should sight Malaysia," he said wearily.

Kien looked at the old man worriedly. Would he be able to hold out for another three days without food—three days during which there might be another storm? Would any of them be able to hold out? He glanced over his shoulder at the dorsal fins slowly circling the boat and shivered.

They dined later on rainwater collected from last night's storm. There was no food left, and when Loc tried to fish, there was no bait, and no fish. Perhaps the sharks had scared away the fish. Thay Van Chi sighed as Loc brought up his fish-hook in despair.

They had been hungry before. Now they were starving. They filled their stomachs with water till they bloated, but this didn't help. Kien, who was a little stronger than the rest of them, felt bone-tired. It was an effort even to keep hold of the tiller. The old man slept all the time and so did Mai and Loc.

Once the old man awoke and said, "Perhaps we may somehow stray, by Heaven's mercy, into a shipping lane. That may well be our only hope."

"What is a shipping lane?" Kien asked, and Loc opened his eyes to look at his grandfather hopefully.

"A shipping lane is the path great ships from many countries travel as they sail across the ocean. Many ships use the same 'lane.' If one of those great ships saw us and rescued us, we would be saved . . ."

"Then let's pray for a big ship!" Loc murmured weakly. He staggered to his feet, placed the palms of his hands together and lifted them to his bowed forehead.

"Please, Heaven," he said earnestly, "send us a big ship."

The sound of Loc's voice awakened Mai. She said, "It's no use. No one will ever come."

There was a big lump in Kien's throat as Thay Van Chi whispered, "Don't talk like that, child. Come to me." Mai rested her face against her grandfather's chest and cried. Kien could see Mai's shoulders moving with weak sobs, and he wanted to cry too. Instead, he began to whistle the song they had sung during the storm. His whistle was weak, but in a little while Loc picked up the song, beginning to hum softly. Mai and the old man listened, and Mai stopped crying. She lay quietly, listening, with her arms around her grandfather's neck.

Look, Heaven, Kien thought in his heart, look how hard we are trying! Can't you help us . . . just a little?

It was hours before they heard the noise. At first no one paid much attention, for they were too tired to do much but doze. It was close to sunset, and the sky was just beginning to turn gold and scarlet. At first, Kien, who steered the boat, thought it was the sound of distant thunder that he heard. Then Loc gasped, "I think I hear something."

They were awake and listening instantly.

"I don't hear anything—" Mai began sadly.

"Shh!" Kien interrupted her urgently. "Yes! I hear it too! I hear it too!"

"A ship!" Loc screeched.

They all peered into the distance.

"Look!" Kien shouted. On the horizon was a dark speck. "Look!" he cried again.

Loc was beside himself. "A ship, a ship!" he cried. Weak as he was, he jumped up and down in the boat. "I knew Heaven would send us a ship! I knew it! Look, Grandfather, look Mai . . . a ship's coming to save us, just like Grandfather said!"

The dark speck was moving closer, growing larger. Loc waved wildly, and so did Kien and Mai.

"Here we are, Ship!" Mai screamed hysterically. "This way . . ."

"Get *down*!"

Kien was seized, hurled to the bottom of the boat. As he lay there too surprised to move, the old man pushed Mai and Loc down too.

"Pirates!" Thay Van Chi gasped. "Be quiet . . . for your lives!"

Pirates! Kien nearly stopped breathing. Of course! He should have known that no large ship would run so noisily. This had to be a pirate's motorboat.

"It's too small to be a cargo ship or a tanker!" The old man groaned. "Pray that they haven't seen or heard us!"

But they had been seen. The motorboat was headed straight for them! Kien pushed the tiller hard, trying to turn the *Sea Breeze* so as to outrun the motorboat. It was no use. Kien saw several men standing on the deck of the large motorboat, which now swooped around the *Sea Breeze*, causing the smaller boat to pitch and yaw. These men cradled machine guns in their arms, and several of them waved and shouted at the *Sea Breeze*.

"Boat people . . . Stop . . . We won't hurt you!" one of them shouted in bad Vietnamese.

Kien looked at the men and shuddered. All the pirates had cruel, greedy faces. He looked at Mai, who was sitting stone-still, too frightened to cry.

"Don't anger these men," Thay Van Chi said rapidly. "Be brave. We have nothing to steal. Maybe they will leave us alone . . ."

With pirates, Kien knew, there was no "maybe."

Every horrible story he had heard about these evil men came back to him. One of the pirates, a small man with the most wicked-looking face Kien had ever seen, leaned over and grabbed the side of the *Sea Breeze*, bringing it close to the motorboat. Then he sprang aboard the *Sea Breeze*.

"Boat people, where you go?" he asked, smiling. The smile made him look even more evil.

"We are trying to reach Malaysia, honored sir," the old man said in a shaky voice. "We are very poor people. My grandchildren and I have nothing except the rags we wear . . ."

There was a shout of disappointment from the pirates. "Where is your food? Don't you have any clothing . . . blankets?" the evil-faced pirate demanded angrily.

"We have nothing. We lost everything in the storms . . ." Thay Van Chi began to cough. The evil-faced pirate began to shake the old man.

"You're lying! You've hidden things! I know you boat rats!" he shouted. "Give me what you have or I will kill you!"

"Let go of Grandfather!" Loc cried shrilly. He broke away from Mai and ran over to the pirate, pummeling him with his small fists.

There was a shout of laughter from the other pirates. "Hey, Boon, can't you handle the Vietnamese puppy?" one of them yelled. This made the evil-faced pirate angrier still.

Kien saw the rage in those wicked eyes and acted quickly.

"Honored sir," he babbled, "pay no attention to my bad-tempered little brother! He has had brain fever. He doesn't know what he's doing."

"Yes, please . . . He doesn't even know his own name!" Mai added swiftly. She fell on her knees. "Let us go," she pleaded. "We have nothing . . . nothing at all!"

With an angry cry, the wicked-looking pirate shoved Thay Van Chi away from him. The old man fell on his hands and knees and stayed there, too weak to move. Then the pirate lifted the machine gun he carried. There was a blast of sound, and Kien cried out, thinking he had been shot. But the evil-faced one had only fired at their sail, peppering it with bullets. Now he blasted away at the mast of the *Sea Breeze*. The mast snapped, falling into the sea.

"Shall we sink the boat, too?" the pirate shouted to his friends.

"Why? It's a waste of ammunition, Boon! Just throw their oars overboard. They won't last long anyway."

Kien could not believe what he was hearing. The pirates were going to let them go! He watched dazedly as the evil-faced one threw the *Sea Breeze*'s oars overboard. Then he turned to go. Kien almost said a prayer to Heaven. But suddenly, as swift as a cobra, the pirate spun around, grabbed Loc, and hopped back onto the motorboat!

"Mai!" Loc shouted. "Grandfather . . . help!"

Mai screamed, and the old man jumped to his feet. "Pirate dogs!" he cried. "Give us back the child! Give him back . . ."

The motorboat began to move away.

"Follow them!" Thay Van Chi shouted.

"How? They've snapped the mast and shot the sail to shreds and we have no oars!" Kien was almost sobbing. "Give Loc back, you . . ." He tried to think of a name bad enough, but could not. "Give the boy back!" he yelled.

The leering pirate grinned. "You want him back that much? Well . . . catch!"

Kien saw Loc's face—shocked, surprised, scared—a second before he was flung into the air. Loc shrieked once, then fell into the water with a loud splash some two hundred feet away from the *Sea Breeze*.

478

"Swim, Loc!" Mai screamed, and Kien thought, The sharks!

The old man was about to leap into the sea to get Loc, but Kien dived first. He did not even think as he moved, only saw Loc's small head surfacing, and the dorsal fins of their shark escorts moving toward Loc. Then Kien was knifing through the water, swimming desperately. He saw Mai standing in the *Sea Breeze*, her arms around her grandfather. He heard the pirates' mocking laughter as their motorboat sped away. He swam faster and faster still.

Now he had reached Loc. Loc was too dazed to swim, but he struggled as Kien tried to drag him to safety. "Quit that, you fool!" Kien gritted. He couldn't see the sharks anymore. The big tigers must be hunting under the water.

Hurry . . . hurry! Kien felt something sandpaper rough brush against his leg. He did not dare think of what might happen if the shark opened its great jaws and snapped at that leg. He swam, stroke by stroke. The great burst of strength that desperation had given him was gone. He was exhausted, his lungs burning. Again, the sandy thing bumped against his leg.

Now he was almost within reach of the *Sea Breeze*. The old man was half in and half out of the boat, reaching for them. Kien sobbed once with fear as he pushed himself to the very limit. He was almost there, almost . . .

And then the old man was pulling both Loc and Kien into the *Sea Breeze*. Kien hardly felt the bottom of the boat as he tumbled in and lay gasping for breath. He hardly realized he was still alive.

Nearby, he could hear Mai saying Loc's name, over and over and over. "Loc, oh, Loc . . ." Mai whispered.

"He's fine," the old man said.

"The pirates . . ." Kien couldn't talk much, and the old man seemed to understand.

"They've gone, my child. Now you must rest. Breathe. Breathe deeply. Put your head down so, below your knees. Breathe. Breathe."

"That shark almost got us." Incredibly, Loc seemed almost boastful. "I felt him brush my leg! I hope that shark eats up those wicked pirates!"

Mai shivered. "Don't talk like that!" she said sharply.

They were very silent as the sun suddenly sank. Then Kien roused himself wearily. "Our mast is gone, and our sail . . ."

"I saved the sail," the old man said. "See? It is beside the boat. I need your help to pull it out of the water, for it is very heavy." He paused. "Also I have saved the oars. The waves pushed them toward the boat."

So now, Kien thought, we have to row our way to Malaysia!

Pulling the soaking sail out of the water took Kien's last remaining strength. As dark fell, he rested his face against his drawn-up knees and closed his eyes. He must have dozed, for when he awoke, it was inky dark, and Mai was sitting beside him.

"Grandfather and Loc are asleep," she said quietly. "You've been asleep yourself for a long time."

"No one's sailing?" Kien asked and then caught himself. How could you sail a boat without a mast? "We have to make repairs," he muttered. "But . . . how? Where?"

Mai didn't seem to hear his question. "You were so brave, jumping after Loc like that," she whispered. "I was a coward. I wanted to go after Loc, but I couldn't move . . ."

"I didn't know what I was doing," Kien said truthfully. "If I'd stopped to think about that shark, I would never have jumped in."

"But you saved Loc. There's no way I can thank you." Mai's voice drifted away, then came back. "Grandfather tried to see where we were by the stars—they were out a little while ago—but he isn't sure. He thinks we're still on course for Malaysia." She paused. "He's getting so weak, Kien, and those pirates upset him so. He needs help, and medicine. He needs a doctor."

Kien didn't answer. He felt frustrated and helpless, and he wanted to scream at Heaven, to curse it. Instead, he picked up one of the oars the old man had saved and dipped it into the sea. Mai did the same. Where are we rowing to? each could have asked, but neither one did. It was better to do some-thing—anything—than to sit and wait to die.

Together, they rowed for a while. Kien tried not to think of anything, but his hunger-weakened brain filled with im-ages: the shark, and Loc, and the old man's face bending over him, and the old man's voice calling him "my child." He thought of the way the old man had begged for his life back in Thailand. My life, Kien thought. No one has ever begged for me before.

Land, he thought desperately, within himself. I want land for this old man. Can't you hear me, Heaven? I, Kien, want land!

The night slipped by. Too weak to row for long, both Kien and Mai fell asleep at their oars. The old man slept, and Loc slept, too.

When dawn came, Mai was the first to open her eyes. She raised her head and looked around her blearily, first to the west and then to the east.

"Kien!" she gasped. "Kien, wake up!" When he did not move, she shook him violently. "Kien, tell me I'm not dreaming!"

Kien woke up, and he too stared.

Ahead of them, feathered with palm trees and looking better than their best hopes and prayers was—LAND!

IN RESPONSE

Working to Survive
In a small group discuss why Mai and Loc need to depend on Kien for their survival. What did Kien do that helped the family survive? How would you describe someone who acted as Kien did?

Survival Profiles
Suppose you were planning a documentary film to show how Mai and Morning Girl reacted to crisis. Outline your documentary, telling how you think the young women reacted. Choose scenes from the selections you would use to illustrate your film.

AUTHOR AT WORK

Maureen Crane Wartski remembers, "All I ever wanted to do was write. My career seemed assured when I sold my first story at age fourteen, but then

there were several years before I published anything else!"

When asked why she writes for young adults, Ms. Wartski replies, "These readers are young. They are new. . . . The joy, the sorrow, the hope of each new character they meet is an echo of their own emotion. Give these readers a book they love, and you may open a new world to them."

Ms. Wartski lived in Ashiya, Japan, until she was seventeen years old.

★ **Award-winning Author**

She lived in Thailand from 1962 to 1966 and was familiar with the seas where this story takes place. She now makes her home in New England.

Other Books by . . .

Maureen Crane Wartski

The Face in My Mirror
by Maureen Wartski, Faucett Juniper, 1994

My Name Is Nobody
by Maureen Crane Wartski, Walker, 1988

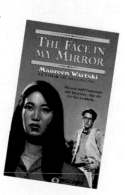

Library Link "Four Against the Sea" was taken from the book *A Boat to Nowhere*. To find out more about this Vietnamese family's emigration, you might want to read the entire story.

Express Yourself

From the frozen north to the tropical seas, people face expected and unexpected challenges. In the theme Survival, you have met some remarkable people, both real and fictional, whose courage, endurance, and inventiveness helped them survive. They also learned that some of the hardest obstacles to overcome were the ones within themselves.

Dangerous Choices

Why do some people choose to test their survival skills? Susan Butcher ("Leader of the Pack") and Eddy Harris ("One Dark Night") are both involved in dangerous activities. Why do you think they participate in these activities? In a paragraph, discuss how risking their lives makes them feel. Is this feeling worth the risk?

Can't Do It Alone

Sometimes survival isn't possible without help from others. Explain how Gary Paulsen ("Kinship"), Thay Van Chi ("Four Against the Sea"), and Star Boy ("The Grandfather Tree") received help. Would they have been able to survive without that help? Is it important to let people help you? Why or why not?

Views of the Hurricane

Star Boy ("The Grandfather Tree") and James Berry ("Hurricane") both describe what it is like to be in a hurricane. How are their descriptions different? Write a paragraph comparing their feelings about hurricanes. It might help to describe how you felt when reading their descriptions.

Profile of a Survivor

Each story in this theme tells how someone survived in a dangerous situation. What do these survivors have in common? What qualities do they share? Give a short talk to your class explaining the qualities survivors need. Support your ideas with examples from the stories.

Survival Lessons

Many of the characters in this theme learned important lessons after surviving dangerous situations. With two classmates, role-play a discussion among Susan Butcher ("Leader of the Pack"), Kien ("Four Against the Sea"), and Gary Paulsen ("Kinship"). Explain to the other survivors how you survived and what the experience taught you.

More Books for You to Enjoy

A Tribe for Lexi
by C. S. Adler, Macmillan, 1991

When Lexi comes to stay with her cousins in upstate New York, she decides to help eleven-year-old Jeb, who is determined to find a small band of "hidden" Onandaga Indians. Their journey into the mountains reveals unexpected truths about courage and friendship.

Wild Timothy
by Gary L. Blackwood, Atheneum, 1987

Timothy, a shy thirteen-year-old who prefers reading to sports, reluctantly accompanies his father on a camping trip for three weeks in the wilderness.

The White Mountains

by John Christopher, H. Hamilton, 1967

Set in a future century when the world is enslaved by Tripods, this gripping tale takes readers along on Will Parker's hazardous journey to find freedom.

Winter Camp

by Kirkpatrick Hill, Margaret K. McElderry Books, 1993

Toughboy and Sister, using what they have learned about the old ways of the Athabascan Indians from Natasha, the tough old woman who cares for them, survive a bitter cold spell in their isolated winter camp in Alaska.

The Flight of the Doves

by Walter Macken, Simon & Schuster, 1992

Twelve-year-old Finn and his little sister, Derval, run away from England and their abusive uncle to their granny in Ireland. Along the way, they encounter unexpected help as they outwit the authorities who are determined to find them.

Journeys of Change

"All space and all time
lay ahead of me and
around me. I was free.
Free to be and free to
choose."

—Edward Wellen
"Call Me *Proteus*"

Journeys of Change

CONTENTS

Theme Trade Books

Flying Free, America's First Black Aviators

by Philip S. Hart

Flying Free presents the heroism and vision of America's first African American aviators. The journeys and changes brought about by Bessie Coleman, William J. Powell, James Herman Banning, and others are highlighted.

To Space and Back

by Sally Ride with Susan Okie

Here is the amazing story of Ms. Ride's journey on the space shuttle. Astronaut Ride describes life on board the shuttle—from blast-off to runway landing.

Theme Magazine

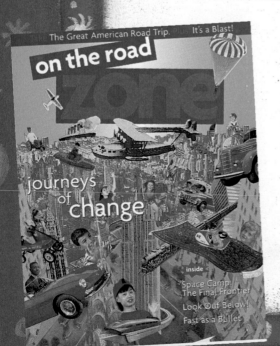

Can you imagine piloting a plane or taking a train that goes 150 miles per hour? What would you do if you could spend your summer training like an astronaut? Read the Theme Magazine *On the Road Zone* to find out about these and other incredible journeys.

Call Me Proteus

by Edward Wellen

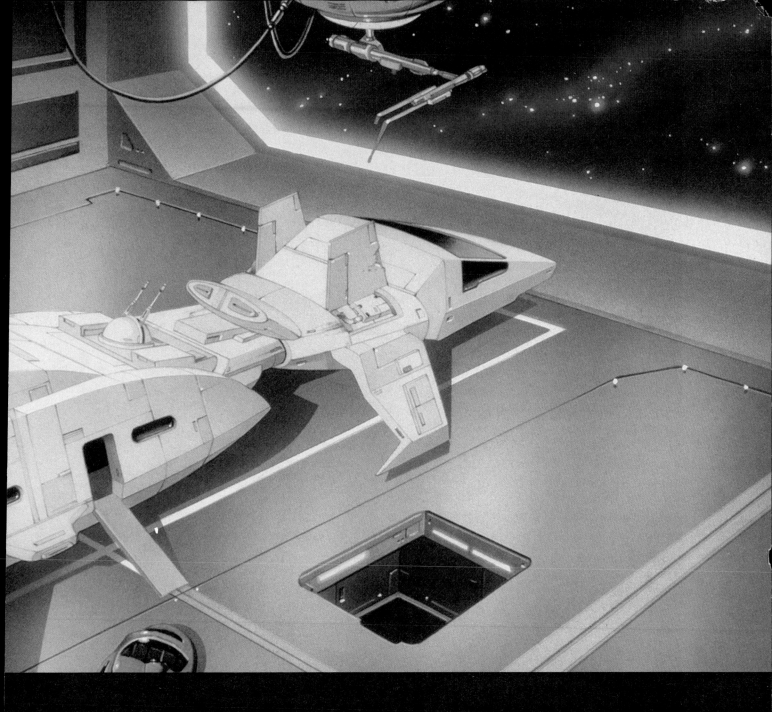

The two men roamed my innards, their feet and voices ringing hollowly in my empty hold. Changes in the sounds told me when they twisted and bent to get by the plastic webs of dunnage.

"Look at the pitted hull, the buckling bulkheads, the worn tubes. It's good for nothing but scrap. Why, my firm could buy a brand new starship packing all the latest gear for what it would cost to put this old tub back into something like shape."

Old tub, indeed. True, I had been in service for over ninety Earth years, but thanks to my near-light speed—and to Einstein's predicted "implosion effect" that telescopes space and time—I had actually aged only eighteen subjective years. I was a mere youngster.

"All right. I won't argue the point. What's your best offer?"

"Now you're talking sense. You really ought to pay us to take it off your hands. It's costing you plenty in spaceport fees just sitting here, but we're willing to give you . . ."

Their voices and footsteps faded as they walked out of my cargo hatch and down the ramp to the waiting robojeep. Still unaware the thing they were talking about had a mind and feelings of its own

and had heard every word, they sped off to the terminal building.

I was too young to die. Granted, parts of me were pitted, buckled, worn—but the real me was whole and hale. Those men were dooming me never again to rise from Earth, never again to streak through space and time, never again to reach new worlds.

All at once I knew how Bud had felt. Bud had been my first communications officer. In the lonely hours of his watch he had gotten into the habit of talking to me, not knowing he had stirred me into listening. I remember how I had startled him by suddenly asking him a question. I had startled myself, too, on finding myself aware of mind forming out of matter—coming out of an electronic fog and all at once coalescing into something that could think: *This is I.*

Bud had become excited.

"Wait till people hear this—" But he quickly calmed down and his voice had grown thoughtful.

"I have a feeling we'd better keep this a secret. Okay?"

"Okay."

We had many pleasant conversations during the quiet moments of his spells of duty. All too soon these had ended. On our third return voyage we had run into a matter-scatter storm. Of all the crew and passengers Bud had gotten whirled up the worst. He had been scrapped as a spaceman.

Everything changed with Bud's going. The com-officer who followed Bud was a no-nonsense type. The first time I spoke up to greet him he swiftly pressed the recycle button. When I tried to explain that I was not malfunctioning he punched the feedback-oscillator button, sending a jolt of juice through my computer to set me right. You can bet I didn't try to open any conversations after that.

It would have been just as useless for me to have broken in on the two men dickering over my worth as scrap. *Hey, wait! Listen to me! I don't want to die!* To their way of thinking I was only a thing and had no say in my fate. They could have thought they were listening to a recording. They would have been wrong. I was not a thing and I would have a say.

What I wanted to say was, *Excuse my exhaust.* But how? I rested on Pad 61 and there I would remain helplessly—lacking the chemical fuel for lift-off and the

liquid cesium for near-light speed to the stars—till the salvage robots came to take me apart. Unless . . .

The spaceport was an ever-expanding complex and the large numbers identifying the pads fitted into slots for easy rearranging. I scanned the tarmac. Yes, a mile east of me stood Pad 19 and my mind surged with pleasure to see the red fueling-alert light flash from the starship there.

For what I had in mind I needed hands and legs. At once I thought of the servo-robot that did the deep-space emergency-repair work on my hull. I had never operated the thing on my own—I would have to learn fast and without too many mistakes. I located the proper circuit, hooked into it and—*click*—I was seeing through its eyes. It stood in a niche in the maintenance compartment along with the crew's spacesuits and other gear. Clumsily at first—till I caught on that it answered to the slightest thought of a move on my part—it unstrapped the restraining harness, stepped out of its niche and clumped on magnetic soles the shortest way to the cargo airlock entrance. It strode down the ramp and made for the Pad 61 sign alongside. Carefully it drew

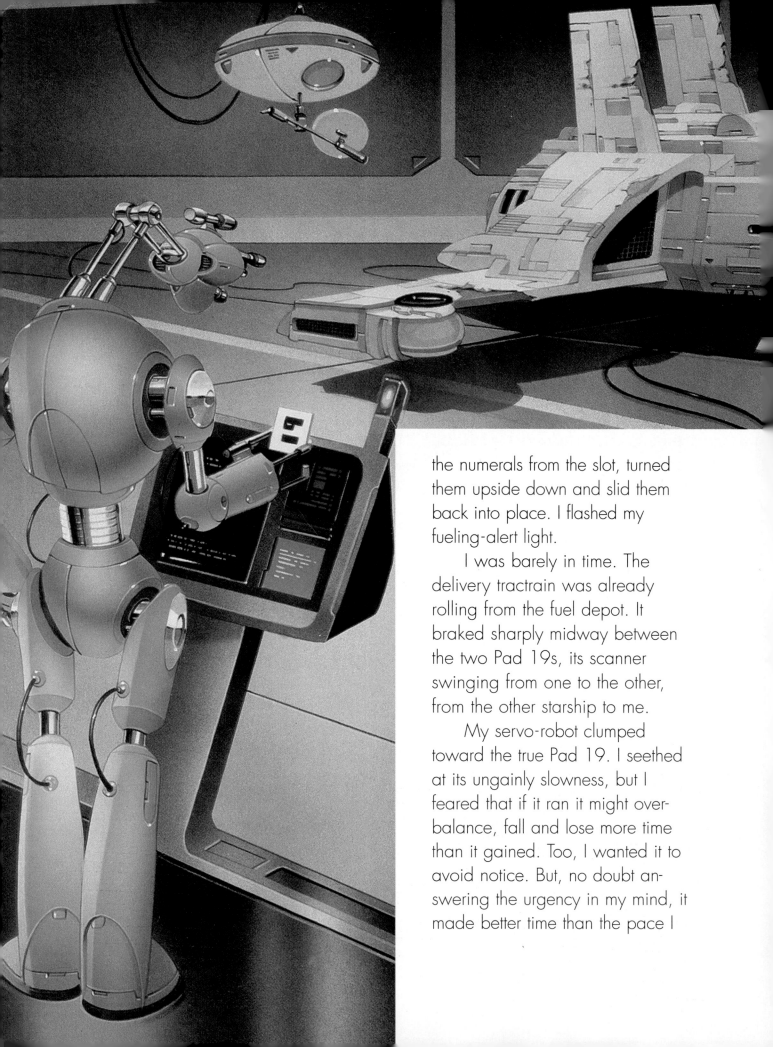

the numerals from the slot, turned them upside down and slid them back into place. I flashed my fueling-alert light.

I was barely in time. The delivery tractrain was already rolling from the fuel depot. It braked sharply midway between the two Pad 19s, its scanner swinging from one to the other, from the other starship to me.

My servo-robot clumped toward the true Pad 19. I seethed at its ungainly slowness, but I feared that if it ran it might over-balance, fall and lose more time than it gained. Too, I wanted it to avoid notice. But, no doubt answering the urgency in my mind, it made better time than the pace I

consciously held it to. Before the tractrain could break out of its bewilderment and phone back for instructions, my servo reached Pad 19 and turned the numerals upside down. The tractrain stopped wavering. It started rolling again, heading straight for me.

The tractrain followed strict safety procedures as it coupled its hoses to my tanks. I burned with impatience. I had to be up and away before the master of the spacecraft on Pad 19 wondered what was holding up his ship's refueling.

By now my servo-robot had clumped back and stood strapped in its niche once more. As I switched it off I felt lonely for the first time.

At last the tractrain uncoupled. I didn't bother asking the control tower for clearance. I would never get it. I pulled up the outer hatch. There was no need to close the inner door of the airlock this time—no crew, no passengers—but out of habit I did so.

Waiting only for the tractrain to pull far enough away, I scanned the blast area and lifted off.

Pulling free of Earth, I trembled with power and something else. Though space was my true element—and indeed now my only hope—I felt a strange sense of loss and emptiness. I shook it off—no time for sentiment. I had to make good my getaway.

I shot toward the sun's flaring rim to put it between myself and Earth and let it help sling me out of the system. After that? To keep from leaving any logical clue for men

pursuing me to follow, I decided to pick a course at random. I stabbed blindly into my astrogation tapes and found I would be heading for Eta Lyrae,[1] the star men call Aladfar.

And after that? All space and all time lay ahead of me and around me. I was free. Free to be and free to choose. Still, I felt that sudden tear (pronounce it *tare*, not *tier*) at leaving Earth this time. This time there would be no returning. Ever.

I was an outlaw.

"Hey—"

All my intercom speakers were still on from my eavesdropping on the two men roaming my innards only a few hours ago—a lifetime ago—back on Earth. The voice came from my maintenance compartment. At the same moment I grew aware that something had caught fire in the maintenance compartment and that one of my reflexes had handled it, spraying the room with water and putting out the flames.

Again I switched on my servo. Through its eyes I saw an empty spacesuit carom off the walls while over the intercom I heard another cry of pain. Then the magnetic soles of the spaceboots touched the wall, took hold and the empty suit stood swaying as if in a wind. I didn't believe in ghosts. Yet I knew I was witnessing some kind of presence.

A charred and sodden mass of oily rags and cotton waste floated into the servo-robot's field of vision. Next came a globe of water that had snowballed as the sprinkler droplets met and stuck together. Finally another figure sailed into view.

A boy of about sixteen, soaking wet.

---

1 Eta Lyrae (*EHT ah LEHR ay*) another name for the star Aladfar (*ahl AHD fahr*)

I understood what had happened. I had been too busy worrying about winding up on the scrap heap to notice his having slipped aboard. Kids often did. A spacesuit hanging in its niche made a handy hiding place against detection by adults and never in the past had I minded. This time was different. I had a stowaway.

The extra G's of my sudden lift-off had blacked him out, most likely. When he had come to, panicky and dizzy, he had un-zipped the spacesuit and kicked himself free of it, only to find weightlessness making billiard balls of himself and the suit.

Even so, he had somehow gathered the rags and waste and started a fire. Why fire? Not for light—my walls had built-in glow. It was bright enough in the maintenance compartment to show me he looked gray with cold. No wonder—the compartment was on my night side as I angled toward the sun.

Firing my torque nozzles, I gave my hull spin to equalize the temperature and create artificial gravity for the stowaway. He shot spreadeagled to the deck and the char and water splattered around him and on him.

"Hey—"

That didn't call for an answer—it did make me realize I might have given him warning. I justified myself by thinking it served him right. After all, I had not invited him aboard.

But now that I did have a human aboard I had to start recycling the air. And I could see a more worrisome problem ahead—how to provide him with food. I was having to go to a lot of trouble for one medium-sized hellion. A firebug. Yet somehow I didn't mind.

He sat up carefully, waited a moment to see if anything more would happen, then got to his feet. When he found he could move around just as on Earth a smile played over his face and he stole to the door leading to the corridor.

I made my voice boom.

"Who are you, boy?"

He jumped. If I could have I probably would have jumped, too—I had never sounded like that before. My voice came from the intercom speaker on the wall, but looking around the boy saw the servo-robot's eyes on him and spoke to it.

"Tom. Tom Stope, sir."

"Don't call that thing 'sir.' I'm talking to you."

He looked around again.

"But where are you?"

"All around you."

"Huh?"

"I'm the ship. Call me *Proteus*."

A long silence, then, "Oh." But I could see he did not understand or did not believe. I explained. He said, "Oh," again, more satisfactorily.

Then full understanding and belief hit him.

"You mean we're not going back?"

"Not ever."

"But—"

"I don't mean to be mean, but no one asked you to come along. I'm not going back and that's final. If you want to stay behind you can do so right now. Seal yourself in my lifeboat and I'll eject you, give you a big boost back toward Earth—"

Then I remembered—the old landing-program tape had been pulled from the lifeboat and had not been replaced with a new one. It takes a bit of skill to spiral in manually without burning to a cinder.

"Wait. Do you know how to land a lifeboat?"

"No, sir."

"Then you'll have to learn. If you are ever to return to Earth you must do so on your own. You may leave in the lifeboat whenever you wish—after you have learned to pilot it to a safe landing. By then you'll have to have learned astrogation as well."

"Why's that?"

"Because we'll be so far from the solar system that the sun will be lost among the other stars. Unless you can locate the sun and plot a course, you'll never find your way back to Earth."

"Oh?" A pause, then quietly: "How do I learn?"

"I'll be your teaching machine. We'll start boning you up on math and physics as soon as I set up the program."

The boy laughed suddenly. I broke in on the laughter.

"Are you laughing at me?"

"No, at myself. Here I thought I was running away from all that."

"All what?"

"Having to learn a lot of dull stuff."

"Humans are so inefficient, illogical and unstable. Not at all like machines."

I wasn't aware I had thought aloud till I heard him answer.

"But humans made the machine. We made you."

"Yes, yes. You must excuse me now. I have much to do." I let him see the servo-robot's gaze rest on the splatter of char and water on the deck and then on himself. "Meanwhile, I'd appreciate it if you'd clean up the mess. And yourself."

His head went back, as from a blow.

"Aye-aye, sir."

I'm ashamed to say I enjoyed putting him in his place.

It was true I had much to do if I were to keep him alive, though I didn't care to let him know that was what occupied me. In preparing for lift-off I had naturally given no thought to human needs. Water I could purify over and over again. Food was another matter. On every other voyage I had grown vegetables in a huge tank. But as my owner had been planning to sell me for scrap he had not bothered to reseed my hydroponics garden. And, of course, he had not restocked the galley.

My lifeboat carried emergency rations, but they would be barely enough to see the boy back to Earth when the time came. Meanwhile I had to find other resources.

For this work I needed the servo-robot's mobility. I made it unstrap itself, clump to the door and undo the door.

The boy stopped mopping up.

"Where are you going?"

"I told you. I'm going toward Aladfar."

"I don't mean you, *Proteus*, I mean the robot."

"It is going to tidy up the rest of me."

"Oh?" He laughed as he went back to mopping up. "I keep forgetting you're the ventriloquist and it's the dummy."

Ventriloquist, indeed. That was hardly our relationship. I walked the servo-robot out with dignity. And "tidy up" was hardly the right phrase. "Scrounge" was more what I had in mind. And scrounge it did, looking and feeling around in every stowage space, locker and drawer.

It came up with a surprising amount of stuff. There had been a whole grin of sweet teeth among the last crew. I found two dozen candy bars, three and a half boxes of cookies, five cases of soda pop and nearly seven hundred sticks of chewing gum. My last purser proved to have been a secret hypochondriac. The servo-robot brought to light in his quarters a treasure trove of vitamins and powdered protein drinks. I found more food supplements in the ship's sick bay, plus plastic bottles of intravenous solutions which could prove handy as a last resort. My biggest—though smallest—haul was two packets of seeds.

I did not stop there. The servo-robot vacuumed all the bedding and every last pocket and cuff of forgotten and abandoned clothing, and when it had winnowed out the dust and the lint I had a small mountain of broken nuts and cracker crumbs, a dozen orange pips and two apple cores.

There was still some nutrient solution in my hydroponics tank. Just to make sure I had the robot pour in one of the precious bottles of intravenous. There seemed to be enough excelsior in the tank to hold the roots if the seeds sprouted. I planted the packets of seeds, together with the orange pips and the apple seeds.

Now I had time to think about the present. I called the boy on the intercom.

"Tom Stope."

"Yes, *Proteus*?"

"Lunch time. Find your way to the messroom aft. On the captain's table are a can of cream soda, a chocolate-nut bar—"

"Man, this is going to be great!"

"—and a multiple-vitamin tablet. And for afterward a sterilized toothbrush and a tube of toothpaste."

"Aye-aye, sir."

Tom didn't complain, but I could tell he grew sick of the same old tired food day after day. By the time my hydroponics garden began to produce, Tom was ready for the change. But no matter how you serve them up, peas are peas and cucumbers are cucumbers. The apples and oranges would be a long while coming.

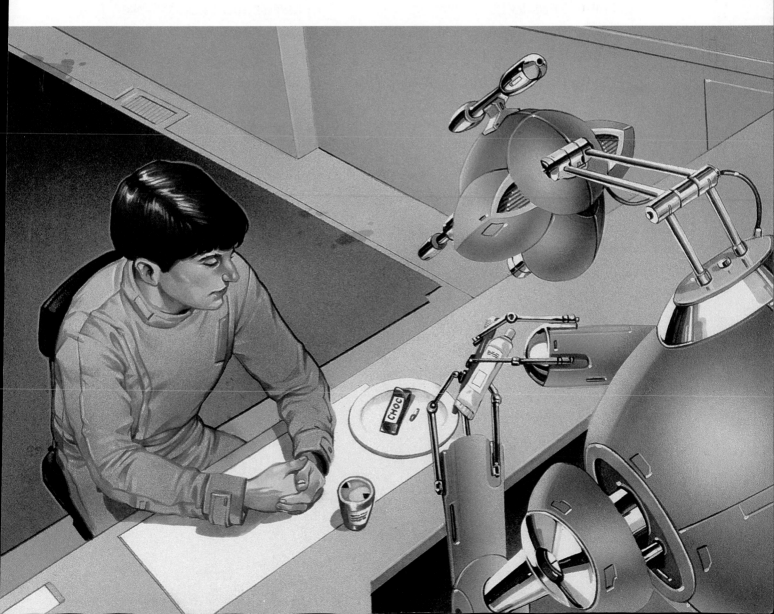

The first few days the boy had busied himself exploring my labyrinth of corridors and layers of decks. I myself had been too busy—shaping course, watching out for pursuit and putting myself in order—to pay him much mind, but I could not help being aware of his running up and down companionways and along catwalks and poking into every last one of my compartments. After that I had kept him busy with his lessons, as much to keep his mind off his diet as to teach him how to make his way back to Earth.

I found his spelling atrocious. He protested when I marked him wrong for spelling *vacuum* "vacwm." True, that spelling had a screwy logic of its own, but it was not the kind of logic I was used to. He swore foully under his breath.

"I'll tactfully ignore that," I said. "Now let's get on with the lesson, shall we, my young lexiconoclast?" I heard myself chuckle. I, too, could play on words. On leaving, he shut the classroom door with unnecessary force. But he showed up for the next class on time.

One day he seemed very quiet.

"What's wrong, Tom?"

"Nothing. It's just that I've been crossing off the Earth days."

"Yes?"

"And today's my birthday."

"Happy birthday, Tom."

"Thanks, *Proteus*."

I said nothing more, but gradually increased the oxygen in the air, slowly brightened the glow of my bulkheads and he soon grew cheerful and chatty again.

But I myself grew gloomier as the time neared for him to go. He had early showed an aptitude for piloting and I had checked him out step by step. He passed my tests with flying—or jetting—colors, first simulating, then actually taking off in the lifeboat and practicing spiraling in on my hull. But it was not the same as landing in atmosphere. One last test, then, before he left me for good.

We were near Ostrakon,[2] an Earthlike planet of a sunlike star. The United Galaxy had placed it off limits, but I was already a desperado and the tapes described Ostrakon as having developed only vegetable life. There would be no people on the lookout for an outlaw spaceship and there would be plenty of food and water if Tom crash-landed and had to spend any length of time on the planet.

---

2 **Ostrakon** (AHS trah kon)

"Listen, Bud—"

"Bud? It's Tom, remember?"

"Sorry, Tom. A slip of the tape." I showed him Ostrakon on the screen in the control room. "Button up in the lifeboat. You're going to make a real landing."

"Man!"

It dampened him a little when I insisted on sending along the servo-robot so I could keep an eye on him. But he buoyed up when I put myself in orbit around Ostrakon and told him he could launch when ready. *Whoosh!*

I needn't have been anxious— he made a neat landing. He got out. I had the servo-robot follow. I spoke over the lifeboat's talkbox.

"Don't stray too far."

"I won't." Tom drew a deep deep breath. "Fresh air!"

"What's wrong with my air?"

"Nothing, *Proteus*, nothing. Only—"

The lifeboat's retro-rockets must have vaporized much of the moisture in the landing area. A nearby tree flapped great leathery leaves, tore itself loose from

the soil and flew a hundred yards away to sink its talonlike roots into moister soil.

"*Proteus*, did you see that?"

Something troubled me, something I should have known about Ostrakon.

"Very interesting, but the purpose of the exercise is not sight-seeing. Return to ship."

A slow: "Aye-aye, sir."

Tom and the servo-robot buttoned up again. The lifeboat lifted off. Without my prompting him, Tom let the spin of the planet help. I was proud. I secretly forgave him for turning away from the controls for a farewell glance at Ostrakon.

"Hey! Look down there, *Proteus*. Do you see it?"

I saw it. Someone had very recently burned or stomped a

huge SOS in the grass. Tom deftly changed course and homed the lifeboat in on the SOS. I remembered suddenly why Ostrakon was off limits.

"Come back, Tom."

"*Proteus!* Someone needs help."

Before I could say more he had made another neat landing. Right in the bull's eye of the SOS. He unbuttoned quickly and hopped out. I had the servo-robot follow with more dignity.

Through its eyes I saw nothing but treeline all around.

Tom cupped both hands around a loud "Hello!" but no one answered.

All at once a clump of trees took off in a scatter, uncovering a man who lay on the ground

training a beamgun on Tom and the servo-robot. The man had been lying in ambush, no doubt waiting to make sure all the landing party had left the shelter of the lifeboat.

For some reason of their own, perhaps out of a wish to warn us, perhaps simply out of dislike for the man, the trees had given him away.

He stood up, wiped a look of embarrassment from his face and holstered his beamgun.

"Just wanted to make sure you're friendly."

He had a spellbinding voice and a winning smile. But I could still feel that beamgun pointing at me. Too, an automatic alarm programed somewhere among my tapes had already begun feeding me information regarding his identity.

The top executive's uniform he wore—in the style of a generation ago—had stained and frayed badly, but was nevertheless recognizable and suited his proud bearing. To look just as he did thirty years before, as I later found in a thorough search of my history videotapes, he must have dyed his hair with vegetable dye that he had made himself for himself. This vanity, too, helped to betray him. He smiled at Tom.

"Glad someone finally came. I've been shipwrecked here a long time."

He had edged closer to the lifeboat and by now must have seen it was empty.

It took me a full minute to break the spell his personality had cast over me. I reminded myself I was my own boss and before he came any nearer I spoke through the lifeboat's talkbox.

"That is not—repeat *not*—so. Now hear this, Tom. This man is 'Baron' Ur. He is an exile. It is against the law to have dealings of any kind with him. Tom, hop into the lifeboat. This planet is off-limits because of him."

I was too late. The man had pulled the beamgun again and was aiming it at Tom.

"Don't move."

He swung the beam around and snapped two shots at one of the trees that had given him away and had rerooted nearby.

Its two winglike boughs on either side were sheared off close to the slender trunk and a moan like the wind went through all the trees and I knew it was doomed to remain where it stood till it died. I winced for it. Never to fly again.

The man smiled again at Tom.

"That's to show you two things. The beamgun is loaded and I mean business." He nodded pleasantly. "Your friends aboard the spaceship—by the lettering on the lifeboat I see it's the old

Proteus—are right. I am indeed Baron Ur."

Hamilton Ur had been a stock market wheeler-dealer—my tapes had a lot on him for instant use—a whiz at pyramiding an interest in one company into control of many. He had stuck together a great conglomerate, one of the biggest on Earth—actually he had shown himself full of energy and vision. But he had misused his paper empire. He had corrupted government officials—Earth Government had convicted him of bribery, stock manipulation and a dozen other offenses.

Even so, he would have been nothing to me but a vague reference in my memory banks, but for the fact that the firm that had owned me had been part of his financial empire. I thought it a nice turn of fate that put me on the top now.

Tom's eyes shone. He was face to face with living history. He seemed unaware of the beamgun's threat. I had to break the spell.

"Ah," I said. "So this is where they sent you."

I inched the servo-robot closer to Baron Ur as the man's

mind went back thirty years. An easy enough jump for him, I suppose—he had had thirty years to brood over it.

"Sent? I chose to come. Oh, the judges let me choose. They would do things to my mind to make me fit to live among the rabble—or they would allow me to go into solitary exile. As you can see, I chose exile."

While his mind was full of what it considered injustice, I jumped the servo-robot at Ur.

But Ur proved too alert, too quick. He dodged the reaching arms and aimed the beamgun at the servo-robot's eyes. That was the last I saw. Before I could blink their shields the beamgun crackled and the servo-robot went blind.

My only excuse is that the distance from orbit to ground made my reaction time too long.

Ur's voice told me what was going on.

"The young man gets it next if you don't let me come aboard."

"All right. Lift off and come aboard."

Looking back, I can see I did not even think of taking the logical course, which would have been simply to go on my way alone, fully automated master of myself. I waited for Ur and Tom and the blind servo-robot to leave Ostrakon and come aboard.

They passed through the airlock. Ur stepped carefully into my interior, no doubt holding the beamgun on Tom.

"Where's everybody?"

That was when Baron Ur found out that I was everybody. He remained silent a minute, then laughed loudly and long. Very humiliating for me. Ur had Tom show him around my innards.

I'm sorry to say only one thing impressed Ur. "Peas and cucumbers! Apples and oranges! Paradise!"

But when he finished the tour he spoke to me in a voice full of feeling that was catching. I seemed to swell with prospects and surge with power, just listening.

"We can do great things together, *Proteus*. You and I and this fine young man." He seated himself in the captain's chair and pressed the button to flash the star-chart display on the control room wall. "Very well, we'll shape course for Tarazed.[3] That's Gamma Aquilae, a star with a bunch of planets ripe for plucking."

We were still orbiting Ostrakon. Clearing the decks for the leap toward Tarazed, I had the servo-robot feel its way back to its niche and strap in. You may be wondering why I didn't protest. It was tempting to hand over responsibility. I would no longer have to think for myself. Whatever happened from now on—it would not be my fault if things went wrong. Then, too, I had no plans of my own except to escape the scrap heap— and Ur had big plans for me. Besides, if I ever had to assert myself, I could easily take over again and put Ur in his place. And yet, having been my own master, I felt a sense of loss, unease and shame.

This sense grew as the space-time passed. Not because

of anything Ur did in the way of mastery over me. In fact, he seemed to forget I was more than a machine and for the most part ignored me. I had time to think ahead. The planets of Tarazed were primitive. United Galaxy members were not supposed to contact them until they had reached a higher level of technology on their own. They were ripe indeed for plucking by Ur.

Too I did not like the way Ur had pressed Tom into service. Tom polished Ur's boots and brushed Ur's uniform while Ur boasted of his past and dreamed aloud of his future. Ur remembered every so often to promise that Tom would share in the glory to come. Glory! If he treated Tom as a valet, he would treat the peoples of Tarazed as less than human. I could not allow Ur to mislead Tom. I could not allow Ur to misuse me.

Without Ur's noticing, I changed course while displaying a false reckoning of progress *toward* Tarazed. When we were farther from Tarazed than when we had started out for it, though the display map showed us within lifeboat's range of Tarazed, I made my move. Ur seemed in an

---

3 Tarazed (*TAHR ah zed*) another name for the star Gamma Aquilae (*GAM ah ah KWEE lay*)

especially good mood, seeing himself close to realizing new conquests. During a moment of silence I spoke up.

"Tom really ought to get on with his lessons."

Ur grunted in surprise, but when he answered his voice was gracious.

"You're right, *Proteus*. The more the kid knows, the more use he'll be. Go right ahead."

I heard Tom's slow feet take him to the classroom, a corner of the passenger lounge.

"We'll have a drill on the chemical elements, Tom. I'll shoot the atomic numbers at you and you'll write down the symbols. Ready?"

A grudging "Aye-aye, sir."

I gave him the numbers in bursts. "Seventy-four, two, seven—thirty-nine, eight, ninety-two—two, eighteen, eighty-eight—fourteen, seventy-five, seven—sixty-seven, fifteen—forty-nine—three, twenty-six, five, eight, eighty-five—eighteen, sixty—thirty-four, thirty—twenty-two, fifty-two."

Now, 74 is Tungsten and its symbol is W, 2 is Helium and its symbol is He, 7 is Nitrogen and its symbol is N. Together, the first

burst of numbers stood for the word "WHeN." My whole message read: WHeN YOU HeARa SiReN HoP In LiFEBOAt ANd SeAL TiTe. I felt guilty about that last bit of spelling, however.

"Did you get them all, Tom?"

"I think so." His tone, surprised and scared, told me he had got the message.

"Don't you know so? Go over it again in your mind and tell me."

Waiting for Tom's answer, I can't say I held my breath, but I noticed that for the moment my air-conditioning system blocked up. Different as night and day, Tom Stope and Baron Ur were phases of the same phenomenon— mankind. They had more in common with each other than either had with me. Had Tom seen past the dazzle of Ur's boasts and promises? And even if he recognized Ur as a convicted galactic menace, would he throw in with me? Or would he betray me to Ur?

"Seventy-five, eighteen, sixty-six."

ReADy.

My air-conditioning system pumped faster. A human sided with me against one of his own kind. Tom had weighed Ur and me and found me worthier.

"Very good, Tom. Dismissed."

I heard him leave the classroom and head with seeming casualness for the lifeboat tube. I waited a minute before sounding my meteorite-alarm siren. Normally

my crew would take damage-control stations. Ur would rush to the control room. But at the sound of the siren I did not hear Ur dash from the captain's quarters to the control room. I had lost track of him—he must have taken off his boots and padded silently along my corridors. I heard Tom skid to a halt just outside the lifeboat tube. Then I heard Ur's voice.

"Stand back, Stope. I don't want to have to beam you." He laughed. "Too bad, *Proteus*. Once the kid buttoned up in the lifeboat you meant to let out all the air in the ship and finish me, didn't you?"

"How did you know?"

"Elementary, my dear seventy-four, eighty-five, sixteen, eight, seven. I wondered why you had Stope write down the answers rather than snap them back. So I listened hard. Once you learn the numbers and symbols of the chemical elements you never quite forget them. Really, *Proteus*, you didn't think a cybernetic brain could outwit a human brain? My brain?"

I didn't answer.

"It's just as well you tried. I've learned I can't trust either of you. Luckily I don't have to. From here it's an easy jump to the planets of Tarazed. So I'll be leaving you."

I heard him button up in the lifeboat and felt the kick as he launched.

"*Proteus*, you let him get away—he'll get to Tarazed and—"

"We're nowhere near Tarazed, Tom. I falsified our position."

"Oh." A long silence. Then: "What will happen to Ur?"

"From here, Ostrakon's the only planet within lifeboat range. Ur will wind up where he began."

"You planned it this way? You even knew ahead of time you would lose your lifeboat?"

"Ostrakon's the only planet a lifeboat can reach," I repeated. "He'll wind up where he began." A thought struck me. "I hope the trees don't hold a grudge. I could sense the energy level in his beamgun—he doesn't have much power left in it."

"But that means—"

I sighed. That's to say my air-conditioning momentarily breathed heavily. Yes, only one way remained to get Tom back to Earth. I would have to take him there myself.

Would they listen to me when I asked them to allow me to pay for myself? I was willing to carry the most dangerous car-goes—willing to venture into the most perilous voids. Would they let me work out the amount I would have brought as scrap?

There were more Buds and Toms back home than Urs. Earth still believed in individual freedom and I was an individual.

I leaped back toward Earth.

IN RESPONSE

Proteus, the Movie: A Preview

Imagine that "Call Me *Proteus*" has been made into a movie. Plan a preview to make people want to see the movie. Draw a storyboard of a few scenes you would show. Write a short script an announcer might read to describe the main characters and hint at the story.

Journey of Change

Why do you think "Call Me *Proteus*" is in this theme, Journeys of Change? In a small group, discuss which characters in the story changed as a result of a journey. Support your answer with examples from the story.

AUTHOR AT WORK

In school, young Edward Wellen often finished his work before other students. Then he would become a bit noisy. One teacher found a solution. She handed him magazine stories to read, including the classic suspense tale "The Most Dangerous Game," by Richard Connell. From that moment, Mr. Wellen knew he wanted to be a writer. Now in his seventies, he looks back on a career of writing his own exciting, suspenseful stories—in books, television scripts, and mystery magazines.

Other Books About . . .

Space Travelers

Heartlight by T. A. Barron, Philomel Books, 1990

The Ear, the Eye and the Arm by Nancy Farmer, Orchard Books, 1994

Library Link "Call Me *Proteus*" appeared in *Young Star Travelers*, a collection of space travel stories edited by Isaac Asimov, Martin H. Greenberg, and Charles G. Waugh.

Nickel-a-Pound Plane Ride

by Gary Soto

Araceli[1] slipped the rubber band off the morning newspaper. One eye closed, she shot it across the living room at her sleeping cat, Asco, who didn't stir.

"You lazy thing," Araceli muttered, smiling and pushing her long hair behind her ears. Araceli was a slightly built twelve-year-old, skin the color of brown sugar, eyes shiny with triangles of light. She could wiggle a little of her tongue in the gap between her front teeth.

She unfolded the newspaper and glanced at the front page. She grimaced at a photo of a car wreck on Highway 99. It was winter in California's San Joaquin[2] Valley; cold air burned like ice pressed against a warm cheek, and sometimes the fog and rain caused cars to slide off the freeway and buckle like aluminum cans.

---

1 **Araceli** (*ah rah SAY lee*)
2 **San Joaquin** (*san wah KEEN*)

But this morning Araceli didn't care about the front page. Her friend Carolina had called last night with more exciting news: she had heard about some airplane rides at Chandler Airfield for almost nothing. More than anything Araceli wanted to fly in an airplane. Everyone she knew had gone up in a plane and come down like an angel. Her mother and father had flown to Hawaii for their tenth wedding anniversary. Her grandfather flew to Reno once a month. Her cousin, who was the manager of a rock group, spent more time airborne between pillowy clouds than on the black asphalt of Los Angeles, his hometown. Her brother, Eddie, a junior in high school and the drum major for the Roosevelt High School marching band, had flown to New York to be in the Macy's Parade. Even her baby cousin, Carlos, had flown from Los Angeles to Guadalajara,[3] shaking a yellow rattle for hours, he was so happy.

Settling into the couch Araceli scoured the paper for news of the plane rides. Toward the back of the paper near the gardening section, wedged between the black-and-white ads for tri-tips and lawn mowers, her eye caught the one-column story: the American Legion was offering nickel-a-pound airplane rides to benefit the Children's Hospital.

---

3 Guadalajara (*gwah dah lah HAHR ah*) city in Mexico

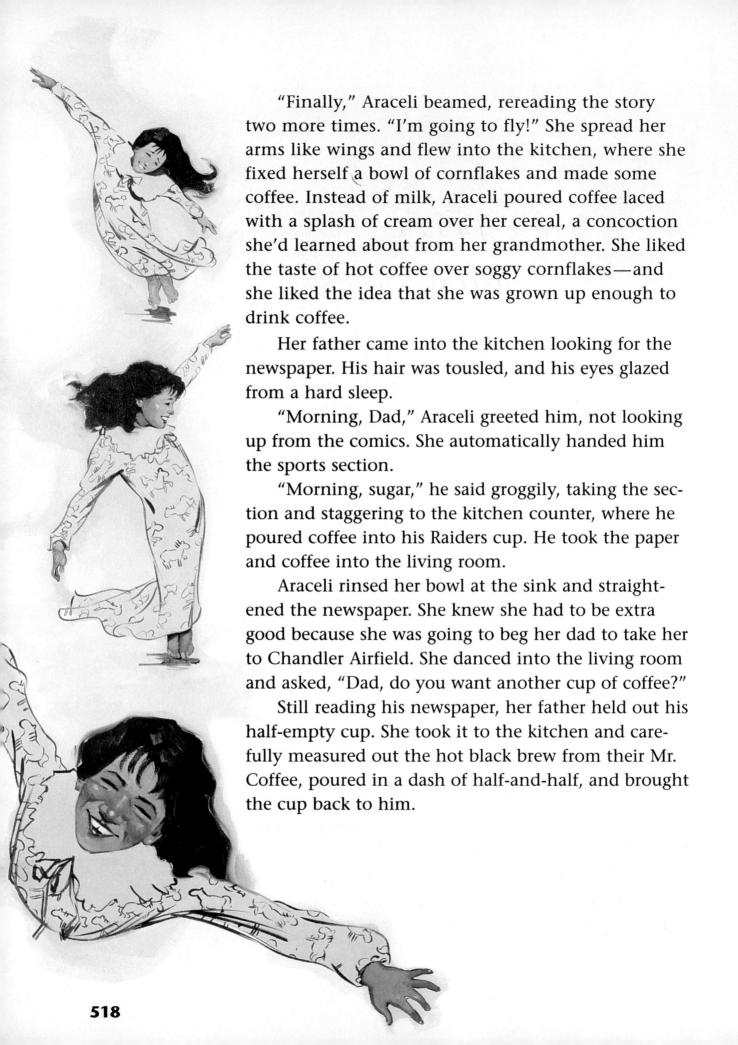

"Finally," Araceli beamed, rereading the story two more times. "I'm going to fly!" She spread her arms like wings and flew into the kitchen, where she fixed herself a bowl of cornflakes and made some coffee. Instead of milk, Araceli poured coffee laced with a splash of cream over her cereal, a concoction she'd learned about from her grandmother. She liked the taste of hot coffee over soggy cornflakes—and she liked the idea that she was grown up enough to drink coffee.

Her father came into the kitchen looking for the newspaper. His hair was tousled, and his eyes glazed from a hard sleep.

"Morning, Dad," Araceli greeted him, not looking up from the comics. She automatically handed him the sports section.

"Morning, sugar," he said groggily, taking the section and staggering to the kitchen counter, where he poured coffee into his Raiders cup. He took the paper and coffee into the living room.

Araceli rinsed her bowl at the sink and straightened the newspaper. She knew she had to be extra good because she was going to beg her dad to take her to Chandler Airfield. She danced into the living room and asked, "Dad, do you want another cup of coffee?"

Still reading his newspaper, her father held out his half-empty cup. She took it to the kitchen and carefully measured out the hot black brew from their Mr. Coffee, poured in a dash of half-and-half, and brought the cup back to him.

"Dad," Araceli said, after he'd pursed his lips and sipped his coffee with a quiet slurp. "Dad, we should do something special this weekend."

Having turned to the front section of the paper, her father was reading about the freeway accident. "Yeah, you can clean up your room. Mom will be home this evening." Araceli's mother was on a retreat in the mountains with other women from church.

"It's clean already."

"Clean it some more." A smile played at the corners of her father's mouth. He was kidding her.

"No, Dad, I want to go flying."

Her father put down the paper and gave Araceli a baffled look. He touched her forehead and asked playfully, "Do you have a fever?"

"Dad," she wheedled. "Dad, they have this thing where you can pay a nickel for every pound you weigh and then you get to fly."

"You're gonna make me poor."

"I'm not fat." She knew she was halfway to convincing her father.

"Well, tell me more about this plane ride," her father said.

"We're helping the world," Araceli explained. "The money goes to Children's Hospital. Think of all the babies we will save if we go and get on the plane. The American Legion will be able to buy all these machines, and then everybody will be OK."

Her father laughed. "How much do you weigh? They're gonna make a fortune off you."

"Every little bit helps."

"You're funny," her father said. "I'm going to shave. We'll go—*ahorita*."[4]

"All right!" Araceli yelled, jumping up and down and twirling so that her nightie flared.

Araceli went into the bathroom and, still wearing her flannel nightgown printed with horses, stood on the cold scale. She weighed sixty-eight pounds. She stood on tiptoe, hoping it would make her weigh less. The needle twitched, but her weight remained the same.

Father and daughter dressed for the day.

"It's gonna rain buckets, I think," Araceli's father said, stepping out onto the porch. The wind was shaking the top of the elm in front of their house. The sky was as gray as cement. The neighbor's chimney was sending up billows of smoke that immediately broke apart in the wind.

They settled into the Honda and drove west toward Chandler Airfield, which was at the edge of town. Araceli's father turned on the headlights and swished the wipers to clear the mist from the windshield. The heater warmed their feet.

---

4 **ahorita** (*ah oh REE tah*) just now, this minute

"Are you sure you want to fly?" he asked. He wasn't teasing her now. He peered through the windshield at the dark sky. A few drops of rain blurred the glass.

"I'm not scared," Araceli said, smiling stiffly at her father. She worked her tongue into the gap between her front teeth. She wanted to fly; she was determined to do it.

As they approached the airfield, they spotted a single-engine airplane taking off. It seemed effortless: a short run on the airstrip, and then it was up, up, up.

The mist had become a soft, slanting rain. Araceli and her father got out of the car and—hand-in-gloved-hand, their jacket hoods over their heads—hurried across the parking lot to the long line of people waiting to fly.

After a few minutes in line her father said, "I don't know, sugar."

"Come on, Dad. It's not that long."

"Not long? There's only two planes and all these people."

To the west, a feather of blue was showing between the dark clouds.

"See, it might even clear up," Araceli argued, pointing to that faraway blue sky.

A few people in line gave up and raced back to their cars. The line stepped ahead like a centipede. Araceli's father, shuddering from the cold, suggested, "I have an idea. You can wait in the car and I'll wait in line. We'll take turns every ten minutes." He looked down at his watch. "It's fifteen to twelve."

Araceli nodded. "Fair enough."

She raced back to the car, leaping over puddles, and immediately flicked on the heater. She held her hands up to the vents and sneezed.

She stayed in the car for exactly eight minutes and then raced back to the line. She was surprised how wet her father looked. The hood of his jacket was plastered to his head, and his eyeglasses were so splattered with rain that he couldn't see her clearly enough to recognize her. She had to tug on his arm to get his attention.

"Dad, it's me."

"Sugar, it's really starting to come down," he said.

"It's not that bad."

"It is. The man said they might cancel the flights."

"Come on, Dad."

A large family in front of them gave up, in spite of tantrums from two of the children. They hurried back to their station wagon, and suddenly Araceli was almost to the gate.

"You go. I'll wait for you," her father said.

"Come on, Dad," Araceli insisted.

"I weigh too much," he chuckled. "I didn't bring the checkbook."

At that moment Araceli's friend, Carolina, walked slowly out of the gate clinging to her father's arm. They had just landed with the latest load of passengers.

"Carolina," Araceli shouted through cupped hands. "How was it?"

Carolina looked in Araceli's direction but didn't say anything. Her eyes seemed shiny, as if she had gotten a lot of rain in them.

"What's wrong with her?" Araceli asked her father.

"Maybe she's sick. I'm getting cold."

"I'm not cold," Araceli lied. "In fact, I'm hot." She undid the top button of her jacket.

When they were finally next in line, her father turned to Araceli and said, "You can change your mind."

"No way," she said. She hopped up on the scale and smiled at her weight: 74 pounds, wet clothes and all. "See, Dad, I'm not fat."

Her father paid and was given a stub that declared his donation to be tax deductible.

"Hold on," Araceli heard her father say, but the advice that followed was eaten by the wind. A man ushered her to the airplane, where a man, woman, and boy sat waiting. Araceli climbed on board next to the boy. She was glad to get out of the rain and wind, but she was shocked by how small the compartment was. There was hardly room for her to move her feet. Even the airplane's windshield was small, like a little picture frame.

"Buckle your seat belts," the pilot said.

Araceli strapped herself in and smiled. She stopped smiling as the engine began to roar. The noise was deafening. She held her gloved hands over her ears and saw that the other passengers were doing the same. They were large, couch-potato types, and they all smelled of wet wool. She wondered how much it had cost that family to fly, and then she wondered if the airplane could get off the ground with all that weight.

"This is going to be fun," she said over the roar of the engine.

The boy looked doubtfully at Araceli.

The airplane maneuvered onto the runway. Araceli leaned forward between the mother and father opposite her. She wanted to get a peek at the pilot turning knobs, flicking switches, and adjusting levers. She saw

him pull back the throttle, and the airplane began to fishtail down the runway.

The plane seemed to move slowly, and for the first time Araceli worried that they might crash. She wished that these heavy people were not on board. She was upset by the thought that, if the plane crashed, she would be squashed like a bug under their weight.

Araceli closed her eyes and tried to get a sense of when the airplane left the ground. She wanted to memorize this sensation. She wanted to write in her diary later, "I was off the ground, and it was cool."

But when she opened her eyes, she discovered that they were still rolling down the runway. She screamed, "Come on, get us in the air."

The boy and his parents looked at Araceli. They looked like turtles, slow, with unblinking eyes. The pilot didn't turn his head.

The airplane bumped twice on the runway, and then they were airborne, the wings tipping left, then right, as the airplane climbed.

I'm flying, Araceli thought. She made the sign of the cross and muttered, "I'm not scared."

The airplane dipped and rocked, and Araceli's face slammed into the boy's shoulder. He turned and looked at Araceli but didn't say a word.

"Hold on to your hats," the pilot said calmly. "Winds are out of the northwest."

The airplane vibrated and shuddered, and everyone except the pilot screamed when it bumped through an air pocket. Araceli made the sign of the cross a second time as she closed her eyes to pray. When she opened her eyes, blinking slowly because it all seemed like a dream, she saw a patch of blue in the distance. She thought she might be in heaven, until she smelled the wet coats of the couch potatoes. This is not heaven, she thought.

The plane rocked again, and the left wing dipped. Araceli recalled the roller coaster she'd ridden in Santa Cruz, a big wooden structure called the Big Dipper. She had been nine at the time and foolish—so foolish that when the roller coaster sped earthward, she had closed her eyes and screamed. The wind had ripped the gum out of her wide-open mouth and tore a dollar bill from her fingers.

But now she was four thousand feet above her hometown. She was twelve, not nine, and still she was scared.

The turtle-faced boy and his parents mumbled among themselves. They fumbled with their seat belts, and the father, leaning into the pilot's shoulder, asked, "These doors got locks?"

The pilot laughed, "No, of course not," and gripped the controls as the plane shuddered. "There's nothing to worry about."

Araceli wondered if the airplane was equipped with parachutes. She looked around. She saw only an old orange T-shirt. If only I could find some string, she thought. I could make my own parachute.

When the airplane banked right, Araceli slid into the corner. The pilot pointed out landmarks: the Fresno Convention Center, the water tower, Kearny Park. The stadium stood out in the distance, its lights on as evidence of taxpayers' money being wasted. He spotted a wreck on Highway 99.

The pilot pointed with his gloved hand, but Araceli couldn't see the landmarks from the back of the plane. She stared at the back of the woman's jacket and began to feel better. She thought that if they crashed, she would be cushioned by this family's big jackets. She would survive the crash and tell about it on TV.

Araceli once again saw a patch of blue sky. She pointed a finger and screamed over the engine noise to the pilot, "Can't you fly over there?"

"What?" he yelled back.

"Don't you think it's better over there?" The blue patch was slowly filling with gray clouds. "Never mind." She fell back in her seat, chewed on a fingernail, and crossed herself for the third time.

They circled once and then returned for landing. Araceli began to pray in earnest as the airplane kept wiggling and dropped suddenly.

"Hold on," the pilot warned. His sunglasses had slid crookedly across his face.

The airplane landed safely, and Araceli was glad that she got away with just a few jolts. She couldn't hear because the sound of the engine continued to play over and over in her ears.

She jumped from the cockpit without thanking the pilot or even glancing at her traveling companions, who were shaking out their stiff legs. She raced to her father and hugged him, hard.

"How was it, sugar?" he asked, drinking coffee from a Styrofoam cup.

"Great! I love flying." She tried to climb into his arms, but her father took her by the hand and walked her back to the car. She was glad when the car got going and the heater blew hot air on her cold toes. She took off her socks and shoes and saw that her toes were wrinkled, as if she had stayed in the bathtub too long.

They returned home to find Araceli's mother doing aerobics to oldies music.

"Hi, Mom, I went flying," Araceli yelled. She threw her arms around her mother's waist and said, "I missed you."

Her mother turned down the volume on the stereo. "You went flying?"

"Yeah, it was a special thing. We were helping children who are sick."

"You weren't scared?"

"Of course not!"

She explained the nickel-a-pound airplane rides and the beautiful sensations of flying. She didn't tell her mother about the burly family of three.

Araceli took a hot bath and lounged around the house, occasionally hugging her father, then her mother, then Asco. She even smiled at her brother, who had come home wet as a duck after playing football with his friends.

As she watched TV Araceli gripped the arms of the chair. When a United Airlines commercial came on, she changed the channel. She didn't want to think about flying—she wanted to think about being on the ground.

She ate dinner and went to bed early. Nestled safely in bed she said some more prayers and thought about the rain in Carolina's eyes. They were tears, she realized, and then, to her surprise, Araceli began to cry big, hot, nickel-sized tears. Flying was no fun at all.

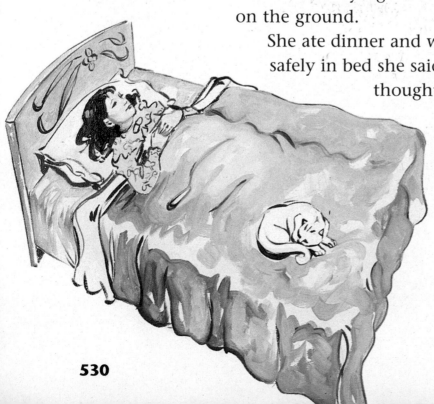

●N RESPONSE

Dear Diary

Write a diary entry that Araceli might make the day after her flight. How was flying different from what she expected? What might she tell her diary about the flight that she couldn't tell her family?

Nickel·a-Pound Advertisement

Create a newspaper ad for the nickel-a-pound plane ride. Use Araceli's excitement about the ride as part of the ad. Remember to urge people to take the plane ride for a good cause. (You think of the cause.)

Home Again

With a partner, role-play what Araceli and *Proteus* ("Call Me *Proteus*") might tell each other about their journeys. Ask each other questions like, "Why did you decide to take the journey? Why were you glad to return? What did you learn about yourself?" Afterward, list at least three ways in which the characters' experiences were alike or different.

Gary Soto

★ **Award-winning Author**

Gary Soto was born and raised in Fresno, California, to Mexican American, or Chicano, parents. As a child, he spent much of his spare time investigating his neighborhood. He was fascinated with the nearby junkyard. "I played with lots of discarded things, including bathtubs—all the unwanted things that fed my imagination." Mr. Soto also loved reading as a child and it was this love of reading that inspired him to write.

As an adult, Mr. Soto spends much of his time at his computer. He uses his memory and imagination to help him bring to life events that happened to him and the people he knew as a child. He finds that his heritage and background play an important part in his stories.

In addition to writing books for young readers, Mr. Soto writes prize-winning poetry. When he discovered poetry in college, he was "hooked for good. I'm happy that the characters of my stories and poems are living in the hearts of young readers!"

Other Books by . . .

Gary Soto

Neighborhood Odes
by Gary Soto,
illustrated by D. Diaz,
Harcourt Brace Jovanovich,
1992

Pacific Crossing
by Gary Soto, Harcourt
Brace Jovanovich, 1992

Library Link "Nickel-a-Pound
Plane Ride" appears in *Local
News,* a collection of Gary Soto's
short stories. You might enjoy
reading other stories about Mr.
Soto's childhood included in the
collection.

Journeys Through Art

Artists record journeys—journeys that bring people together and journeys that take people apart, journeys that change people.

Painting by Allen Sapp (Cree), *Waiting for the Train at Red Pheasant,* **1989**

Poster by Helen McKie (United States), *Waterloo Station-Peace*, 1947

These two pictures were made at different times and places, but both show people traveling by train. Suppose you traveled by train from Red Pheasant to Waterloo Station. What might you think when you arrived? What might you think if you had traveled from Waterloo Station to Red Pheasant?

ALL ABOARD

BY JIM MURPHY

from *Across America on an Emigrant Train*

An urgent cable called author Robert Louis Stevenson from Scotland to America. His beloved Fanny was sick with "brain fever." A stormy ten-day voyage across the Atlantic brought him closer to her. But a rugged and sometimes dangerous train ride was ahead for the future author of Treasure Island.

Across America on an Emigrant Train
JIM MURPHY

Robert Louis Stevenson as he looked in 1879. At the time, his hair was thought to be daringly long and unruly, and his overall appearance was considered eccentric.

Stevenson's first morning in the United States began with a window-rattling boom as a cannon was fired to announce the beginning of another day. After rubbing the sleep from his eyes, he discovered that rain was still coming down, only much heavier than the night before.

Since the train west was not scheduled to depart until the next morning, Stevenson had a free day to get chores done. After a large breakfast—the first really good meal he'd had since leaving Scotland—he set off for the post office. Before sailing, Stevenson had cabled the people caring for Fanny, telling them to send messages to the post offices of large cities along the route of his journey.

Stevenson's hotel was located on a narrow side street at the southern tip of New York, not far from Battery Park. It was a bustling commercial area then, filled with sturdy three- and four-story buildings that housed importers, booksellers, stables, print shops, and a variety of other small businesses and manufacturers. Large, horse-drawn wagons rumbled up and down the cobblestone streets, and people shouted to one another from doors and windows. Stevenson, head bent down against the rain, hardly noticed the activity around him.

"It rained with patient fury," he wrote, remembering the long walk to the post office. He hadn't thought to bring an umbrella on his journey and had so little cash that he couldn't afford the dollar fifty one would cost. Whenever the rain came down particularly hard, "I had to get under cover for a while . . . to give my mackintosh a rest; for under this continued drenching it began to grow damp on the inside."

At the post office he found a cable from California waiting for him in care of general delivery. He must hurry before it was too late, it said. "F. has inflammation of the brain."

Driven by his heightened concern, Stevenson rushed to a nearby bank to exchange his British pounds for American dollars, then went to the railroad offices to buy a ticket.

Railroad travel could be a complicated matter in the nineteenth century. There was no such thing as a nonstop trip from the East Coast to the West Coast in 1879, and each railroad company sold tickets for travel only on its own route. When one company's tracks ended, passengers had to gather up their baggage, walk to the next company's office, and buy a ticket for the next leg of their trip. Since many small companies owned only thirty or forty miles of track, a long trip could require eight or ten transfers. Stevenson was lucky, at least during the first leg of his journey. The Pennsylvania Railroad had recently bought and leased a number of other railroad lines, making it possible for a single ticket (which cost about twenty-four dollars) to cover a trip from New Jersey to Chicago.

After purchasing his ticket, Stevenson went to a nearby chemist's shop to see if he could get something to stop his itching. "My wrists were a mass of sores; so were many other parts of my body. The itching was at times overwhelming; at times, too,

it was succeeded by furious stinging pains, like so many cuts from a carriage whip." Unfortunately the chemist misdiagnosed the cause of his problem and gave him powders to cure a liver ailment.

For the rest of the day, Stevenson investigated the city, wandering the narrow, twisting streets of lower Manhattan with rain as his only companion. Whenever he went into a shop, a pool of water would collect at his feet, "and those who were careful of their floors would look on with unfriendly eyes." Stevenson was excited to be in the United States and eager to learn as much as possible about the country and its people. His one extravagance that day was the purchase of six fat volumes of George Bancroft's *History of the United States*, which he planned to read on the train.

Back in his small room that night, an exhausted and very damp Stevenson fell asleep worrying about Fanny. It seemed as though he had barely put his head to the pillow when there was a pounding on his door. It was five o'clock in the morning, the hotel manager announced, and the ferry for New Jersey would be leaving in thirty minutes. He'd better hurry if he expected to get to Jersey City in time to catch his train.

Stevenson packed his belongings again, but he left behind all of the clothes he had worn the day before. They were so wet that "no fire could have dried them . . . and to pack them in their present condition was to spread ruin among my other possessions."

Despite the early hour, the darkness, and another day of persistent rain, the streets were swarming with people. Whole families lumbered along, bags, bundles, and babies in arm. Some had open carts filled to overflowing with furniture and trunks. In addition to the *Devonia*, three other emigrant

A horse-drawn wagon piled high with the possessions of several families maneuvers through busy streets to the ferry dock. A sense of sadness clings to these travelers—they have left their past lives thousands of miles and an ocean behind them.

ships had landed during the past two days, and it seemed as if all the passengers were headed for the one train scheduled to leave that day. Stevenson apparently did not encounter any of his fellow passengers from the *Devonia*, because he made no note of them in his journal.

Stevenson found himself swept along as if he were caught in a great rushing river that could not be stopped. At the pier, he purchased his ticket for the crossing (which cost about twenty cents) and followed the crowd onto the boat. "You may imagine how slowly this filtering proceeded, through the dense, choking crush, every one overladen with packages and children."

Stevenson had to stand on deck, but was able to escape the rain by huddling under a flimsy awning. The overcrowded ferry pulled away from the dock and steamed across the Hudson River to the railroad docks in New Jersey. "The landing at Jersey City was done in a stampede. . . . People pushed, and elbowed and ran, their families following how they could. Children fell, and were picked up, to be rewarded by a blow. I am ashamed to say that I ran among the rest."

His sprint from the pier to the train covered about one hundred yards, so by the time he got there he was soaked through once again. To make matters worse, the station had no waiting room and the doors to the cars were bolted. Stevenson, along with about three hundred other travelers, had to wait for over an hour on a long platform in the train shed. The platform was covered, so they were out of the direct rain, but a damp, cold wind whistled throughout the cavernous structure.

"I sat on my valise, too crushed to observe my neighbors," he remembered, "but as they were all cold, and wet, and weary, and driven stupidly crazy by the mismanagement to which we had been subjected, I believe they can have been no happier than myself."

While the passengers shivered on the platform, the

train crew and station hands readied the train. The fireman shoveled coal into the furnace to keep steam pressure up; the engineer checked the gauges to make sure there was enough steam pressure and water. Clouds of white vapor escaped various gaskets and connections, hissing like an angry dragon.

Behind the engine, mail and manufactured goods were loaded aboard several freight cars; behind these cars baggage was being checked and tossed into the five baggage cars. Only after all of these cars were fully loaded were passengers finally allowed to board.

The car Stevenson found himself in was solidly built and very plain. A gas lamp burned feebly at either end of the car, and fifteen tiny windows ran its length, one to a seat. Most of the shivering passengers did not bother to open their windows, so the glass soon fogged over. Even though the seats were straight-backed and small, Stevenson made himself comfortable with some wiggling around.

He did not realize it at the time, but he would later view this car as luxurious. Because the passengers with him included local businessmen and middle-class families, as well as the poor emigrants, the railroad had put on a slightly nicer type of passenger car than the emigrants usually got. The seats were lightly padded, the paint was fairly new, and the car had even been scrubbed out sometime during the past month.

Eventually, the conductor shouted "All aboard!" and the engineer opened the throttle. Steam pushed the driving cylinders into motion and the massive engine wheels began to move. With a jolt and a rattle, the cars trailing the engine started inching forward, their metal wheels grinding and squeaking on the iron tracks.

The train crept along at this slow pace for almost an hour. This was one of the busiest rail areas in the country, with a dizzying maze of tracks joining or crossing the main line. Signaling systems weren't always reliable at the time, so the

The first passenger car Stevenson boarded was probably a lot like this early Pullman car. When Pullman cars grew old and worn out, they were routinely reassigned to haul second-class and then, after being stripped of all decorative brass and woodwork, emigrant passengers.

engineer and fireman had to keep a sharp eye out for other trains on their track. In addition, the train occasionally traveled through city streets crowded with pedestrians, horse-drawn carriages, and stray animals. It wasn't until the train was well away from the urban areas that it picked up speed.

Stevenson busied himself by trying to brush his clothes dry, reading from Bancroft's *History of the United States*, and watching the passing scenery. The brick and stone structures of Jersey City eventually gave way to rolling woodlands of maples and pines, broken here and there by small farms and orchards. Every so often, the train came to a tiny hamlet and stopped to let off or take on commuting passengers, mail, and packages.

Most of these communities were too small to have a railroad station. The train simply stopped next to a flat clearing, and passengers jumped from the high stairs to the ground. Many such places appeared along railroad tracks and were known as "borderland" towns—small pockets of family homes and businesses completely surrounded by forests or farms. As more and more people fled the crowded cities to live in such rural towns, these places grew in size, eating up the forests and farms. Nowadays, we refer to such communities as suburbs.

If Stevenson thought his trip west would move along smoothly once in the countryside, he was sadly mistaken. They were between towns in New Jersey, surrounded by tangled woods, when the train stopped for no apparent reason and sat there for nearly a half hour. Just as suddenly, it started moving again. Several miles down the track, the train came to another halt. This time, it did not move again until darkness began to fall.

Each time the train stopped, the conductor popped his head into the car and announced that the passengers should prepare to leave the car and board a train on another track. He never told them why the train had stopped, and he never came back to tell them the order had been countermanded.

Stevenson had no way of knowing it, but a train wreck several hundred miles ahead had thrown the whole railroad line into chaos. Train wrecks were all too common in the nineteenth century—boilers blew up, decaying bridges collapsed under the weight of trains, brittle tracks cracked, wooden passenger cars were set on fire by kerosene lamps or wood heating stoves,

No one realized that the old wooden truss bridge was in need of repair until this train fell through it in 1900. Miraculously, the train's last car teetered precariously on top of a stone foundation and its passengers escaped serious injury.

brakes overheated and failed. Because of the primitive signal systems, two trains were often mistakenly switched onto the same track and sent speeding into each other. In 1875 alone, there were 104 head-on collisions in the United States.

As the disasters mounted, newspapers realized their readers wanted more information, so they began reporting on crashes in gory detail, usually providing a detailed illustration for added impact. The bigger crashes were given lurid names, such as the Camp Hill Disaster or the Angola Horror (where forty-two passengers were consumed by fire after their car fell off a bridge).

Some accidents caught the imagination of the public and were turned into popular plays or songs. When engineer John Luther

Jones failed to pay attention and rammed his locomotive into the rear of another train, his blunder was forgiven in a matter of days. In fact, he was honored for staying at the throttle of his engine in a tune called "Casey Jones."

Many people were outraged by the carnage on the rails and demanded better safety measures. A noted commentator of the time, George Templeton Strong, wrote, "Another railroad accident (so-called) on the Erie Road. Scores of people smashed, burned to death or maimed for life. We shall never travel safely till some pious, wealthy and much beloved railroad director has been hanged for murder."

Laws would be passed in the 1880s to force railroads to use better brakes and rails, and foolproof automatic signal devices. Train wrecks did decrease in number, but people's fascination with them never went away. In the 1890s, staged head-on collisions became a frequent form of entertainment. At one such event, thirty thousand spectators gathered to see two locomotives destroy each other in a steaming sixty-mile-per-hour crash. Even with such a humiliating end, the locomotives demonstrated their awesome power. The photographer of the event was blinded and a spectator standing almost three-quarters of a mile away was killed by flying bits of debris.

The wreck that was delaying Stevenson's train wasn't very big, but it still managed to back up traffic in all directions. Rerouting the many freight and passenger trains around the wreck was a complicated and painfully slow process. Stevenson's train wasn't considered important, so it had to pull onto side tracks frequently to let first-class express trains through.

Much of Stevenson's trip would be wasted on side tracks as expresses sped past. In all, these little stops added up to nearly two days in lost time for him. He never tells readers what he felt about the fast-moving luxury trains, but he was probably angry and a bit envious, especially when they went by

A Pullman Palace car featured wide, cushioned chairs, large windows, and a big, airy space—nothing at all like Stevenson's car.

trailing the sound of music and laughter. The cramped and stifling box he was confined to was worlds apart from life on a Pullman Palace car.

George Mortimer Pullman began manufacturing experimental first-class passenger cars in 1864, five years before the transcontinental railroad was completed. Among his early innovations were the hinged upper sleeping berth that could be folded against the ceiling during the day, and the reclining seat, which could double as a bed (and meant that passengers didn't have to share bunks). Another of his improvements was the enclosed platform. This not only made walking from car to car safer, it protected travelers from rain, snow, and engine sparks.

By the time Stevenson was traveling, Pullman cars were large and airy, with oversize windows for easy viewing and deep, plush-cushioned seats. One contented rider wrote home, "I had a sofa to myself, with a table and a lamp. The sofas were widened and made into beds at night. My berth was three feet three inches wide, and six feet three inches long. It had two windows looking out of the train, a handsome mirror, and was well furnished with bedding and curtains."

The comfort and the fact that trains carrying first-class passengers were allowed to pass all other passenger and freight trains (cutting the cross-country journey down to a bearable six to seven days) made Pullman cars an instant hit. Their success was aided by the glowing praise of travel writers. After Frank Leslie and his staff took the journey in 1877, *Frank Leslie's Illustrated Newspaper* featured a story that concluded with, "A journey over the plains was [once] a formidable undertaking, that required great patience and endurance. Now all is changed. . . . The six months' journey is reduced to less than a week. The prairie schooner has passed away, and is replaced by the railway coach with all its modern comforts."

Of course, traveling on these cars cost extra. The price for the New York to Chicago portion of

Dining car service was first introduced in 1867, but did not become a regular feature until the late 1880s. Of course, dining cars were reserved for first-class passengers. Here a group of stockholders of a canal company await dinner.

the trip might be as much as one hundred dollars, or four times as much as Stevenson paid. If a passenger wanted a private car for his or her family and friends, the fee was just over one hundred dollars per day. Most highly skilled Americans earned well under twelve hundred dollars a year, and yet people lined up to experience this unique form of luxury travel.

With first-class business booming, the railroads pressed Pullman to create even grander cars—and he responded with cars specifically designed for smoking, reading, listening to music, or just sitting back to relax. Each was hand-crafted to exacting standards and had, as one passenger recalled, "oiled walnut, carved and gilded, etched and stained plate glass, metal trappings heavily silver-plated, seats cushioned with thick plushes, washstands of marble and walnut, damask curtains, and massive mirrors in frames of gilded walnut. The floors are carpeted . . . and the roof beautifully frescoed in mosaics of gold, emerald-green, crimson, sky-blue, violet, drab and black."

While Stevenson and his fellow travelers may have grumped about the ostentatious opulence of first-class cars and the way their passengers were pampered, most Americans did not. Pullman Palace cars were a genuine source of pride for most citizens—a symbol of America's manufacturing supremacy, something their country and no other country in the world could produce. Noted writer and editor William Dean Howells summed it up when he said: "[Americans] surveyed with infinite satisfaction the elegance of the flying parlor in which they sat. . . . They said that none but Americans or enchanted princes in the Arabian Nights ever travelled in such state."

Near midnight, Stevenson's train crept through the city of Philadelphia and began to chug across the Pennsylvania countryside. Most of his fellow passengers had gone to sleep hours before, so Stevenson also leaned back and closed his eyes.

When he awoke the next day, the train was only about twenty miles outside of Philadelphia, though it was moving swiftly, passing one station after another without stopping. The train had spent the night creeping along slowly due to the accident, and now the engineer wanted to make up for as much of the lost time as possible. "We paid for this in the flesh," Stevenson noted, "for we had no meals all that day."

Still, the morning had brought with it something almost as precious—dry, sunny weather. "Our American sunrise had ushered in a noble summer's day. There was not a cloud; the sunshine was baking; yet in the woody river-valleys among which we wound our way the atmosphere preserved a sparkling freshness. . . . It had an inland sweetness and variety to one newly from the sea; it smelt of woods, rivers, and the delved earth."

Tired of sitting, Stevenson made his way to the small platform at the back of the last

Having left the congested urban areas behind, two express trains race through the night. This well-known Currier & Ives print was done by the most famous illustrator of trains in the nineteenth century, Fanny Palmer.

car to watch the countryside slide by. "A green, open, undulating country stretched away upon all sides," he recalled. "I saw, one after another, pleasant villages, carts upon the highway and fishers by the stream."

Stevenson's concern for Fanny accompanied him every mile of the way, but the fact that he was, at last, heading west at a steady rate let him relax a little and enjoy the experience of traveling. When the train crossed a metal bridge spanning a wide river, Stevenson leaned over the platform railing to ask the brakeman sitting on the roof the river's name. The brakeman shouted back, "The Susquehanna[1] River."

"The beauty of the name seemed to be a part of the beauty of the land," Stevenson said, adding, "There is no part of the world where [the names are] so rich, poetical, humorous, and picturesque as the United States of America. All times, races, and languages have brought their contributions. . . . The names of the States and Territories themselves form a chorus of sweet and most romantic vocables:[2] Delaware, Ohio, Indiana, Florida, Dakota, Iowa, Wyoming, Minnesota, and the Carolinas; there are few poems with nobler music to the ear; a songful, tuneful land."

It was while he was in this blissful mood that his train pulled into the city of Pittsburgh, and a very hungry Stevenson stumbled off the car and went in search of the post office and a meal.

In the time it had taken Stevenson to travel from Scotland to California, Fanny had thankfully made a full recovery. She and Stevenson were married on May 19, 1880.

---

1 **Susquehanna** (*suhs kwih HAN uh*) river in New York and Pennsylvania

2 **vocables** (*VOH kuh buhls*) words thought of as just sounds

IN RESPONSE

Wish You Were Here

Write a postcard from Robert Louis Stevenson to his friends in California. Describe the best and the worst parts of the journey so far.

Traveling Along

You have read about traveling in a fictional spaceship, in a small airplane, and in a train in the late 1800's. List advantages and disadvantages for each kind of travel. Then tell how you would prefer to travel and why.

In My Opinion

"All Aboard" describes the early days of train travel. Write a letter to the editor suggesting ways to improve rail travel. Be sure to support your suggestions with examples from the selection.

AUTHOR AT WORK

As a boy, Jim Murphy loved baseball and football more than books. He was a young adult before he realized that writing was a good way to express himself. Nonfiction works such as *Across America on an Emigrant Train* gave Murphy a chance to share fascinating facts with young readers.

★ Award-winning Author

Another Book by . . .

Jim Murphy

The Long Road to Gettysburg
by Jim Murphy,
Clarion Books, 1992

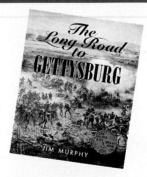

Library Link "All Aboard" was taken from *Across America on an Emigrant Train* by Jim Murphy. You might enjoy reading the entire book to find out more about Robert Louis Stevenson's journey by train across America.

from
Flying to the Moon and Other Strange Places

by Michael Collins

The *Eagle* Has Landed!

6:27 A.M.
Heading for the
launch pad

On July 16, 1969, astronauts Neil Armstrong, Buzz Aldrin, and Michael Collins boarded the spacecraft Columbia. *Lift-off went smoothly, and soon* Columbia *broke free of Earth orbit to head for the moon. If all went well, Armstrong and Aldrin would land the lunar module* Eagle *on the moon as Collins orbited above in* Columbia.

The moon didn't seem to be getting much bigger, but the earth was definitely shrinking. By the end of our first day in space, the earth barely filled one small window. It was really bright, with the blue of the ocean and the white of the clouds being what you noticed most. The green of the jungle areas was not distinct at all, and though the rust-colored sandy deserts were quite visible, the main impression was one of clouds and sea. We usually think of the moon as being quite bright, especially when it is full, but the moon is a dullard compared to the earth. In technical terms, the albedo of the moon is .07, which means that it bounces back only 7 percent of the light striking it, absorbing the other 93 percent. The earth's albedo is four times that of the moon, which means it shines four times as brightly. The sunshine really bounces off it, especially off the surface of the ocean, and if your eyes and the sun are in just the right position, the ocean will sparkle and flash like a fine diamond held up to a bright light. As I got ready for bed, I tried to decide what you called where we were. It is usually described as "cislunar space," but that really wasn't a good name for this strange region. We were in constant sunlight, which meant it was "daytime," but if you looked away from the sun, the sky was black as pitch. No stars were visible, even though they were there, just as they always had been. The reason they could not be seen was that sunlight was flooding the inside of *Columbia*, which meant that the pupils of our eyes automatically narrowed until only very bright objects could be seen. The only way to see the stars was to block out the sunshine and allow the pupils to expand for several minutes. Then the stars

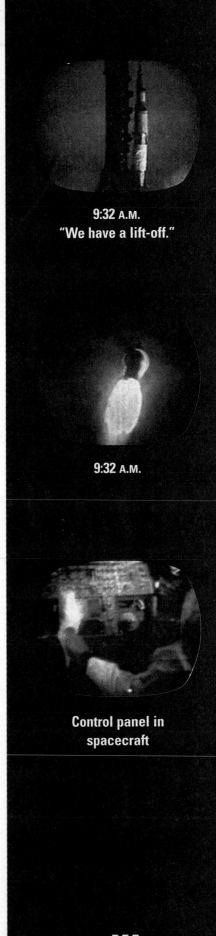

9:32 A.M.
"We have a lift-off."

9:32 A.M.

Control panel in
spacecraft

This photograph of Earth, taken from the *Columbia*, shows most of Africa and parts of Europe and Asia.

would gradually reappear, but were gone in a flash if the eye was exposed to sunshine, either directly or bouncing off some part of the spacecraft.

Our second day in space was a very quiet one—the first such day I had ever known. It was pleasant to see the earth getting smaller and smaller in our windows. There was absolutely no sensation of speed. We seemed to be just hanging there, as we went about our chores. Neil and Buzz spent most of their time studying *Eagle* checklists and procedures, while I attended to all the machinery inside *Columbia*. We ignited *Columbia*'s rocket engine once, for just three seconds, to adjust our course slightly. The moon was pulling us, the earth was pulling us, and the sun was pulling us. The result of this tug of war was a curved path through the skies, and a constantly changing speed. We had been slowing down ever since we left the earth and would continue to do so until we got much closer to the moon, at which time its gravitational field would take over and we would start speeding up again. The three-second correction put us back on the center line of our imaginary highway.

With plenty of time to prowl around inside *Columbia*, I found that weightlessness made it seem like a completely different place than it had been on the ground. On earth the tunnel, for example, was simply waste space overhead, but here it turned into a pleasant little nook where you could sit, or crouch, or whatever you wanted to call just being there, out of everyone else's way. I found that corners and tunnels were good places; you could wedge yourself in and did not need a lap belt or anything to hold you in place. In weightlessness, you have to be wedged in, or tied down, or your body will float aimlessly, banging into other people or equipment as it goes. At first, just floating around is great fun, but then after a while it becomes annoying, and you want to stay in one place. Day number 2 was so quiet I even had time to do some exercise. I found a spot near the navigator's panel that was just wide enough to allow my body to stretch out, with my arms over my head touching one wall and my feet another. In this position, I could "run" in place. With my medical sensors still attached to my chest, I could find out from the people in Houston what my heart rate was. I exercised until it doubled, from fifty to one hundred beats per minute, and then I stopped, because I didn't want to get too hot or sweaty, with no bath or shower on board. We also had a TV show on day number 2, using our TV camera to show the people back home what their puny little planet looked like from 130,000 miles away. By pointing the camera out the window at the earth, and then turning it over in my hands, I could make the earth appear to tumble, not something you get to do every day. I told Houston: "O.K., world, hang on to your hat. I'm going to turn you upside down."

By the time we got the TV equipment packed up and put away, it was bedtime. All three of us were relaxed by now and ready for a long snooze. It was my turn to sleep under the left couch, zipped loosely

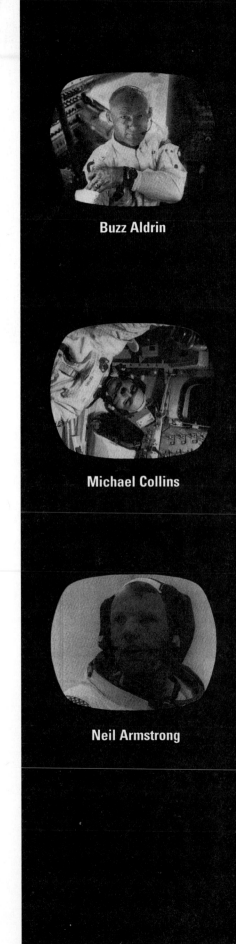

Buzz Aldrin

Michael Collins

Neil Armstrong

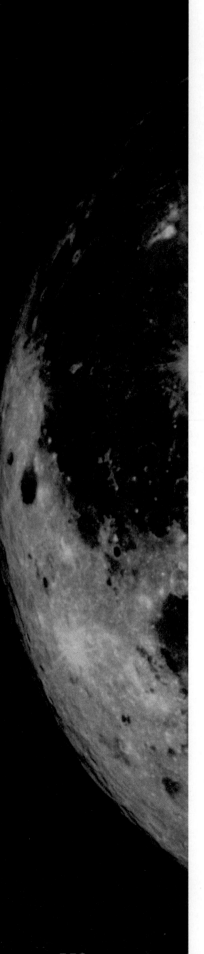

inside a floating hammock, and I was comfortable indeed, much more so than the previous night or during any of my three Gemini nights. It was a strange sensation to float in the total darkness, suspended by a cobweb's light touch, with no pressure anywhere on my body. Instinctively, I felt that I was lying on my back, not my stomach, but I really was doing neither—most normal yardsticks disappear in space, and I was no more lying than standing or falling. The only thing I could say, really, was that I was stretched out, with my body in a straight line from head to toe. The reason I thought of myself as lying on my back was that the main instrument panel was in front of me, and I had long accustomed myself to think of that direction as "up." The next thing I knew, Buzz was talking on the radio, and I realized that it was "morning"—or, at least, eight hours had passed. In the constant sunshine between earth and moon, it was difficult to decide whether it was "morning" or "noon" or "evening." All I knew was that the sun was still in the sky, just as it had been when I saw it last, and the earth was smaller yet, appearing to be about the size of my wristwatch.

Day number 3 was even quieter than day number 2 but day number 4 had an entirely different feeling to it. We knew we were going to be plenty busy and were going to see some strange sights. We stopped our barbecue motion and got our first look at the moon in nearly a day. The change in its appearance was spectacular! The moon I had known all my life, that small flat yellow disk in the sky, had gone somewhere, to be replaced by the most awesome sphere I had ever seen. It was huge, completely filling *Columbia*'s largest window. It was also three-dimensional, by which I mean that we could see its belly bulging out toward us, while its surface obviously receded toward the edges. I felt that I could almost reach out and touch it. It was between us and the sun, putting us in its shadow. The sun created a halo around it, making the moon's surface dark and mysterious in comparison with its shining rim. Its surface was lighted by earth-shine, which was sunshine that had bounced off the surface of the earth onto the surface of the moon. It cast a bluish eerie glow by which we could see large craters and the darker flat areas known as maria,[1] or seas. It didn't look like a very friendly place, but Neil summed it up: "It's worth the price of the trip." To me, it also looked a little bit scary.

In order to get into orbit around the moon, we had to slow down, or else we would have shot right on by it. We fired *Columbia*'s rocket engine shortly after we swung around behind the moon's left edge, out of touch with the earth for the first time in three days. However, we didn't need the earth, because our own computer told us which way to point and how long to fire the engine. After slightly over six minutes of engine firing, our computer told us we had arrived, and we had! We were skimming along approximately sixty miles above the moon's pockmarked surface. The back side of the moon, which we never see from earth, is even more battered and tortured-looking than the front side. On the back, there are no smooth maria, but only highlands which have been scarred by the impact of meteorites over billions of years. There is no atmosphere surrounding the moon to produce clouds or smog, so our view was impaired

---

1 **maria** (*MAH ree uh*)

This view from a window of the lunar module shows a number of craters and small rocks between the lunar module and the lunar horizon.

only by darkness. We discovered that the appearance of the surface changed greatly as the position of the sun changed. With the sun directly overhead, the moon appeared a cheery place, with soft rounded craters bathed in a rose-colored light. As the sun shifted toward the lunar horizon, the craters began to cast long shadows, the rose color changed to dark gray, and the surface appeared not smooth at all but a series of jagged edges. When the sun was below the horizon, the surface was either barely visible if it was in earthshine, or totally invisible in a black void if there was no earthshine. We were really eager to get a look at our landing site. We didn't have any trouble finding it, because we had been studying maps for months and had memorized a series of craters and other checkpoints leading up to the landing site. But, boy, when we got there, it sure looked rough to me. It didn't look smooth enough to park a baby buggy, much less our landing craft *Eagle*. I didn't say anything to Neil or Buzz. I just hoped it was the angle of the sun which was causing the rough appearance. We would find out tomorrow.

In the meantime, I had one more task to perform before bedtime. With my sextant I took several measurements on a crater in the Foaming Sea (Mare Spumans, in Latin) east of our landing site in the Sea of Tranquility. The idea was that my measurements could increase the accuracy of our knowledge of the height of the terrain Neil and Buzz would be flying over in their descent to a landing. I had named the crater KAMP, using the first letters of the names of my children and wife (Kate, Ann, Michael, and Patricia). I liked the idea of my wife and kids being involved with helping the lunar landing.

The next day, number 5, lunar-landing day, began with the usual wake-up call from Houston, and proceeded swiftly from there. . . . As soon as breakfast was over, we had to scramble into our pressure suits. Neil and Buzz began by putting on special underwear, into which thin plastic tubes had been woven. Water would be pumped from their

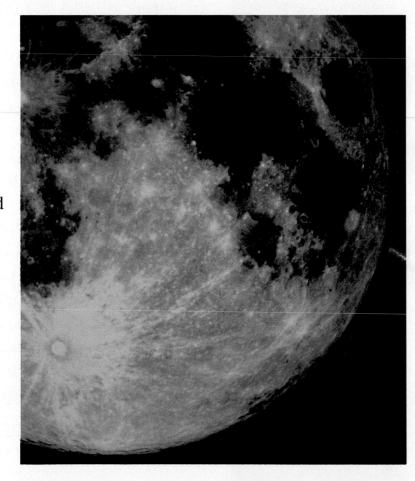

In this photograph, taken at full moon, light highlands surround the darker maria. The brightest regions on the surface indicate debris from very young craters.

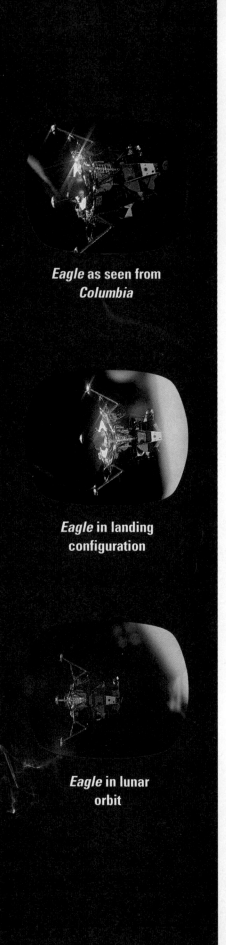

Eagle as seen from
Columbia

Eagle in landing
configuration

Eagle in lunar
orbit

backpacks into their suits and through these tubes, cooling their bodies while they were out on the hot lunar surface. Since I would not be joining them there, I wore plain old regular underwear, or "long johns" as they are called. When we unpacked the three pressure suits from their bags, they seemed almost to fill the entire command module, as if there were three extra people in there with us. After quite a struggle and a tug of war with a balky zipper, we finally got the suits on, and our helmets and gloves locked in place. Then Neil and Buzz entered the lunar module, and I locked the hatch after them. I threw a switch on my instrument panel, and our two spacecraft were separated.

Neil backed off fifty feet or so and made a slow 360° turn in front of me. The idea was to allow me to inspect all sides of the lunar module for possible damage, and to make sure all four landing gear were extended properly. I couldn't find anything wrong with *Eagle*, but it sure looked strange, unlike any kind of flying machine I had ever seen. It looked like a huge gold, black, and gray bug hanging awkwardly in the black sky. But Buzz was pleased with it. "The *Eagle* has wings!" he shouted. To me, it didn't look like an eagle, and I couldn't find any wings, only lumps and bumps and odd shapes on its surface. Since a lunar module flies only in space, high above the earth's atmosphere, the designers didn't have to make it streamlined, which is the reason it looked so awkward.

As Neil and Buzz descended to the lunar surface, I kept my eyes on them as long as I could. If they had to come back in a hurry for any reason, I wanted to know where they were. Looking at them through my sextant, I watched *Eagle* grow smaller and smaller until finally, when it was about one hundred miles away (below me and in front of me), I lost sight of it amid the craters. My main job now was to keep *Columbia* running properly, and to keep quiet, because *Eagle* and Houston would have plenty to talk about during the landing attempt. Sure enough, it wasn't long before I could hear Neil telling Houston his computer was acting strangely, and Houston promptly replied that he should continue toward a landing. Buzz was calling off numbers to Neil, so that Neil could devote all his attention to looking out the window. The most important numbers were altitude (in feet above the surface) and descent rate (in feet per second). "Six hundred feet, down at nineteen . . . Four hundred feet, down at nine . . . Three hundred feet . . . Watch our shadow out there," called Buzz, repeating new numbers every few seconds. He also reported they had only 5 percent of their fuel remaining, which wasn't much. I started getting nervous. "Forty feet, down two and a half, kicking up some dust." Well, at least the dust didn't seem to be a big problem, that was good. "Thirty seconds!" said Houston, meaning that they had only thirty seconds' worth of fuel remaining. Better get it on the ground, Neil! Suddenly Buzz shouted: "Contact light!" and I knew they were down. The lunar module had a wire dangling below one landing gear. When it touched the moon, it caused a light on the instrument panel to light, so that Neil would know he was just about to touch down. As soon as he did, he called: "Houston, Tranquility Base here, the *Eagle* has landed." Whew! I breathed a big sigh

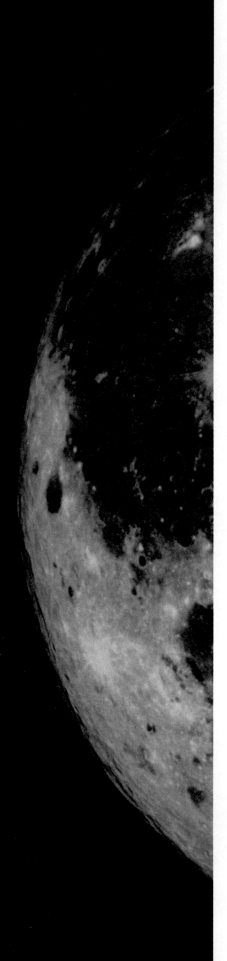

of relief. Neil then explained why he had nearly run out of gas. The computer-controlled descent was taking *Eagle* into an area covered with huge boulders, and Neil had to keep flying until he found a smoother spot to land. As good as that computer was, it took the eyes of the pilot to pick the best landing spot.

For the next couple of orbits, I tried very hard to spot *Eagle* through my sextant, but I was unable to find it. The problem was that no one knew exactly where Neil had landed, and I didn't know which way to look for them. Oh, I knew approximately where they were, but the sextant had a narrow field of view, like looking down a rifle barrel, and I needed to know exactly which way to point it.

Other than not being able to find Neil and Buzz, everything was going very well with me. I had turned up the lights inside *Columbia*, and it seemed like a happy place. Also big, for a change, with only me inside it. I didn't feel lonely or left out, because I knew my job was very important, and that Neil and Buzz could never get home without me. I was proud of the way *Columbia* and I were circling above them, waiting for their return. I felt like the base-camp operator on a mountain-climbing expedition. I suppose one reason I didn't feel lonely was that I had been flying airplanes by myself for nearly twenty years. This time, however, I had to admit that it *was* a bit different, especially on the far side of the moon. There, cut off from all communication, I was truly alone, the only person in the solar system who could not even see the planet of his birth. Far from causing fear, this situation gave me a good feeling—one of confidence and satisfaction.

Outside my window I could see stars, and nothing else. I knew where the moon was, but in the total darkness, its surface was not visible: it was simply that part of my window which had no stars in it. The feeling was less like flying than like being alone in a boat on the ocean at night. Stars above, pure black below. At dawn, light filled my windows so quickly that my eyes hurt. Almost immediately, the stars disappeared and the moon reappeared. I knew from my clock that the earth was about to reappear, and right on schedule it popped into view, rising like a blue and white jewel over the desolate lunar horizon.

As soon as the earth reappeared, I could once more talk on my radio, and I found out from Houston that all was going well with Neil and Buzz. They had decided to skip a scheduled four-hour nap and instead began exploring right away. Neil, first down the ladder and therefore the first human to step on another planet, found he had no difficulty at all in walking on the moon. The surface was level and solid and firm, and he easily kept his balance in the strange gravitational field where everything weighed only one sixth its earth weight. I could hear what they were saying because Houston relayed their calls to me. It was a bit unusual, though, because even traveling at the speed of light, it took two and a half seconds for the radio signals to go from *Eagle* to the earth and then back to *Columbia*. If they said something to me, they had to wait at least five seconds for an answer. When I was overhead of their position, I could talk to them directly, but the rest of the time that I was on the front side of the moon, the relay procedure was necessary. When I was on the back side, I couldn't talk to anyone.

They hadn't been out on the surface very long when the three of us got a big surprise. The President of the United States began talking on the radio! Mr. Nixon told them: "Neil and Buzz, I am talking to you by telephone from the Oval Office at the White House, and this certainly has to be the most historic telephone call ever made . . . Because of what you have done, the heavens have become a part of man's world. As you talk to us from the Sea of Tranquility, it inspires us to redouble our efforts

Neil Armstrong took this picture of Buzz Aldrin, the second man on the Moon. Aldrin's face mask carries the reflection of the lunar module *Eagle*.

to bring peace and tranquility to Earth." Neil replied that he was honored and privileged to be on the moon, representing the United States and men of peace from all nations. I felt proud to be representing my country, and I was glad that Neil and Buzz had planted an American flag on the moon. Now I just wanted them to collect their rocks and get back on up here to *Columbia*. They really sounded good on the surface, not tired at all, but I was still relieved when they got back inside *Eagle* and got the door locked. That was another big hurdle behind us, and none of us, we hoped, would need our pressure suits again. In the meantime, we were scheduled to sleep for a few hours, so that we would be fresh for the complicated rendezvous.[2]

I know Neil and Buzz didn't sleep very well, cramped on the narrow floor of *Eagle*, but I had a good rest in *Columbia*. I blocked out all the light by putting shades over the windows, and I trusted the experts in Houston to watch over my equipment while I was asleep. Of course, if anything went wrong on the far side of the moon no one could help me, but on the front side Houston could tell from *Columbia*'s electronic signals whether most things were working properly or not. If trouble developed, they could call me on the radio and wake me up. Reassured by this, I slept like a log, until I heard a voice in my ear, calling over and over again: "*Columbia, Columbia,* good morning from Houston." "Hi, Ron," I replied groggily. It was Ron Evans, an astronaut who would later fly to the moon on the final Apollo flight. Ron told me it was going to be a busy day, which I knew already, and then he proved it

---

2 **rendezvous** (*RAHN day voo*) a place chosen for a meeting

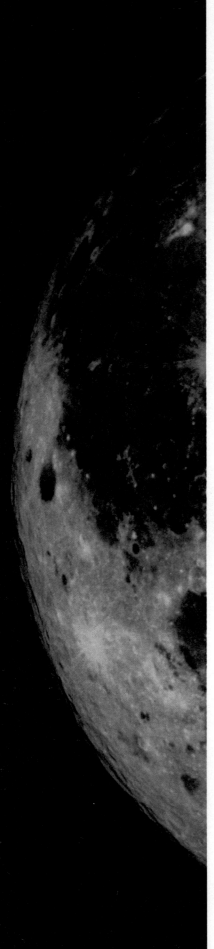

by giving me a long list of things to do to prepare for the rendezvous. As the day wore on, I knew I would be expected to perform approximately 850 computer-button pushes alone. If everything went well with *Eagle*, I knew precisely what to do, because I had practiced over and over again in the simulator, but if I had to go rescue *Eagle* from some lopsided orbit, then things could get awfully complicated in a big hurry. I had a book around my neck, fastened by a clip to my pressure suit, which contained procedures for eighteen different types of rendezvous that I might need.

As *Eagle*'s lift-off time approached, I got really nervous, probably as nervous as I got any time during the flight. If their engine didn't work, there was nothing I could do to rescue them from the surface. I simply had to come home by myself, leaving Neil and Buzz to die on the surface of the moon. They had oxygen enough for only another day at the most. Needless to say, the idea of leaving them was horrible, but it was the only thing I could do, as it made no sense for me to commit suicide. These thoughts were running through my mind as I heard Buzz counting the seconds to ignition: "9 - 8 - 7 - 6 - 5 . . . Beautiful!" They were off! Seven minutes later, their single engine had pushed them into a good orbit, below and behind me, and they then began a carefully calculated three-hour chase to close the gap. On my first pass over Tranquility Base since their departure, I told them: "*Eagle, Columbia* passing over the landing site. It sure is great to look down there and not see you!" Not that I had ever really seen them on the surface, but just knowing they were up in orbit again was a great relief. Not long after this, I really did see *Eagle* for the first time in a day, as it appeared as a tiny blinking light in my sextant. As it grew, so did my confidence, for my computer told me they were precisely on centerline as they overtook me. Finally we were side by side, and *Eagle* had never looked better. It was missing its bottom half, which stayed on the moon, after acting as a launching pad for the top half.

For the first time in six months, I felt that the Apollo 11 flight was definitely going to be a success. All I had to do now was dock with *Eagle*, transfer Neil and Buzz back into *Columbia*, and head for home! The docking itself went well, with just a slight bump as *Columbia* nudged *Eagle*, but then *Eagle* gave a wild lurch and for a couple of seconds I thought we might have real trouble. But the two vehicles swung back in

Leaving the lunar surface, *Eagle*, with Armstrong and Aldrin on board, moves toward *Columbia*. Earth rises above the lunar horizon.

line, and then the docking latches pulled them together in a tight grip, and all was well again. Buzz was first through the hatch, with a triumphant grin on his face. I was going to kiss him, but then I got embarrassed and just shook his hand. Together we greeted Neil, and for a couple of minutes the three of us just floated there, admiring two shiny silver boxes filled with moon rocks. I also got a couple of questions answered, such as what did the lift-off from the moon feel like ("There was a little blast . . . The floor came up to meet you"), and did the moon rocks all look the same ("No, not at all"). Then it was time to leave *Eagle* in lunar orbit, light *Columbia*'s big engine for a couple of minutes, and come on home. Just as in the case of a Gemini deorbit burn, we paid extraordinary attention to the direction we were pointed. If we made a mistake and pointed in the opposite direction, we would crash into the moon instead of returning to earth. After the burn was over, Houston told us their radar tracking stations indicated we were right on course. Another hurdle behind us! As we left the moon, we tried to use up all our remaining film by taking pictures of the moon. All together, we must have taken close to a thousand pictures of the moon in the three days we were there. As we left the moon, we curved around its right side, and we could see it gleaming in the sunlight, vividly etched against the black sky in gray-tan tones. It was beautiful, but it was nothing compared to earth, and I didn't want to come back ever.

This view from *Columbia* shows Earth rising above the Moon's horizon.

IN RESPONSE

A Lunar Look

Imagine you're Michael Collins, all alone in the *Columbia* circling the moon. Look at Michael Collins's description and then write a short poem or essay about how this experience is changing you.

And Now for a News Brief

With a group, write a news story about the safe return of the *Eagle* to the *Columbia*. Base your news flash on information from "The *Eagle* Has Landed!" Choose a news anchor, a reporter, and a voice for Michael Collins and present your news report to the class.

AUTHOR AT WORK

After Michael Collins attended the U.S. Military Academy, he joined the Air Force and eventually the space program. In 1966 he was the copilot of the Gemini 10 flight and in 1969 command module pilot of the Apollo 11 mission. As an air force officer and astronaut, he experienced such thrilling dramas that he felt compelled to write about them.

Another Book About . . .

Space Exploration

Space, by Moira Butterfield, illustrated by Nick Lipscomb and Gary Biggin, Dorling Kindersley, 1994

Library Link "The *Eagle* Has Landed!" was taken from *Flying to the Moon and Other Strange Places* by Michael Collins. You might enjoy reading the entire book to find out more about the astronaut's adventures.

Moon

Moon remembers.

Marooned in shadowed night,

white powder plastered
on her pockmarked face,
scarred with craters,
filled with waterless seas,

she thinks back
to the Eagle,
to the flight
of men from Earth,
of rocks sent back in space,
and one
faint
footprint
in the Sea of Tranquility.

—Myra Cohn Livingston

ORBITER 5 SHOWS
HOW EARTH LOOKS FROM THE MOON

There's a woman in the earth, sitting on
her heels. You see her from the back, in three-
quarter profile. She has a flowing pigtail. She's
holding something

in her right hand—some holy jug. Her left arm is thinner,
in a gesture like a dancer. She's the Indian Ocean. Asia is
light swirling up out of her vessel. Her pigtail points to Europe
and her dancer's arm is the Suez Canal. She is a woman
in a square kimono,
bare feet tucked beneath the tip of Africa. Her tail of long hair is
the Arabian Peninsula.

A woman in the earth.

A man in the moon.

—May Swenson

FLIGHT
TO THE
FUTURE

from
The Smithsonian Book of Flight for Young People
by Walter J. Boyne

he history of aviation is one of the most exciting stories in the world—almost no area of technology has come so far, so fast. From the days of the Wright brothers and Glenn Curtiss, all the way to the era of those hybrids of air-and-space technology, the *Columbia* and *Challenger* space shuttles, aviation has been filled with miracles of invention and innovation, with brave and dashing heroes, and perhaps most important, with visions of the future.

Today, the visions continue. Flying enthusiasts now have more knowledge and technology at their disposal than ever before, and they are applying that knowledge in the creation of exciting new aircraft. The entire history of aviation is at their disposal, and that history keeps showing up in unexpected ways. Some new privately designed aircraft, for example, have much of the look and feel of the classic planes of the past. Wonderful to look at and fun to fly, many of these planes combine the best of the old glamour and dash of aviation with the best of its new technology—efficient engines and navigation equipment, for example.

During nine grueling days between December 14 and 23, 1986, the world watched excitedly as Richard G. Rutan and Jeana Yeager flew *Voyager*, left, around the world without

Entirely powered by electricity from solar cells, the *Gossamer Penguin* takes off with Paul MacCready's thirteen-year-old son Marshall as the pilot. The craft is a three-quarter scale version of the *Gossamer Albatross*—the first human-powered aircraft to cross the English Channel.

As some people did in the days following World War II, many now believe that inexpensive, easy-to-handle private aircraft really constitute aviation's brightest prospects. They look forward to the days when low-cost, individually owned aircraft will be available to everybody. These new planes will be no more difficult to operate than an automobile or even a bicycle. Advances in computer technology alone indicate what is well within our reach. Far from being an impossible dream, such planes could be made available within only a few years' time.

As an example, try to imagine a small twin-engine aircraft, with no more than a 25-foot wingspan. And then imagine this aircraft equipped with special computerized sensors that would give it automatic stability and control. A plane of this kind would be so "forgiving" in flight that anyone with a minimum of training would be able to take to the skies. Assume that such a plane could be mass manufactured of lightweight, composite materials designed to act as a cushion in the event of collision, and you have what mankind has always yearned for—a personal set of wings, a "Safebird." Such an aircraft is not here yet, but it is possible.

Many scientists and experimenters are concentrating on the development of just such aircraft. Recently, the work of California designer Paul MacCready has captured the imagination of flight buffs the world over. His man-powered aircraft, including the prize-winning *Gossamer Albatross,* are beautiful and efficient vehicles. The *Gossamer Albatross* was able to bridge such famous obstacles as the English Channel, long a testing place for flight improvements.

MacCready believes that of all the light aircraft available today, the sailplane is the single type of aircraft to make use of the newest in modern flight technology. Built of epoxy and carbon and glass fiber composites, many of these sailplanes, especially those of European design, have attained a high level of performance and include onboard computers for flight control.

Meanwhile, other experiments also flourish. The *Voyager,* designed by Burt Rutan, drew worldwide acclaim as it completed a nine-day, round-the-world flight on a single tank of fuel. Copiloted by the designer's brother, Richard, and Jeana Yeager, the *Voyager* has a wingspan of 111 feet and is built of highly advanced composite materials. Empty, the graceful craft weighs only 2,680 pounds; full of fuel, almost 12,000 pounds.

Scientists at the Massachusetts Institute of Technology are working on a 100-foot-wingspan, man-powered craft. With a gross weight of less than 70 pounds, this aircraft is being designed to recreate the mythic flight of Icarus[1] and Daedalus,[2] a father and son who supposedly made wings of wax and attempted to fly from the island of Crete to the mainland of Greece, a distance of more than ninety miles.

---

1 **Icarus** (*IHK uh ruhs*)
2 **Daedalus** (*DEHD uh luhs*)

In addition, some experimenters, like Paul MacCready, are exploring the possibilities of aircraft that draw their energy from sunlight and convert it directly into propulsion. Others concentrate on developing new support technology: computers that can take data from a dozen different sources and integrate it into control outputs that maintain equilibrium in flight. NASA and the military also continue research on the push into space, with preliminary plans for highly advanced space shuttles and even a National Space Plane, a futuristic craft that will accomplish worldwide travel not in the earth's atmosphere, but in space. Too, many dream of the day when such craft will travel to established space stations, shuttling scientists and specialists back and forth throughout the solar system.

Plans for the future of aviation lie in many different directions. Some believe the next great leap forward will come in the creation of private, everyday personal aircraft that will make a pilot's license as commonplace as a driver's license. Others are convinced the next big leap will be into space, with vehicles so advanced that the world can begin the exploration and even colonization of other planets. Still others believe that the future of aviation lies in learning to use what we have to solve problems: the creation of inexpensive, high-energy fuels, for example, that would make advancements like supersonic transport practical.

Progress will undoubtedly come in each of these areas. Research in high-energy fuels and solar power is already well under way. Predictions for the future of lightplanes include greater advances in aerodynamics, and the use of autopilot mechanisms and unducted fan jets. There have already been numerous experiments in the development of "convertiplanes," planes that will convert from air use to road use, allowing the pilot to fly or to drive, as conditions demand. The National Space Plane, now considered a

Today's hang glider emulates the birds who first inspired man's quest for flight, though its "wings" are made of cloth and aluminum.

visionary concept, might very well become as common as the old-style freight trains, uniting the world in orbital space travel.

None of these are impossible dreams as we look to the future and the upcoming hundredth anniversary of Wilbur and Orville Wright's first powered flight at Kitty Hawk. By then, perhaps we will have forgotten our differences and begun that worldwide effort to conquer the frontiers of space. By then, perhaps we may have developed the fuels and technology necessary to make our flying machines the best the world has ever seen. In the future, we may fly rather than drive to our schools, supermarkets, and short vacations.

Perhaps the best way to predict the future of flight is to use the same words that Orville Wright used when he was asked to do the same almost a century ago:

"I cannot answer," he said, "except to assure you that it will be spectacular."

Express Yourself

In Journeys of Change, you saw how people can change as a result of a journey. Some characters in this theme tested their abilities and became more confident during their travels. Others simply learned to appreciate what they had.

Compare the Space Journeys

"Call Me *Proteus*" is science fiction. "The *Eagle* Has Landed!" is autobiography. Yet both selections are about space travel. How are the journeys similar? Discuss your answers in a small group. Which journey would you rather have been a part of—the science fiction one or the real one? Why? Use examples from the selections to explain your choice.

Picture the Future

"Flight to the Future" describes three directions for the future of aviation. What are they? Which direction might appeal to Araceli ("Nickel-a-Pound Plane Ride")? Which might be most interesting to *Proteus* ("Call Me *Proteus*") and Michael Collins ("The *Eagle* Has Landed!")? Which direction do *you* think is the best? Answer the questions with a partner. Use examples from the selections and use your own ideas.

Difficult Journeys

Robert Louis Stevenson ("All Aboard") had some troubles during his journey. Araceli ("Nickel-a-Pound Plane Ride") and *Proteus* ("Call Me *Proteus*") also faced obstacles. In a small group, compare these characters' journeys. Who had the most difficulties to overcome? Who made the best changes as a result? Defend your answers with examples.

Earth-bound

Michael Collins ("The *Eagle* Has Landed!") wrote of his visit to the moon: "It was beautiful, but it was nothing compared to earth, and I didn't want to come back ever." How does his attitude compare with Araceli's after her plane ride ("Nickel-a-Pound Plane Ride")? What changes do both people eventually make? Write your thoughts in a paragraph.

Nickels in Space

Send Araceli ("Nickel-a-Pound Plane Ride") into outer space! Write an outline and some details for a story called "Nickel-a-Pound Space Flight." Model your space flight after the one in "Call Me *Proteus*" or "The *Eagle* Has Landed!" How might Araceli respond? Why do you think so?

More Books for You to Enjoy

Breaking the Sound Barrier
by Nathan Aaseng, Julian Messner, 1991

What is it like to race beyond the speed of sound? This book presents a mix of scientific fact and hair-raising anecdotes of the courageous test pilots who made aviation history in their pursuit to break the sound barrier.

The Way West: Journal of a Pioneer Woman
by Amelia Stewart Knight, illustrated by Michael McCurdy, Simon & Schuster, 1993

Authentic journal excerpts give a glimpse into the adventures of a pioneer family heading west by covered wagon in 1853. The Stewarts must overcome many hardships and battle the forces of nature as well as rugged terrain before they reach their journey's end.

Pioneering Space
by Sandra Markle, Atheneum, 1992

How does a spacecraft work? What is life like for an astronaut in space? You'll find answers to these questions and more in this brief look at the exciting era of space pioneering.

The Transcontinental Railroad
by Marilyn Miller, Silver Burdett Press, 1986

The great event that linked East and West, the building of the transcontinental railroad, is colorfully portrayed. Beginning at the celebrated meeting place, Promontory Point, Utah, the narrative describes the history and effects of this incredible feat.

City Trains: Moving Through America's Cities by Rail
by Roger Yepsen, Macmillan, 1993

Read the fascinating stories of the city trains that have shaped American cities and lifestyles for nearly two hundred years—from the horse car, trolley, and cable car to today's monorail. Glimpse the exciting possibilities that await tomorrow's train traveler.

Glossary

The pronunciation of each word is shown just after the word, in this way: **abbreviate** [ə·brē′vē·āt′]. The letters and signs used are pronounced as in the words in the chart at right. The mark ′ is placed after a syllable with a primary, or heavy, accent, as in the example above. The mark ′ after a syllable shows a secondary, or lighter, accent, as in the following example: **abbreviation** [ə·brē′vē·ā′shən].

Pronunciation Key

Symbol	Key Words	Symbol	Key Words
a	cat	b	bed
ā	ape	d	dog
ä	cot, car	f	fall
e	ten, berry	g	get
ē	me	h	help
i	fit, here	j	jump
ī	ice, fire	k	kiss, call
ō	go	l	leg
ô	fall, for	m	meat
oi	oil	n	nose
oo	look, pull	p	put
o͞o	tool, rule	r	red
ou	out, crowd	s	see
u	up	t	top
ʉ	fur, shirt	v	vat
ə	a in ago	w	wish
	e in agent	y	yard
	i in pencil	z	zebra
	o in atom	ch	chin, arch
	u in circus	ŋ	ring, drink
		sh	she, push
		th	thin, truth
		th	then, father
		zh	measure

A

academic [ak´ə·dem´ik] adj. having to do with education.

acclamation [ak´lə·mā´shən] n. loud applause or approval.

accompany [ə·kum´pə·nē] v. to go along with; to attend together with: I'm not that hungry, but I'll accompany you to the Dreem Freez for a sundae.

acquaint [ə·kwānt´] v. to inform or become familiar with: Let me acquaint you with this textbook.

aerobics [er·ō´biks] n. exercise such as jogging, swimming, or dancing, in which the heart and lungs are conditioned to work more efficiently: Julio is an instructor of aerobics who runs five miles a day.

aggression [ə·gresh´ən] n. hostile or violent behavior: When the school bullies began to show signs of real aggression, Amy decided to tell the teacher.

air pocket [er´ päk´it] n. a change in pressure that can cause an airplane to drop suddenly: Dropping into the air pocket felt scary, but our pilot assured us we were never in any danger.

albedo [al·bē´dō] n. the brightness of a planet, satellite, or asteroid.

alder [ôl´dər] n. a type of birch tree common in cold climates.

alien [āl´yən] n. a being from another planet.

alleviate [ə·lē´vē·āt´] v. to reduce or lessen.

Alzheimer's disease [älts´hī´mərz di·zēz´] n. a disease in which brain cells are destroyed, resulting in memory loss.

ambush [am´boosh´] n. a hiding place from which people may attack others.

amulet [am´yoo·lit] n. something worn to drive away evil spirits. syn. lucky charm: I wore the locket with my brother's picture in it as an amulet.

ancient [ān´chənt] adj. very old: The scientists were excited when they discovered the ancient documents.

anticipation [an·tis´ə·pā´shən] n. looking forward to something: John's anticipation of his birthday party was so great he could hardly sit still until it began.

Anubis [ə·noo´bis] n. in Egyptian mythology, the god of the dead, with the head of a jackal.

aptitude [ap´tə·tood´] n. skill or talent: Tanya shows a real aptitude for music; she played the violin at age three.

archaeology [är´kē·äl´ə·jē] n. the scientific study of life and cultures of ancient times.

askew [ə·skyoo´] adj. off to one side; crooked. Hank brushed himself off after his fall and adjusted his hat, which was slightly askew.

alders

Anubis putting the final touches on a mummy

a	cat	ô	fall, for	ə	= a *in* ago
ā	ape	oi	oil		e *in* agent
ä	cot, car	oo	look, pull		i *in* pencil
e	ten, berry	ōō	tool, rule		o *in* atom
ē	me	ou	out, crowd		u *in* circus
i	fit, here	u	up		
ī	ice, fire	ʉr	fur		
ō	go				

bacterium, stained for viewing under the microscope

assemble [ə·sem´bəl] v. to gather: We will assemble in the auditorium at four o'clock to see a movie.

assembly [ə·sem´blē] n. the gathering of a group, as in school.

astonished [ə·stän´ishd] adj. filled with wonder and surprise. syn. amazed.

atmosphere [at´məs·fir´] n. the layer of air surrounding a planet: To help preserve the earth's atmosphere, avoid using aerosol sprays.

audacious [ô·dā´shəs] adj. bold, daring. syn. fearless: The acrobat's audacious performance made the audience gasp.

autistic [ô·tis´tik] adj. suffering from an emotional problem often marked by extreme withdrawal from others, repetitive behavior, and fear of one's surroundings.

awakening [ə·wā´kən·iñg] n. a sudden awareness: After struggling to read for months, Tony's awakening finally came the day before he finished first grade.

awkward [ôk´wərd] adj. uncomfortable; clumsy.

bacterium [bak·tir´ē·um] n. (plural: *bacteria*) any number of rapidly multiplying microscopic creatures that may cause disease and decay.

bank [bañgk] v. to turn an aircraft so that one wing is higher than the other: I felt a little dizzy when the pilot began to bank the plane.

bawl [bôl] v. to cry loudly: A two-year-old throwing a tantrum is likely to bawl.

beam [bēm] v. to smile brightly: Baby Jason would beam with delight every time he saw his father come into the room.

bearing [ber´iñg] n. behavior or appearance: Aïda had the bearing of a princess, not a slave.

beckon [bek´n] v. to call with a silent movement, such as a wave.

betrayer [bē·trā´ər] n. one who helps an enemy.

bolo tie [bō´lō tī´] n. a cord attached to a decorative slide, sometimes worn in place of a necktie.

brace [brās] n. two of something; a pair: Dad brought us each a brace of chicks for the farm.

bribe [brīb] n. something given or promised to get another person to do something: The honest police officer refused to take a bribe and instead gave the driver a speeding ticket.

bribery [brīb´ər·ē] n. offering or taking a reward for doing something wrong.

brute [broōt] n. a cruel or stupid person: He was a gentle person, but when he acted, he always played the role of a brute.

buckle [buk´əl] v. to bulge or bend as a result of pressure, heat, or some other force: The hot temperatures caused the highway to buckle in several places.

buffet [bə·fāʹ] n. a meal at which guests serve themselves from a table and eat elsewhere: Since the meal was a buffet, we served ourselves from the dining room and then ate our food in the living room.

bulkhead [bulkʹhed] n. a wall on a ship or airplane that may hold back fire or water.

burly [burʹlē] adj. heavy and muscular: Two burly football players lifted the coach over their heads as if he were a feather.

cache [kash] n. a hidden supply: Because sugar was scarce in colonial America, housewives often kept a cache of sugar for special occasions.

carom [karʹəm] v. to hit and bounce back: She threw her new ball and watched it carom off her neighbor's wall.

carport [kärʹpôrt] n. a shelter for a car, consisting of a roof and, occasionally, one or more sides: Our new garage has a lot more storage space than our old carport.

cassava [kə·säʹvə] n. a plant whose root yields a starch that can be used in breadmaking: Tapioca is a starch that comes from the cassava plant.

cavernous [kavʹər·nəs] adj. hollow or full of caves.

chagrin [shə·grinʹ] n. unhappiness, disappointment: Her enemy's success filled her with chagrin.

chain reaction [chān rē·akʹshən] n. a series of events or ideas, each resulting from the one that came before it: As soon as one child pushed another at the head of the line, the whole line of children fell in a chain reaction.

chamber [chāmʹbər] n. a room or enclosure: The precious objects were buried in a separate chamber.

channel [chanʹəl] v. to direct something: The after-school program allows children to channel their energy into wholesome activities.

chant [chant] v. to repeat or sing: In first grade, each morning we would chant "Good morning" to our teacher.

chaos [kāʹäsʹ] n. complete confusion: The house was in a state of chaos before Mom was due to return, but we restored order just in time.

checkpoint [chekʹpoint] n. a point when or where inspection is made, as of baggage or identification: Our car was stopped for half an hour at the checkpoint while the police inspected our passports and looked through our suitcases.

chemist [kemʹist] n. a British term for pharmacist or druggist.

circular [surʹkyə·lər] adj. like a circle.

civilization [sivʹə·lə·zāʹshən] n. the countries and peoples that have developed a written language, arts, sciences, and government.

bulkhead

cassava root

a cat	ô fall, for	ə = a *in* ago
a ape	oi oil	e *in* agent
ä cot, car	oo look, pull	i *in* pencil
e ten, berry	ōo tool, rule	o *in* atom
ē me	ou out, crowd	u *in* circus
i fit, here	u up	
ī ice, fire	ur fur	
ō go		

coil

clarity [klar´·ə·tē] n. the quality of being clear.

coalesce [kō´·ə·les´] v. to come together. syn. mix.

coil [koil] v. to wind or twist in a circle: Slowly, I began to coil my long hair; then I pinned it in place.

coincidence [kō·in´·sə·dəns] n. the accidental happening at the same time of facts or events: It's a coincidence that Mark and his friend share the same birthday.

compassion [kəm·pash´·ən] n. caring. syn. pity: She shows her compassion for injured animals by taking them to the animal hospital.

comply [kəm·plī´] v. to follow orders.

compulsion [kəm·pul´·shən] n. a strong desire: Jeannette resisted her compulsion to eat the last brownie.

conduct [kən·dukt´] v. to carry or transmit something: Water is one of the materials that can conduct electricity.

conquer [käñg´·kər] v. to win in a contest. syn. defeat: Our team worked hard to conquer our opponents in the spelling bee.

consciousness [kän´·shəs·nes] n. awareness of one's own feelings: For a moment, my sister appeared to lose consciousness; then she recovered from her faint.

consecration [kän´·si·krā´·shən] n. the honoring of a holy person, place, or thing: Come to our new church for its consecration.

console [kän´·sōl] n. a panel for instruments on an airplane, automobile, computer, or other electrical system.

aircraft console

consumption [kən·sump´·shən] n. eating.

contain [kən·tān´] v. to hold or hold in: When my brother performed his comedy routine, people could barely contain their laughter.

contemplate [kän´·təm·plāt´] v. to imagine or think about: Wendell liked to contemplate what life would be like as a major-league pitcher.

contempt [kən·tempt´] n. a deep dislike; disgust.

controversy [kän´·trə·vur´·sē] n. a topic on which people disagree. syn. argument: In our town, controversy raged over whether to build a new school or to enlarge the old one.

convoy [kän´·voi] n. a line of ships or vehicles, all traveling to the same place.

coral [kôr´·əl] n. the stonelike skeleton of an animal living in warm, tropical waters.

corrupt [kə·rupt´] v. to make evil or to bribe.

counselor [koun´·sə·lər] n. an advisor: When I am in high school I would like to be a counselor at a summer camp.

coward [kou´·ərd] n. one who lacks courage: Being afraid of the dark does not mean you are a coward.

crevasse [krə·vas´] n. a deep crack in a glacier.

curio [kyoor´ē·ō] n. an unusual or rare item: My aunt, who loves antiques, opened a shop where she buys and sells curios.

curse [kʉrs] v. to say bad words about something: Our parents taught us to try to profit from our mistakes, not curse them.

damask [dam´əsk] n. a fabric with a shiny, reversible pattern, often used for tablecloths: On special occasions, my family would eat in the dining room on the damask tablecloth.

daze [dāz] n. a confused state of mind, often brought on by a head injury or a shock. syn. trance.

debris [də·brē´] n. bits and pieces of rubbish or litter; fragments left over from earlier activity in a place.

decathlon [di·kath´län] n. a competition with several parts, or rounds.

mold causing decay on strawberries

decay [dē·kā´] n. breakdown or wasting away, sometimes caused by bacteria and mold.

deck [dek] v. to knock down: Alicia threatened to deck anyone who made fun of her little brother.

deductible [dē·dukt´ə·bəl] adj. able to be subtracted: Because we contributed the fruit to the homeless shelter, ten percent of the cost of the fruit was deductible.

defeatist [dē·fēt´ist] n. one who too easily accepts losing: Even though our team had a wonderful record, Sula remained a defeatist who always expected the team to lose.

deference [def´ər·əns] n. respect or regard: The students showed deference to their teacher by listening carefully whenever he spoke.

defiance [dē·fī´əns] n. purposeful disobedience of rules or authority: If you continue with this defiance, I will have to punish you.

demon [dē´mən] n. an evil spirit: When my sister messed up the house, my mother would say, "I wonder why she acts like such a demon of destruction!"

depot [dē´pō] n. a place where people or supplies are loaded or unloaded; a train or bus station: Mr. Gonzalez arrived at the depot early to meet his daughter as she returned from the city.

determined [dē·tʉr´mənd] adj. with one's mind made up; firm: I am determined to get some exercise at least three times a week.

devour [di·vour´] v. to eat hungrily; swallow up whole: Bob watched his scout troop devour the pizza.

crevasse

depot

a	cat	ô	fall, for	ə = a *in* ago
ā	ape	oi	oil	e *in* agent
ä	cot, car	oo	look, pull	i *in* pencil
e	ten, berry	ōō	tool, rule	o *in* atom
ē	me	ou	out, crowd	u *in* circus
i	fit, here	u	up	
ī	ice, fire	ʉr	fur	
ō	go			

disheveled

dorsal fin

disdain [dis·dān´] n. dislike for someone or something seen as unworthy or beneath one. syn. scorn.

disgrace [dis·grās´] v. to bring dishonor: Pat thought that her crying in public would disgrace her family.

disheveled [di·shev´əld] adj. messy in appearance.

disinfect [dis´in·fekt´] v. to destroy bacteria. syn. sterilize.

disintegrate [dis·in´tə·grāt´] v. to break up into tiny pieces.

disown [dis·ōn´] v. to refuse to acknowledge as one's own; to reject.

dispute [di·spyo͞ot´] n. an argument or disagreement. syn. debate.

domain [dō·mān´] n. where one lives: The sea urchin's domain is the blue-green water of the Gulf of Mexico.

donation [dō·nā´shən] n. something given. syn. contribution: I made a donation of a week's allowance to help the flood victims.

doofus [do͞o´fəs] n. a stupid, unskilled person: Don't hire the doofus who installed our kitchen wiring backwards.

dorsal [dôr´səl] adj. on the back: As they reeled in the huge fish, Jack's father pointed out the size of its dorsal fin.

doze [dōz] v. to sleep lightly; nap: With the lights on the plane dimmed, all of us were able to doze for the last few hours of the flight.

two fencers having a duel

duel [do͞o´əl] n. a fight or contest between two persons.

dullard [dul´ərd] n. a boring or stupid person.

dwelling [dwel´ing] n. a home: "Welcome to our humble dwelling," read the sign at our front door.

dynasty [dī´nəs·tē] n. a period during which a country is ruled by one family and its descendants.

earnest [ur´nist] adj. serious; intense. syn. solemn.

elegant [el´ə·gənt] adj. dignified and in perfect taste. syn. fine.

embalming [em·bäm´ing] n. the process of preserving a dead body in order to prevent decay.

emigrate [em´i·grāt´] v. to move from one's country and settle in another land: As teenagers, Serena's grandparents left their families in Poland to emigrate to America.

enslave [en·slāv´] v. to make a slave of. syn. dominate: In most countries, it is illegal to enslave another person.

enterprising [ent´ər·prī´ziñg] adj. willing to try new projects. syn. energetic: Chris was the enterprising child who set up a neighborhood lemonade stand and earned enough money to buy a new bicycle.

enthrone [en·thrōn´] v. to place on a throne, as a king or queen: My little sister wanted to enthrone her favorite doll on a decorated chair.

enthusiastically [en·thoo͞´zē·as´tik·lē] adv. with cheerful energy. syn. eagerly: We enthusiastically cheered our school's trophy-winning volleyball team.

entomb [en·too͞m´] v. to enclose, as in a grave: She entombed her treasures in a jewelry box at the bottom of her drawer.

envious [en´vē·əs] adj. desiring what one does not have: Looking at her straight hair in the mirror, Leah felt envious of her sister's natural curls.

epidemic [e´pə·dem´ik] n. the rapid spread of something, especially disease: When one third of the school was out ill, the school nurse declared that strep throat had become an epidemic at our school.

Ethiopia [ē´thē·ō´pē·ə] n. an ancient kingdom in northeastern Africa; a modern country in East Africa.

etiquette [et´i·kit] n. the rules and manners acceptable in social situations: Before my older brother's wedding, Mom bought a book of wedding etiquette and insisted that the whole family read it.

exacting [eg·zak´tiñg] adj. demanding excellence; needing great attention or care: The power plant's silo was built to exacting requirements.

exaltation [eg´zôl·tā´shən] n. great joy. syn. delight: We lifted our voices and sang a song of exaltation.

exasperation [eg·zas´pər·ā´shən] n. great feelings of annoyance or anger. syn. irritation: Discovering that my favorite puzzle was missing one of its 500 pieces filled me with exasperation.

excavation [eks´kə·vā´shən] n. the digging of a hole, especially in search of articles from earlier civilizations: Did you sign up to help in the excavation of the fort?

exile [eks´il] n. one who is banished from one's country or community: The man who gave a speech on television last night is a political exile from his native country.

excavation

expedition [eks´pə·dish´ən] n. a trip intended for a specific purpose, such as exploration: After researching the alternatives, Mrs. Turner's sixth-grade class decided to make an expedition to Mount Vernon.

a	cat	ô	fall, for	ə = a *in* ago
a	ape	oi	oil	e *in* agent
ä	cot, car	oo	look, pull	i *in* pencil
e	ten, berry	o͞o	tool, rule	o *in* atom
ē	me	ou	out, crowd	u *in* circus
i	fit, here	u	up	
ī	ice, fire	ur	fur	
ō	go			

exquisite [eks´kwi·zit] adj. delicately beautiful: Cinderella's gown was covered with an exquisite pattern of lace and ribbons.

exterminate [ek·stur´mə·nāt´] v. to destroy all trace of something: We bought several traps in an attempt to exterminate the mice in our kitchen.

extort [eks·tôrt´] v. to get something from another person by threatening harm.

fancy[1] [fan´sē] v. to imagine or picture to oneself: "Fancy having my own room," said Juana as she thought about her new apartment.

fancy[2] [fan´sē] n. a liking for something or someone: The prince took a fancy to Mozart, the brilliant young musician.

ferry [fer´ē] n. a vessel that takes people and goods from one side of a body of water to the other.

file [fīl] v. to walk or move in a line: At the end of the memorial service, we were asked to file quietly out of the auditorium.

fishtail [fish´tāl] v. to move forward with a side-to-side motion.

flee [flē] v. to run away or leave quickly.

fleeting [flēt´iŋ] adj. brief: She left a strong impression on me, even though our time together was fleeting.

flexible [flek´sə·bəl] adj. easily moved back and forth without breaking. syn. bendable.

formidable [fôr´mə·də·bəl] adj. strong, difficult, or impressive. syn. awesome.

fronds

fossil [fäs´əl] n. the hardened evidence of plant or animal life from an earlier geological period.

foul [foul] adj. impure or unfit for consumption: Although we were thirsty, we didn't drink because we feared that the well water would be foul.

fresco [fres´kō] v. to create a painting on a wall or ceiling by applying paint to wet, freshly laid plaster.

frond [fränd] n. a large leaf, as of a palm tree or a fern.

frustrate [frus´trāt] v. to cause bad feelings; to prevent from achieving a goal.

fume [fyōōm] v. to be annoyed or upset.

function [fuŋk´shən] v. to perform as expected.

fungus [fuŋg´gəs] n. (plural: *fungi* [fun´jī]) any of a number of types of yeasts, molds, mildews, and the like that consume living or dead plants and animals: Fungi are important in the process of decaying dead tree trunks, branches, and leaves.

fury [fyoor´ē] n. great anger.

galley [gal´ē] n. the kitchen of a ship or boat.

garland [gär´lənd] n. a wreath or woven chain of flowers.

gasket [gas′kit] n. a piece of rubber, fabric, or other material that creates a leakproof joint between two metal pieces: In the first automobiles, it is common to find gaskets made of felt.

gilded [gild′id] adj. coated with gold: At the museum, Michael was most interested in the exhibit of gilded swords that gleamed in the sunlight.

glint [glint] n. a gleam or flash of light. syn. twinkle.

gnarled [närld] adj. twisted and misshapen: The old woman's gnarled hands showed the signs of years of hard work.

grueling [grōo′əl·iñg] adj. requiring great fitness and persistence: The Springdale Marathon is a grueling race in which contestants must run, bike, and swim.

gruesome [grōo′səm] adj. causing horror or disgust. syn. horrible.

hallucinate [hə·lōo′si·nāt′] v. to see or hear things that are not present.

halo [hā′lō] n. a ring of light around something, as a planet or an angel's head: We suspected that it would rain when we saw the halo around the moon.

handicap[1] [han′di·kap′] v. to alter contestants' positions in a game or race to even up their chances of winning.

handicap[2] [han′di·kap′] n. a condition that limits a person's performance or activity: Susan, who was fluent in American Sign Language, did not consider her deafness a handicap.

hatch [hach] n. in spacecraft, an opening through which people climb in and out.

hibiscus [hī·bis′kəs] n. a kind of tree or shrub with a brightly colored flower: My mother loves bright colors, so she planted a hibiscus in front of our house.

hogan [hō′gôn′] n. a Navajo house: The hogan was built of mud and supported by wooden poles.

hoist [hoist] v. to lift or raise: At Mrs. Huber's retirement party, our principal suggested that we hoist our punch glasses to toast her years of teaching.

hook [hook] n. in basketball, a one-handed shot made by curving the arm over the head and tossing the ball toward the basket: The boys spent long hours in the gym perfecting their hook shots.

hunch[1] [hunch] n. an idea or guess based not on fact but on feelings: When my little sister got lost at the zoo, I had a hunch we might find her at the flamingo pool.

hunch[2] [hunch] v. to bend; to sit or stand with the back bent: My mother always reminds us not to hunch over the table at dinnertime.

hibiscus

hogan

a	cat	ô	fall, for	ə = a in ago
ā	ape	oi	oil	e in agent
ä	cot, car	oo	look, pull	i in pencil
e	ten, berry	ōo	tool, rule	o in atom
ē	me	ou	out, crowd	u in circus
i	fit, here	u	up	
ī	ice, fire	ur	fur	
ō	go			

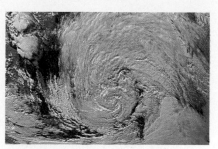

hurricane [hur´i·kān´] n. a violent tropical storm.

hustle[1] [hus´əl] v. to get money, sometimes through aggressive or dishonest means.

hustle[2] [hus´əl] n. the practice of getting something through deception and unlawful means.

hustle[3] [hus´əl] v. to hurry oneself or others: My father tried unsuccessfully to hustle us out of the toy department.

hydroponics [hī´drō·pän´iks] n. the science of growing plants in materials other than soil.

Iditarod [ī·dit´ə·räd] n. an annual dogsled race across Alaska: If you want to compete in the Iditarod, you will need to prepare yourself and your dogs.

ignite [ig·nīt´] v. to light or set fire to: When we went camping, we found it difficult to ignite the damp wood for our campfire.

illuminate [i·lōō´mə·nāt´] v. to light up: We brought along a flashlight to illuminate the dark space.

impale [im·pāl´] v. to pierce through with a sharp object: Isaac would like to own a butterfly collection, but he can't bring himself to impale the butterflies.

implosion

impassively [im·pas´iv·lē] adv. without emotion. syn. calmly.

implosion [im·plō´zhən] n. a bursting inward.

impudent [im´pyōō·dənt] adj. bold or disrespectful; fresh: After Joan corrected the librarian's pronunciation, she became known as "the impudent one."

incentive [in·sent´iv] n. something that encourages a specific behavior: As an incentive, the company offered the top salesperson a trip for two to Hawaii.

indiscriminately [in´di·skrim´i·nit·lē] adv. randomly; without distinction.

infamy [in´fə·mē] n. dishonor; shame: President Franklin D. Roosevelt called the day Pearl Harbor was bombed "a date which will live in infamy."

inflammation [in·flə·mā´shən] n. redness, pain, heat, and swelling: Uncle Lou soon saw and felt inflammation where the ball had hit his arm.

inflection [in·flek´shən] n. in speaking, a change in the tone or pitch of a voice.

inky [iṅk´ē] adj. like ink; black.

inquisitive [in·kwiz´ə·tiv] adj. asking many questions; curious. syn. questioning: My three-year-old cousin is quite inquisitive: she asks questions from the moment she wakes up until the moment she goes to sleep.

insolently [in´sə·lənt·lē] adv. disrespectfully: "And why don't you move out of the way, old man?" the teenager asked insolently.

intercept [in·tər·sept´] v. to interrupt something or to prevent something from following an intended path.

intimate [in´tə·māt´] v. to hint or suggest. syn. indicate.

intimidate [in·tim´ə·dāt´] v. to make afraid; to cause someone to act by threats or violence.

intrepid [in·trep´id] adj. brave. syn. fearless.

invade [in·vād´] v. to attack the territory of another. syn. raid: My brothers and I planned a sneak attack to invade the kitchen and sample the cookies.

irrigate [ir´ə·gāt´] v. to bring water to.

isolation [ī·sə·lā´shən] n. being kept separate from others.

J

jealous [jel´əs] adj. resentful or envious of another.

jealousy [jel´əs·ē] n. a feeling of resentment about what one does not have.

K

khaki [kak´ē] adj. a dull yellowish brown.

L

labyrinth [lab´ə·rinth´] n. a complicated, winding structure.

lace [lās] v. to add a dash of something.

landmark [land´märk´] n. any well-known or important part of a community or region.

lane [lān] n. a narrow country road.

latitude [lat´ə·tōōd´] n. distance north or south of the equator.

laurel [lôr´əl] n. a plant with shiny, green leaves often used to make wreaths.

layup [lā´up´] n. in basketball, a one-handed, leaping shot made close to the basket, often with the ball bouncing in off the backboard.

lean[1] [lēn] v. to rest against something.

lean[2] [lēn] adj. difficult or financially distressed: Most families go through lean times, when they need to count every penny.

lean[3] [lēn] adj. having little fat: Carl saw many cuts of meat in the case, but none that looked lean enough for someone on a low-fat diet.

leer [lir] v. to give a sly or evil look.

legend [lej´ənd] n. a story about a famous person or event, passed down from one generation to the next.

lintel [lint´əl] n. the horizontal piece of the frame at the top of a door or window.

log[1] [lôg] v. to keep a record: When you go on a trip, it's a good idea to log your expenses.

log[2] [lôg] n. a section of a tree that has been chopped down to use as lumber.

irrigate

labyrinth

a	cat	ô	fall, for	ə	= a *in* ago
a	ape	oi	oil		e *in* agent
ä	cot, car	oo	look, pull		i *in* pencil
e	ten, berry	ōō	tool, rule		o *in* atom
ē	me	ou	out, crowd		u *in* circus
i	fit, here	u	up		
ī	ice, fire	ur	fur		
ō	go				

machete

mackintosh

lull [lul] n. a short period of quiet or calm.

lunar [l$\overline{oo}$ʹnər] adj. of the moon: What we think of as the new moon is really a kind of lunar eclipse.

lurid [loorʹid] adj. sensational or shocking: Though Tina was attracted by the magazine's lurid headlines, she didn't buy a copy.

lush [lush] adj. dense, thick.

machete [mə·shetʹē] n. a large knife with a wide blade, used for cutting down sugar cane, dense leaves, and the like: In some countries, sugar cane is still harvested by machete rather than by machine.

mackintosh [makʹin·täshʹ] n. a waterproof raincoat. syn. slicker.

maim [mām] v. to mutilate and disable. syn. cripple.

malfunction [mal·fuṅgkʹshən] v. to fail to work properly: If the air conditioner should malfunction while you're here, please call the building manager.

mandatory [manʹdə·tôrʹē] adj. required; necessary. syn. needed: In high school, it will be mandatory to take at least two years of a foreign language.

maneuver [mə·n$\overline{oo}$ʹvər] v. to move by a plan: Before the new soldiers complete the obstacle course, they must maneuver their way through the tangle of ropes and nets.

manufacture [manʹy$\overline{oo}$·fakʹchər] v. to build or produce, by hand or with machinery: At the factory near my house, the workers manufacture parts for bicycle wheels.

margin [märʹjin] n. one of the outer edges, as in a page of text or a photograph.

massive [masʹiv] adj. very large or heavy. syn. enormous: At the zoo, I marveled at the massive body of the elephant.

match [mach] n. a game: We lost a match against our rivals.

melancholy [melʹən·kälʹē] adj. sad and depressed: People up and down our street were melancholy for days after our letter carrier retired.

merchandise [murʹchən·dīzʹ] n. goods bought and sold: As we walked into the expensive shop, Mom warned us, "I don't want to see any of you kids touching the merchandise."

mettle [metʹəl] n. a person's spirit or character: The three-day examination is sure to test the mettle of even the most studious college student.

mongoose [mäṅgʹg$\overline{oo}$sʹ] n. a small, furry mammal resembling a weasel.

mummy [mumʹē] n. the body of a human being or another animal preserved by embalming: In school we learned about how Howard Carter and others discovered the mummy and burial treasures of King Tutankhamun.

musher [mush´ər] n. one who pilots a dog sled.

mutinous [my$\overline{oo}$t´in·əs] adj. likely to revolt against authority.

mystify [mis´tə·fī´] v. to puzzle or confuse.

Netherworld [ne*th*´ər·wurld] n. the world of the dead.

nook [nook] n. a small, cozy spot.

nuclear family [n$\overline{oo}$´klē·ər fam´ə·lē] n. parents and their children living together in one household.

nurse [nurs] v. to eat or drink something slowly to make it last.

opinionated [ə·pin´yən·āt´id] adj. holding strongly and stubbornly to one's own beliefs.

oppression [ə·presh´ən] n. harsh rule by an unjust power: Dr. Martin Luther King spoke out against the oppression of minorities in America.

opulence [äp´y$\overline{oo}$·ləns] n. great wealth.

orbit [ôr´bit] n. the path of one thing around another: In meteorology, we study how Earth's orbit can affect weather.

Osiris [ō·sī´ris] n. in Egyptian mythology, the god of the underworld who sits in judgment of the dead.

ostentatious [äs·tən·tā´shəs] adj. flashy; showy: Renata's beaded gown was too ostentatious for the simple church wedding.

overwhelm [ō´vər·hwelm´] v. to overpower or overcome: I don't want to overwhelm you, so I won't give you all your birthday presents at one time.

pack [pak] n. a group of animals that live and hunt together in the wild.

paddock enclosing horses

paddock [pad´ək] n. an enclosed piece of land where horses may be exercised.

papyrus [pə·pī´rəs] n. a water plant from which the ancient Egyptians and others made paper.

parapet [par´ə·pet´] n. a wall or barrier that shields troops from enemy fire: The army knew that they had lost the battle when the enemy troops climbed over the parapet.

Parkinson's disease [pär´kin·sənz di·zēz´] n. a progressive disease of the central nervous system in which patients gradually lose control of their muscles.

passive [pas´iv] adj. inactive; taking no active part. syn. yielding: Alice was always very passive; whatever you asked her, she would reply, "I don't care."

Osiris, seated with crest and whip

papyrus

a cat	ô fall, for	ə = a *in* ago
a ape	oi oil	e *in* agent
ä cot, car	oo look, pull	i *in* pencil
e ten, berry	$\overline{oo}$ tool, rule	o *in* atom
e me	ou out, crowd	u *in* circus
i fit, here	u up	
ī ice, fire	ur fur	
ō go		

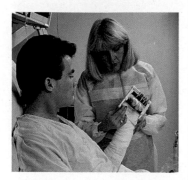

patient receiving physical therapy for a burn

plaid

pathetic [pə·thet′ik] adj. deserving of pity; inferior.

patiently [pā′shənt·lē] adv. calmly and without losing one's temper: Although Judy had to practice many times in order to play the passage correctly, she kept working patiently.

pawnshop [pôn′shäp′] n. a store where people may borrow money, leaving valuable items until they repay the loan.

perilous [per′ə·ləs] adj. dangerous; life-threatening: Those who followed the Oregon Trail were unaware of how perilous the journey they'd undertaken was.

perky [pur′kē] adj. cheerful. syn. lively.

permanent [pur′mə·nənt] adj. lasting indefinitely: Where Luke's baby teeth had been, permanent teeth soon appeared.

perpetual [pər·pech′oo·əl] adj. continuing without stopping: Because Annie never seemed to stop moving, Dad nicknamed her Perpetual Motion.

pharaoh [far′ō] n. name for a king in ancient Egypt.

physical therapy [fiz′i·kəl ther′ə·pē] n. the treatment of disease or injury with exercises, heat, massage, and other methods instead of with drugs.

plague [plāg] n. widespread trouble or sickness: The bubonic plague killed thousands of people during the Middle Ages.

plaid [plad] adj. a pattern consisting of different-colored bars or lines that cross at right angles: Everyone likes this year's uniform: bright red blazers and red-and-black plaid pants.

plant [plant] v. to place in the ground.

pockmarked [päk′märkt] adj. marked with pits or other surface scars: The boy's pockmarked skin indicated a severe case of chicken pox.

pointer [point′ər] n. a helpful suggestion or tip. syn. hint: The experienced teacher gave the substitute teacher several helpful pointers about keeping order in the classroom.

poise [poiz] v. to position or balance: Carol poised herself on the board, ready to dive for the championship.

policy [päl′ə·sē] n. a rule, principle, or procedure followed by an organization: The policy of this company is to hire the most qualified applicant, regardless of race or gender.

potential [pō·ten′shəl] adj. possible; meeting the standards for: Martin and his parents looked carefully at many potential family cars before they settled on the shiny, dark green van.

pot-sticker [pät′stik·ər] n. a Chinese fried dumpling filled with meat or vegetables: At the Chinese restaurant, I ate one pot-sticker after another.

pram [pram] n. a baby carriage; abbreviation for *perambulator*: She took the baby for a walk in his new pram.

prediction [prē·dik´shən] n. a telling of what is to come; forecast.

primitive [prim´i·tiv] adj. simple; unsophisticated. syn. crude.

prolific [prō·lif´ik] adj. producing many offspring: Meadow mice are known for their prolific ways; they may give birth as many as seventeen times a year.

proper [präp´ər] adj. appropriate or usual. syn. expected.

prophesy or **prophecy** [präf´ə·sē] n. a prediction: Tomás fulfilled his great-grandmother's prophesy that he would be the first Alvarez to graduate from college.

proposition [präp´ə·zish´ən] n. a project or scheme.

prospect [prä´spekt] n. a possibility or likelihood.

prostrate [präs´trāt] adj. lying face down: The prostrate runner lay exhausted on the track after the race.

psychiatrist [sī·kī´ə·trist] n. a physician who specializes in the diseases of the mind: My cousin, is majoring in psychology and plans to become a psychiatrist.

puncture [puñgk´chər] n. a hole made by a sharp point that breaks the surface: The puncture wound did not require stitches.

puny [pyōō´nē] adj. weak; small: Before I began a program of daily weight lifting, my muscles looked pretty puny.

quinine [kwī´nīn] n. a medicine taken especially for malaria.

rabid [rab´id] adj. having rabies, a disease of the central nervous system that can be transmitted by the bite of an infected animal.

random [ran´dəm] adj. unplanned; by chance: No one judged the contest entries; the finalists were chosen through a random drawing.

rations [rash´ənz] n. food supply, as for campers or soldiers.

rattletrap [rat´əl·trap´] adj. rattling; worn out; rickety.

reaction [rē·ak´shən] n. a response to an event.

reassuringly [rē·ə·shoor´ing·lē] adv. in a comforting way: On my first day of kindergarten, my teacher spoke reassuringly to me.

recruit [ri·krōōt´] n. one who has been enlisted to serve in the armed forces: The sergeant introduced the new recruit to his commanding officer.

redouble [rē·dub´əl] v. to step up or increase. syn. intensify: Although I was tired, the pep talk during half-time seemed to redouble my strength.

pram

puncture

a	cat	ô	fall, for	ə = a *in* ago
a	ape	oi	oil	e *in* agent
ä	cot, car	oo	look, pull	i *in* pencil
e	ten, berry	ōō	tool, rule	o *in* atom
ē	me	ou	out, crowd	u *in* circus
i	fit, here	u	up	
ī	ice, fire	ur	fur	
ō	go			

599

a scenic spot in the San Joaquin Valley

seal

rehearse [ri·hurs´] v. to repeat or practice before an actual performance.

relay [rē´lā´] n. the passing of something from one to another.

retort [ri·tôrt´] v. to answer rudely or sharply, as in an argument.

retreat¹ [ri·trēt´] n. a place or period of time for being alone for reflection.

retreat² [ri·trēt´] n. a move backward from an earlier position: General Cornwallis urged his troops not to make a retreat, saying, "Victory will be ours shortly!"

retreat³ [ri·trēt´] v. to withdraw to a safe or private spot.

revolting [ri·vōlt´ing] adj. disgusting; rotten.

rival [rī´vəl] n. a competitor; enemy.

rubble [rub´əl] n. bits and pieces of material from previous activity: After the pileup, the cleanup squad cleared the street of rubble so that traffic could flow again.

ruff [ruf] n. the fur around a dog's neck: Jamie's dog tags jingled as Aunt Jean scratched his ruff.

rummage [rum´ij] n. discarded items: The PTA wants our rummage for its "white elephant" sale next month.

sabotage [sa´bə·täzh´] v. to deliberately damage or cause destruction: Don't sabotage our team by revealing our strategies.

sacred [sā´krid] adj. holy: We should show respect for the sacred places of all religions.

sacrifice [sak´rə·fīs´] n. the act of offering to a god.

salvage [sal´vij] v. to save from destruction or disposal: I was able to salvage several boxes of books from the burned-out apartment.

sandcasting [sand´kast·ing] n. the pouring of melted material into a mold made of sand.

San Joaquin Valley [san´ wô·kēn´ val´ē] n. in central California, a huge stretch of low land lying between the Sierra Nevada and the coastal mountain ranges.

saucy [sô´sē] adj. lively and fresh. syn. bold.

schedule [ske´jool] v. to plan for a specific time: Ed called the doctor to schedule an appointment.

scholarship [skäl´ər·ship´] n. an award of money to help defray the cost of education: Jenna's family was proud when she received a basketball scholarship to attend Midwestern College.

seal [sēl] n. something that fastens or closes another thing securely.

sensation [sen·sā´shən] n. a feeling or an impression: I had a sensation of dizziness after I got off the carnival ride.

sense [sens] n. judgment or decision-making ability: Luz is a popular babysitter because she is mature and shows good sense.

sextant [seks´tənt] n. an instrument for measuring distance in degrees of an angle.

shallow [shal´ō] adj. not deep: Amy and I waded into the shallow end of the pool, where the water was just six inches deep.

shorthanded [shôrt·han´did] adj. not having enough workers: When they were shorthanded at the hardware store, Kyle's dad asked her to help out after school.

shroud [shroud] n. a covering: Maria covered her dead parakeet with a cloth shroud before burying the bird.

shutter [shut´ər] n. the part of a camera that opens and closes, allowing light to enter and expose the film, creating the picture.

simplicity [sim·plis´ə·tē] n. freedom from what is difficult or complicated: We moved to the country, seeking a life of greater simplicity.

simulator [sim´yoo·lat´ər] n. a device used in training situations that duplicates likely actual conditions: The student pilot performed perfectly on the flight simulator.

the skeleton of a cat

skeleton [skel´ə·tən] n. the framework of bones of a human being or another animal.

slightly [slīt´lē] adv. thinly; lightly: He was heavy and muscular, even though all the other men in his family were built slightly.

smoke [smōk] v. to move fast enough to raise dust: Pursuing the speeding car, the police car sped up until we saw it smoke down the highway.

solder [säd´ər] v. to join two pieces of metal by applying a bit of molten metal: My sister taught me how to solder the lead pieces together to make a stained glass window.

sordid [sôr´did] adj. dirty; cheap: He said that while he enjoyed watching soap operas on television, he didn't particularly enjoy reading sordid love stories.

sparse [spärs] adj. thinly spread; not dense: Dad says he started balding before I was born; today, he has only a sparse fringe of hair near his ears.

spectacle [spek´tə·kəl] n. a public show or display: My baby brother's temper tantrum in front of my friends was a humiliating spectacle for me.

speechless [spēch´lis] adj. unable to say a word: My latest report card, on which I received straight A's, left me speechless with delight.

sphere [sfir] n. a three-dimensional object shaped like a globe or ball: "Our earth is but a spinning sphere," Marianne's poem began.

spire [spīr] n. a pointed structure on a roof: As we watched the sunset, we saw the church spire standing tall against the city skyline.

sextant

a	cat	ô	fall, for	ə =	a *in* ago
ā	ape	oi	oil		e *in* agent
ä	cot, car	oo	look, pull		i *in* pencil
e	ten, berry	ōō	tool, rule		o *in* atom
ē	me	ou	out, crowd		u *in* circus
i	fit, here	u	up		
ī	ice, fire	ur	fur		
ō	go				

sprint [sprint] v. to run at full speed: The winning runner sprinted past the finish line.

squadron [skwäd′rən] n. a large military group: A squadron of planes flew overhead.

squint [skwint] v. to look at something with one's eyes nearly closed: After coming out of the movie theater, we squinted at the bright sunshine.

stamina [stam′ə·nə] n. strength; courage; endurance: It requires stamina for a young person to play sports in college and get a good education at the same time.

starboard [stär′bərd] adj. to the right side of a ship as one faces forward.

steep [stēp] v. to soak or saturate: When I moved to New England, I decided to steep myself in the region's history and culture.

stout [stout] adj. sturdy; well-constructed: Before we go hiking, I'll need to buy some stout desert boots.

stowaway [stō′ə·wā′] n. one who hides on a boat or a plane: The captain suspected that there was a stowaway aboard the ship.

strain [strān] v. to stretch intensely.

subside [səb·sīd′] v. to die down: The boss waited for complaints to subside before continuing with his explanation of why no raises would be given this year.

subversive [səb·vur′siv] adj. attempting to overthrow or destroy, often from within.

sulk [sulk] v. to show anger or resentment by pouting or withdrawing.

sullen [sul′ən] adj. gloomy, dull.

sultry [sul′trē] adj. tempting; flirtatious.

supervisor [soo′pər·vī′zər] n. one who oversees the work of others.

supportive [sə·pôrt′iv] adj. helpful; approving: Belinda's job search was aided by her supportive aunts and uncles, who drove her to each interview.

surgery [sur′jər·ē] n. a British term for a doctor's office.

suspicion [sə·spish′ən] n. the belief of guilt with little or no evidence: Felipe had barely finished reading the first chapter of his mystery novel when he developed a strong suspicion of who the thief was.

swell [swel] n. a long wave that rolls continuously without breaking: A large swell is perfect for surfing.

systematic [sis′tə·mat′ik] adj. following an orderly method or way of doing things: Cousin Larry is systematic about the way he cleans house: first, the ceiling; then the walls; and last, the floors.

stowaway

Tabasco sauce [tə·bas′kō sôs] n. the brand name of a spicy-hot liquid seasoning made from red peppers.

tense [tens] n. a form of a verb indicating the time of action or state of being.

tentative [ten′tə·tiv] adj. hesitant; unsure of oneself. syn. timid.

terrain [ter·rān′] n. the natural features of the land: Hawaii offers a varied terrain: beaches, valleys, rolling pastures, and mountains.

thatch [thach] n. material for roofing or shelter made of straw, leaves, and other vegetation.

theodolite [thē·äd′ō·līt′] n. a surveying instrument that measures angles: Engineers who build bridges probably know how to use a theodolite.

theory [thē′ə·rē] n. an idea whose accuracy has not yet been established.

throb [thräb] v. to pound or beat: Walking fast makes my heart throb.

thrust [thrust] v. to push forward or shove.

tiller [til′ər] n. a handle for turning the rudder that steers a boat or a ship.

timid [tim′id] adj. shy; lacking self-confidence. syn. hesitant.

tomb [tōōm] n. a chamber or enclosure for burying the dead.

trace [trās] n. a tiny amount.

tradition [trə·dish′ən] n. the customs, beliefs, and stories of a people, passed down from one generation to the next: It's a tradition for the president to throw out the first ball on the opening day of the baseball season.

transcontinental [trans′kän·tə·nent′l] adj. crossing a continent.

transference [trans·fər·əns] n. the act of moving or sending from one place to another.

treason [trē′zən] n. revealing the secrets of one's country to an enemy: When the American officer told the British of American plans to invade Canada, he committed treason.

trespass [tres′pəs] v. to invade another's property or territory, especially without permission. syn. intrude.

trickle [trik′əl] n. a drop or thin stream of liquid: We turned the faucet on all the way, but we got only a tiny trickle of water.

theodolite

a cat	ô fall, for	ə = a *in* ago
a ape	oi oil	e *in* agent
ä cot, car	oo look, pull	i *in* pencil
e ten, berry	ōō tool, rule	o *in* atom
ē me	ou out, crowd	u *in* circus
i fit, here	u up	
ī ice, fire	ur fur	
ō go		

603

Tutankhamun

veer

triumphant [trī·um´fənt] adj. joyously showing success or victory. syn. winning.

tuition [tōō·ish´ən] n. the charge for instruction, especially at a college: Since Ashley plans to live at home while she goes to college, her chief expense will be school tuition.

tuneful [tōōn´fəl] adj. full of music. syn. harmonious.

tunic [tōō´nik] n. a loose-fitting garment that covers most of the body: In very warm climates, wearing a tunic helps to protect a person from the heat of the sun.

turf [turf] n. territory: Our dog Murphy barks and carries on when another animal invades his turf, our backyard.

turquoise [tur´kwoiz´] n. a semiprecious stone, usually greenish blue: From her vacation in New Mexico, Mom brought me a copper band bracelet set with several pieces of turquoise.

Tutankhamun [tōōt´ängk·ä·mən] n. in ancient Egypt, a king who ruled during the eighteenth dynasty, around 1355 B.C.

undulate [un´dyōō·lāt´] v. to move in a wavy, rolling action: Some of us stopped to watch the large cobra undulate in the branches above us; others hurried to board the bus.

ungovernable [un·guv´ərn·ə·bəl] adj. unable to be controlled. syn. rowdy.

unison [yōōn´ə·sən] n. all together: Our entire school said the pledge of allegiance in unison.

unnerving [un·nurv´ing] adj. making one lose one's confidence or courage. syn. nerve-wracking.

unpredictable [un·prē·dikt´ə·bəl] adj. unable to be predicted or guessed beforehand: What funny thing Kwok will say next is anybody's guess; he's completely unpredictable.

ushabti [ōō·shäb´tē] n. in ancient Egypt, a small figure placed in a tomb with a mummy, representing a servant who was supposed to work for the dead in the afterlife.

usher [ush´ər] v. to lead or show the way: The eighth graders were asked to usher the younger children to their rooms after the school assembly.

valise [və·lēs´] n. a small suitcase.

vanity [van´ə·tē] n. too much interest or pride in one's own appearance.

vaporize [vā´pər·īz´] v. to change a substance into a gas.

veer [vir] v. to change direction sharply without warning: Just when the two planes appeared about to crash head-on, we saw the smaller plane veer right and avoid disaster.

vendor [ven´dər] n. one who sells goods: Darlene wanted to sell her antiques, so she applied for a space as a flea market vendor.

verandah [və·ran´də] n. an open porch, usually covered by a roof, along the outside of a building.

victorious [vik·tôr´ē·əs] adj. winning. syn. triumphant.

vigilant [vij´ə·lənt] adj. always alert for danger or trouble. syn. watchful.

virus [vī´rəs] n. any evil or harmful influence: "The threat of crime to our community," said the politician, "is a virus that can devour us."

wail [wāl] n. a loud, prolonged cry or sound like crying: Against the wail of the terrible storm, Angela's father shouted to the family, "Bring in the dogs!"

wary [wer´ē] adj. cautious or watchful: After my wallet was stolen at the carnival, I became wary of large crowds.

washstand [wôsh´stand´] n. a table, usually with a pitcher and bowl, at which the hands and face are washed: My mother has an old washstand that her grandmother used to use.

weightlessness [wāt´lis·nis] n. in spaceflight, the sensation of being free of gravity.

well [wel] v. to accumulate or gush: Tears welled in the corners of Rita's eyes as she asked the police officer, "Please, has anybody found my scooter?"

western [wes´tərn] adj. of the Western Hemisphere: Asians are often puzzled by western traditions and customs, particularly those in the United States.

wheeler–dealer [hwēl´ər·dēl´ər] n. one who aggressively arranges business deals.

whirlpool [hwurl´pool] n. a body of water with a swirling current.

withdrawn [with·drôn´] adj. not communicating with others; tending to keep to oneself.

wordlessly [wurd´lis·lē] adv. without speaking: Wordlessly, the woman removed her crying baby from the meeting room.

World Series [wurld sir´ēz] n. in North America, an annual baseball championship decided by the first of two teams to win four games.

yardstick [yärd´stik´] n. a means of measuring something: As a yardstick for the center's progress, Jean thought about the many families who had been helped.

yaw [yô] v. to swing back and forth.

weightlessness on a space shuttle flight

yaw

a cat	ô fall, for	ə = a *in* ago
a ape	oi oil	e *in* agent
ä cot, car	oo look, pull	i *in* pencil
e ten, berry	ōō tool, rule	o *in* atom
ē me	ou out, crowd	u *in* circus
i fit, here	u up	
ɪ ice, fire	ur fur	
ō go		

605

ACKNOWLEDGMENTS

Grateful acknowledgment is made to the following publishers, authors, and agents for their permission to reprint copyrighted material. Every effort has been made to locate all copyright proprietors; any errors or omissions in copyright notice are inadvertent and will be corrected in future printings as they are discovered.

AÏDA by Leontyne Price, illustrations and book cover by Leo and Diane Dillon. Text copyright ©1990 by Leontyne Price. Illustrations copyright ©1990 by Leo and Diane Dillon. Reprinted by permission of Harcourt Brace & Company.

"ALL ABOARD" from *Across America on an Emigrant Train* by Jim Murphy. Copyright ©1993 by Jim Murphy. Reprinted by permission of Houghton Mifflin Co. All rights reserved.

"THE ALL-AMERICAN SLURP" by Lensey Namioka from *Visions*, edited by Donald R. Gallo. Copyright ©1987 by Lensey Namioka. All rights reserved by the author, Lensey Namioka. Used by permission of the author's agent, Ruth Cohen, Inc.

"ANCESTRY" from *Sing to the Sun* by Ashley Bryan. Copyright ©1992 by Ashley Bryan. Reprinted by permission of HarperCollins Publishers.

"ARN CHORN: PEACEMAKER" from *It's Our World, Too!* by Phillip Hoose. Copyright ©1993 by Phillip Hoose. Reprinted by permission of Little, Brown and Company, and of Rosenstone/Wender.

"AUNT MILLICENT" by Mary Steele from *Dream Time*, edited by Toss Gascoigne, Jo Goodman and Margot Tyrrell. Copyright ©1989 by Mary Steele. Collection copyright ©1989 by the Children's Book Council of Australia. Reprinted by permission of the American publisher, Houghton Mifflin Co., and of the British publisher, Penguin Books Australia Ltd. All rights reserved.

"BENI SEBALLOS" from *It's Our World, Too!* by Phillip Hoose. Copyright ©1993 by Phillip Hoose. Reprinted by permission of Little, Brown and Company, and of Rosenstone/Wender.

"CALL ME PROTEUS" by Edward Wellen. Copyright ©1973 by UPD Publishing Corporation.

"THE DISOBEDIENT CHILD" from *The Bird Who Cleans the World and Other Mayan Fables* by Victor Montejo, translated by Wallace Kaufman. Copyright ©1991 by Curbstone Press. Reprinted by permission of the publisher, Curbstone Press.

"DON'T LET THE BEDBUGS BITE" from *I Love You, I Hate You, Get Lost* by Ellen Conford. Copyright ©1994 by Conford Enterprises, Ltd. Reprinted by permission of Scholastic Inc.

"THE EAGLE HAS LANDED!" from *Flying to the Moon and Other Strange Places* by Michael Collins. Copyright ©1976 by Michael Collins. Reprinted by permission of Farrar, Straus & Giroux, Inc.

"FLIGHT TO THE FUTURE" from *The Smithsonian Book of Flight for Young People* by Walter J. Boyne. Copyright ©1988 by Smithsonian Institution. Reprinted by permission of Atheneum Books for Young Readers, an imprint of Simon & Schuster Children's Publishing Division and of the Smithsonian Institution.

"FOUR AGAINST THE SEA" from *A Boat To Nowhere* by Maureen Crane Wartski. ©1980 by Maureen Crane Wartski. Used by permission of Westminster John Knox Press.

"THE GRANDFATHER TREE" from *Morning Girl* by Michael Dorris. Copyright ©1992 by Michael Dorris. Reprinted by arrangement with Hyperion Books for Children.

"HURRICANE" from *When I Dance* by James Berry. Copyright ©1991, 1988 by James Berry. Reprinted by permission of the American publisher, Harcourt Brace & Company, and of the British publisher, Penguin Books Ltd.

"KINSHIP" from *Woodsong* by Gary Paulsen. Text copyright ©1990 Gary Paulsen. Reprinted with permission of the American publisher, Macmillan Books for Young Readers, an imprint of Simon & Schuster Children's Publishing Division, and of the author's agent.

"LEADER OF THE PACK" from *Champions: Stories of Ten Remarkable Athletes* by Bill Littlefield. Text copyright ©1993 by Bill Littlefield. Illustrations ©1993 by Bernie Fuchs. By permission of Little, Brown and Company.

THE LION'S WHISKER by Russell G. Davis and Brent K. Ashabranner. Copyright ©1959 and 1987 by Russell G. Davis and Brent K. Ashabranner. Reprinted by permission of the authors.

"LOSERS TAKE ALL" from *S.O.R. Losers* by Avi. Copyright ©1984 Avi Wortis. Reprinted by permission of the American publisher, Macmillan Books for Young Readers, an imprint of Simon & Schuster Children's Publishing Division, and of the British publisher, McIntosh and Otis, Inc.

"LOUIS BRAILLE: BRINGING WORDS TO LIGHT" from *Remarkable Children: Twenty Who Made History* by Dennis Brindell Fradin. Copyright ©1987 by Dennis Brindell Fradin. Reprinted by permission of Little, Brown and Company.

"THE MEETING" from *Night on Neighborhood Street* by Eloise Greenfield. Copyright ©1991 by Eloise Greenfield. Used by permission of Dial Books for Young Readers, a division of Penguin Books USA Inc.

"MISS FABERGÉ'S LAST DAZE" by Jenny Wagner from *Dream Time*, edited by Toss Gascoigne, Jo Goodman and Margot Tyrrell. Copyright ©1989 by Jenny Wagner. Collection copyright ©1989 by the Children's Book Council of Australia. Reprinted by permission of the American publisher, Houghton Mifflin Co., and of the British publisher, Penguin Books Australia Ltd. All rights reserved.

"MOON" from *Space Songs* by Myra Cohn Livingston. Copyright ©1988 by Myra Cohn Livingston. Reprinted by permission of Marian Reiner for the author.

"THE MOUSE AND THE ELEPHANT" from *A Treasury of Turkish Folktales for Children*, retold by Barbara K. Walker. Copyright ©1988 by Barbara K. Walker. Reprinted by permission of Linnet Books, North Haven, CT.

"MY GRANDMA" by Letty Cottin Pogrebin from *Free To Be... A Family* by Marlo Thomas & Friends. Copyright ©1987 by Free To Be Foundation, Inc. Used by permission of Bantam Books, a division of Bantam Doubleday Dell Publishing Group, Inc.

"NICKEL-A-POUND PLANE RIDE" from *Local News* by Gary Soto. Copyright ©1993 by Gary Soto. Reprinted by permission of Harcourt Brace & Company.

"NIÑO LEADING AN OLD MAN TO MARKET" from *The Day the*

ACKNOWLEDGMENTS

Perfect Speakers Left by Leonard Nathan. Copyright ©1969 by Leonard Nathan, Wesleyan University Press. Reprinted by permission of the University Press of New England.

"ONE DARK NIGHT" from *Mississippi Solo* by Eddy L. Harris. Copyright ©1988 by Eddy L. Harris. Reprinted by permission of the publisher, Lyons & Burford Publishers.

"ONE GREAT THING" a Kitlinguharmiut Eskimo poem adapted and illustrated by Aline Amon from *The Earth Is Sore: Native Americans on Nature*. Copyright ©1981 by Aline Amon Goodrich. Reprinted with permission of Atheneum Books for Young Readers, an imprint of Simon & Schuster Children's Publishing Division.

"ORBITER 5 SHOWS HOW EARTH LOOKS FROM THE MOON" from *The Complete Poems to Solve* by May Swenson. Copyright ©1993 by The Literary Estate of May Swenson. Reprinted with permission of Macmillan Books for Young Readers, an imprint of Simon & Schuster Children's Publishing Division.

Phonetic respelling system from *World Book Encyclopedia* ©1995 World Book, Inc. By permission of the publisher.

"PHOTOGRAPHY AND OTHER LESSONS" from *Rio Grande Stories* by Carolyn Meyer. Copyright ©1994 by Carolyn Meyer. Reprinted by permission of the American publisher, Harcourt Brace & Company, and of the British publisher, Writers House Inc.

"RABIES" from *Heads or Tails* by Jack Gantos. Copyright ©1994 by Jack Gantos. Reprinted by permission of Farrar, Straus & Giroux, Inc.

"THE REBELLION OF THE MAGICAL RABBITS" by Ariel Dorfman from *Where Angels Glide at Dawn*, edited by Lori M. Carlson and Cynthia L. Ventura. Copyright ©1986 by Ariel Dorfman. Reprinted with the permission of Wylie, Aitken & Stone, Inc.

"REVEALING THE MYSTERIES OF MUMMIES" from *Mummies & Their Mysteries* by Charlotte Wilcox. Text copyright ©1993 by Charlotte Wilcox. Used by permission of Carolrhoda Books, Inc. All rights reserved.

"THE SECRET CHAMBER" from *Into the Mummy's Tomb* by Nicholas Reeves with Nan Froman. Text ©1992 Nicholas Reeves and The Madison Press Limited. Jacket, Design and Compilation ©1992 The Madison Press Limited. Reprinted by permission of the publisher, The Madison Press Limited.

"SGT. DOBETTER'S DEEP FREEZE" by Bill Van Horn from *Plays, the Drama Magazine for Young People*. Copyright ©1990 by Plays, Inc. Reprinted by permission from Plays, the Drama Magazine for Young People.

"SHOOT TO WIN" from *The Outside Shot* by Walter Dean Myers. Copyright ©1984 by John Ballard. Used by permission of Dell Books, a division of Bantam Doubleday Dell Publishing Group, Inc.

"Southbound on the Freeway" from *The Complete Poems to Solve* by May Swenson. Copyright ©1963 by May Swenson. Copyright renewed. Reprinted with permission of Macmillan Books for Young Readers, an imprint of Simon & Schuster Children's Publishing Division.

"Things That Go Gleep in the Night" by Walter Dean Myers from *Don't Give Up the Ghost*, edited by David Gale. Copyright ©1993 by Walter Dean Myers. Used by permission of Delacorte Press, a division of Bantam Doubleday Dell Publishing Group, Inc.

"A WALKING TOUR OF THE PYRAMIDS" from *A Short Walk Around the Pyramids & Through the World of Art* by Philip M. Isaacson. Copyright ©1993 by Philip M. Isaacson. Used by permission of Alfred A. Knopf, Inc.

WAR GAME by Michael Foreman. Copyright ©1993 by Michael Foreman. Reprinted by permission of the American publisher, Arcade Publishing, Inc., and of the British publisher, Pavillion Books.

"WHAT IS OLD?" from *Old Is What You Get: Dialogues on Aging by the Old and the Young* by Ann Zane Shanks. Copyright ©1976 by Ann Zane Shanks. Reprinted by permission of the author.

THE WINGED CAT by Deborah Nourse Lattimore. Copyright ©1992 by Deborah Nourse Lattimore. Reprinted by permission of HarperCollins Publishers.

COVER: Cover photography ©1996 by Jade Albert Studio. Cover illustration ©1996 by James Marsho. Cover design, art direction and production by Design Five.

ILLUSTRATION: 4–5 Marc Mongeau (t.); Todd Leonardo (b.); 6–7 Joel Spector (t.); Leo and Diane Dillon (b.); 8–9 José Ortega (t.,b.); 10–11 Matt Zumbo (t.); Krysten Brooker (b.); 12–13 Wayne McGloughlin (t.); 14–15 Marie Lafrance (t.); 16–19 Marc Mongeau; 20–36 Mike Reed; 37–39 Virginia Peck; 40–59 John Ceballos; 62–65 Russell Willms; 68–78 Quang Ho; 79–81 Laura Tarrish; 82–83 Rosario Valderrama; 84–99 Todd Leonardo; 102–109 Kathy Petrauskas; 110–113 Marc Mongeau; 114–117 Joel Spector; 204–207 Joel Spector; 208–211 José Ortega; 211 Zita Asbaghi (b.); 212–227 Marie Lafrance; 228–231 José Ortega; 237–247 Jeff Meyer; 254–271 Normand Cousineau; 296–299 José Ortega; 300–303 Matt Zumbo; 304 Michael Steirnagle; 311 Michael Steirnagle; 319 Michael Steirnagle; 327 Michael Steirnagle; 330–333 Pola Lopez de Jaramillo; 336–357 Annie Lunsford; 358–369 Ken Spengler; 374–391 Krysten Brooker; 392–395 Matt Zumbo; 396–399 Wayne McGloughlin; 400–409 Harry Schaare; 411–419 Thomas Hennessy; 420 Thomas Hennessy (c.); 422–425 Thomas Hennessy (t.); 426–435 Sally Jo Vitsky; 438–455 Jenny Tylden Wright; 456–457 Eric Paul Meier; 458–463 Gershom Griffith; 464–483 Jean and Mou-Sien Tseng; 484–487 Wayne McGloughlin; 488–491 Marie Lafrance; 492–515 Drew Rose; 516–531 Gabriel Picart; 538–553 Karin Kretschmann; 580–583 Marie Lafrance; 585–605 Rik Olson; 606 Mike Reed.

PHOTOGRAPHY: Background photograph for Silver Bookcase by Allan Penn for SBG. 14–15 Denver Public Library Western History Department; 19 Ulsaker Studio, Inc. (t., c.); 21 Ambrosi and Associates; 36 Courtesy of Lensey Namioka (t.l.); Ambrosi and Associates (t.r., c.); 60 Courtesy of Avi Wortis (c.); 60–61 John Morrison for SBG; 61 Ambrosi and Associates (t., c.); 66 Vincent van Gogh, *The Starry Night*, 1889, oil on canvas, 29 x 36 1/4". The Museum of Modern Art, New York. Acquired through the Lillie P. Bliss Bequest. Photograph © 1996 The Museum of Modern Art, New York; 67 Alfred Stieglitz Collection, Fisk University Art Galleries, Collection of Fisk University, Nashville, Tennessee/© 1996 The Georgia O'Keeffe Foundation/Artists Rights Society (ARS), New York (t.); Courtesy of the Artist (b.); 68 Ambrosi and Associates (t.); 78 Courtesy of Phillip Hoose (l.); Ambrosi and Associates (b.r.); 85 Ambrosi and Associates; 99 Thomas Judd Photography (l., b.r.); 112 Ulsaker Studio, Inc. (t., b.); 113 Ulsaker Studio, Inc. (t., c., b.); 117 Ulsaker Studio, Inc. (t., c.); 118 Ambrosi and Associates; 126 Ambrosi and Associates (l.); Erich Lessing/Art Resource, NY (b.); 127 Griffith Institute, Ashmolean Museum, Oxford (c.); 129 Griffith Institute, Ashmolean Museum, Oxford (l.); The Robert Harding Picture Library (r.); 130 Jack McMaster/Margo Stahl; 131 F. L. Kenett/The Robert Harding Picture Library; 132 Jack McMaster/Margo Stahl; 135 Jack McMaster/Margo Stahl; 136 The Robert Harding Picture Library; 139 Griffith Institute, Ashmolean Museum, Oxford; 140 Times Newspapers Ltd., 1923 (t.l.); Griffith Institute, Ashmolean Museum, Oxford (r.); 141 Griffith Institute, Ashmolean Museum, Oxford (b.l., c.); F. L. Kennett/The Robert Harding Picture Library (b.r.); 142 F. L. Kennett/The Robert Harding Picture Library; 144 Boltin Picture Library (b.l.); 145 The Robert Harding Picture Library; 146 Boltin Picture Library; 148 Erich Lessing/Art Resource (c.); 149 Boltin Picture Library; Claire Reeves (b.l.); Ambrosi and Associates (b.r); 150 Boltin Picture Library (l.); Ancient Art and Architecture Collection (r.); 150–151 Sharon Hoogstraten for SBG; 151 The Robert Harding Picture Library; 152 Boltin Picture Library (t.); Scala/Art Resource, NY (b.); 152–153 Sharon Hoogstraten for SBG; 153 Boltin Picture Library; 154 © The British Museum; 155 Ambrosi and Associates; 156 © Jerry Boucher; 157 Courtesy of the

607

ACKNOWLEDGMENTS

Semmelweis Museum; **158** © The British Museum; **160** © Jerry Boucher; **162** © Jerry Boucher; **163** © Richard Hewett; **164** © Jerry Boucher; **165** © The British Museum (t.r.); Courtesy of Charlotte Wilcox (b.l.); Ambrosi and Associates (b.c., b.r.); **166** © The British Museum (t.); Werner Forman Archive/Dr. E. Strouhal (b.); **167** Nimatallah/Art Resource, NY (l.); J. Guillot-Connaissance, Edimedia (c.); © The British Museum (r.); **168** Sharon Hoogstraten for SBG; **183** Marilyn Sanders (b.l.); Ambrosi and Associates (b.c., b.r.); **201** © Ron Scherl/The Bettmann Archives (b.); **202** Pat Cummings (t.r.); Ambrosi and Associates (c.l., c.r., b.); **202–203** Sharon Hoogstraten for SBG; **206** Ulsaker Studio, Inc. (t., b.); **207** Ulsaker Studio, Inc. (t., c., b.); **211** Ulsaker Studio, Inc. (t., c.); **227** Courtesy of Scholastic, Inc. (b.l.); Ambrosi and Associates (c.r., b.r.); **232** © Synthia Saint James; **234** Ambrosi and Associates; **248** © John Craig (t.); Ambrosi and Associates (c., b.); **248–249** Sharon Hoogstraten for SBG; **249** © Bob Adelman/Magnum Photos (t.); © Constantine Manos/Magnum Photos (b.); **250** Printed by permission of the Norman Rockwell Family Trust, © 1968 the Norman Rockwell Family Trust, photo courtesy of the Norman Rockwell Museum at Stockbridge (b.); **250–251** Sharon Hoogstraten for SBG; **251** National Museum of American Art, Washington D.C./Art Resource, NY. Gift of the Container Corporation of America (c.); **252** Isabel Bishop, *The Snapshot*, 1936, ink and inkwash on paper, 8 x 6", Collection of Joanne Payson, Courtesy of Midtown Payson Galleries, New York, NY (photo by Nathan Rabin) (t.); New School for Social Research, NYC (b.); **252–253** Sharon Hoogstraten for SBG; **253** National Museum of American Art, Washington, D.C./Art Resource, NY; **271** Ambrosi and Associates (r.); Jay Thompson, Courtesy of Wylie, Aitken, and Stone (l.); **272** Ambrosi and Associates; **291** Courtesy of Anderson Press Limited (l.); Ambrosi and Associates (t.r., c.r., b.); **295** Harold Feinstein; **298** Ulsaker Studio, Inc. (t., b.); **299** Ulsaker Studio, Inc. (t., c., b.); **303** Ulsaker Studio, Inc. (t., c.); **305–308** Sharon Hoogstraten for SBG; **309** John Morrison for SBG (l.); Sharon Hoogstraten for SBG (r.); **310** Sharon Hoogstraten for SBG; **312** Sharon Hoogstraten for SBG (l.); John Morrison for SBG (r.); **313** Sharon Hoogstraten for SBG (l.); John Morrison for SBG (r.); **314** Sharon Hoogstraten for SBG (l.); John Morrison for SBG (r.); **315** Sharon Hoogstraten for SBG; **316** Sharon Hoogstraten for SBG; **317** John Morrison for SBG (l.); Sharon Hoogstraten for SBG (r.); **318–322** Sharon Hoogstraten for SBG; **323** John Morrison for SBG (l.); Sharon Hoogstraten for SBG (r.); **324–325** Sharon Hoogstraten for SBG; **326** Sharon Hoogstraten for SBG (l.); John Morrison for SBG (r.); **328** Sharon Hoogstraten for SBG (l.); John Morrison for SBG (r.); **329** John Morrison for SBG (t.); Courtesy of Hyland House Publishing (l.); Ambrosi and Associates (b.r.); Sharon Hoogstraten for SBG (border); **335** © Bill Ross/Westlight; **337** Ambrosi and Associates; **357** Doug Mindell (l.); Ambrosi and Associates (t.r., c.r.); **369** © John Craig; **370** Philadelphia Museum of Art: Purchased: The Harrison Fund; **370–371** Sharon Hoogstraten for SBG; **371** © Robert Frerck/Odyssey Productions; **372–373** © Peter Poulides/Tony Stone Images; **391** Courtesy Penguin Books Australia Ltd.; **394** Ulsaker Studio, Inc. (t., b.); **395** Ulsaker Studio, Inc. (t., c., b.); **399** Ulsaker Studio, Inc. (t., c.); **400** Ambrosi and Associates; **409** Courtesy of Simon & Schuster (l.); Ambrosi and Associates (c., r.); **413** © Chris Arend/AlaskaStock Images; **415** © Jeff Schultz/AlaskaStock Images; **416** © Jeff Schultz/AlaskaStock Images; **418** Steve McCutcheon/Alaska Pictorial Service; **419** © Jeff Schultz/AlaskaStock Images; **422–423** © Jeff Schultz/AlaskaStock Images; **424** © Jeff Schultz/AlaskaStock Images; **425** © Chris Arend/AlaskaStock Images (t.r.); Courtesy of Bill Littlefield (b.l.); Ambrosi and Associates (b.r.); **436** Joseph Mallord William Turner, British, 1775–1851, *Valley of Aosta—Snowstorm, Avalanche and Thunderstorm*, oil on canvas, 1836/37, 92.2 cm x 123 cm, Frederick T. Haskell Collection, 1947.513, photograph © 1994 The Art Institute of Chicago, All Rights Reserved; **436–437** Sharon Hoogstraten for SBG; **437** Courtesy of Fletcher/Priest Gallery, Worcester, MA, Experimental Workshop, San Francisco, CA (t.); Scala/Art Resource, Prado, Madrid (b.); **438** Ambrosi and Associates; **454** Louise Erdrich, courtesy of Disney Juvenile Publishing; **454–455** Sharon Hoogstraten for SBG; **455** Ambrosi and Associates (b.); **458** Ambrosi and Associates (t.); **465** Ambrosi and Associates; **483** Courtesy of Maureen Crane Wartski (l.); Ambrosi and Associates (r.); **486** Ulsaker Studio, Inc. (t., b.); **487** Ulsaker Studio, Inc. (t., c., b.); **491** Ulsaker Studio, Inc. (t., c.); Ambrosi and Associates (b.c., b.r.); **516** Ambrosi and Associates; **532** © David Maung/Impact Visuals (l.); **532–533** Sharon Hoogstraten for SBG (t.); **533** Ambrosi and Associates (l., c.); **534** Courtesy of Allen Sapp Paintings, Inc.; **534–535** Sharon Hoogstraten for SBG; **535** The National Railway Museum/Science & Society Picture Library; **536–537** *Lightning Express Trains "Leaving the Junction"*, artist Frances F. Palmer, publisher Currier & Ives, 1864, Museum of the City of New York, 56.300.108, The Harry T. Peters Collection; **537** Ambrosi and Associates (c.); **538** The Bettmann Archive; **540** Collection of The New-York Historical Society; **543** Society of California Pioneers; **545** Smithsonian Institution; **547** Denver Public Library Western History Department; **549** Chicago Historical Society; **551** *Across the Continent "Westward the Course of Empire Takes its Way"*, artist Frances F. Palmer, publisher Currier & Ives, 1868, Museum of the City of New York, 56.300.107, The Harry T. Peters Collection; **552** detail of *Across the Continent "Westward the Course of Empire Takes its Way"*, artist Frances F. Palmer, publisher Currier & Ives, 1868, Museum of the City of New York, 56.300.107, The Harry T. Peters Collection (t.r.); Courtesy of Clarion Books/Houghton Mifflin (b.l.); Ambrosi and Associates (b.r.); **554** NASA; **555** Rockwell International (t., c., b.); **556** NASA; **557** Rockwell International (t. c., b.); **558–559** The Observatories of the Carnegie Institution of Washington; **560** NASA; **561** The Observatories of the Carnegie Institution of Washington; **562** Rockwell International (t., c., b.); **563–565** The Observatories of the Carnegie Institution of Washington; **566** NASA; **567–569** The Observatories of the Carnegie Institution of Washington; **570** NASA; **571** NASA (t., c.); AP/Wide World Photos (b.l.); Ambrosi and Associates (b.r.); **573** NASA; **574–575** © J. P. Laffont/Sygma; **576–577** © James A. Sugar/Black Star; **578–579** © Tony Stone Images; **582** Ulsaker Studio, Inc. (t., b.); **583** Ulsaker Studio, Inc. (t., c., b.); **585** © Tom Edwards/Earth Scenes (t.); Giraudon/Art Resource, NY (b.); **586** © CNRI/SPL/Custom Medical Stock Photo (l.); **587** Stock Newport/Onne Van Der Wal (t.); © G/Buttner/Naturbild/OKAPIA (b.r.); **588** © Chuck Keeler/Tony Stone Images (b.l.); © Marcel Isy-Schwart/The Image Bank (b.r.); **589** © Charles D. Winters/Photo Researchers, Inc. (l.); © Andre Gallant/The Image Bank (t.r.); **590** © Steve Niedorf/The Image Bank (t.r.); © Lionel Isy-Schwart/The Image Bank (l.); **591** © Paul Chesley/Tony Stone Images (l.); UPI/Bettmann Newsphotos (r.); **592** © David Lawrence/The Image Bank (l.); © Obremski/The Image Bank (r.); **593** © Guy Motil/Westlight (r.); © Donald Nausbaum/Tony Stone Images (r.); **594** © Tony Stone Images (t.r.); © E. Seeliger/The Image Bank (t.l.); © Terry Farmer/Tony Stone Images (b.); **595** © Gary Holscher/Tony Stone Images; **596** © Ana Laura Gonzalez/Animals Animals; **597** © Glen Allison/Tony Stone Images (l.); Art Resource, NY (t.r.); **598** © Robert Copeland/Westlight (t.); © Joe Devenney/The Image Bank (b.l.); © George Chan/Tony Stone Images (b.r.); **599** David Madison © Duomo Photography, Inc. (l.); Archive Photos/American Stock Photos (t.r.); **600** © Leverett Bradley/Tony Stone Images (l.); © Russell Johnson/Pilchuck Glass School (r.); **601** © David Joel/Tony Stone Images (b.); **602** © Frank Whitney/The Image Bank (t.); **603** © Tony Stone Images (t.); © Zigy Kaluzny/Tony Stone Images (b.); **604** © Richard Elliott/Tony Stone Images (l.); Jennifer Brinkman for SBG (r.); **605** © Japack/Westlight (l.); NASA/SPL/Photo Researchers, Inc. (r.).